A SELF-MADE WO

'*A Self-Made Woman* ha
– characters that come a
intriguing point of view.
Fre
author of Century *and* Ellis Island

'Ruth Harris has cleverly dissected two generations of women. She writes about feminist issues with wit and without anger or *angst.*'
The Times

'A provocative novel.'
Daily Express

'A contemporary novel of achievement and fulfilment. Compelling.'
The Literary Guild

'It's an enlightening book as well as an entertaining one – an emotional, searching story revealing how women define their own happiness.'
Sunderland Echo

'A book about love, work, women's aspirations and ambitions.'
Eastern Daily Press

'Wonderful! I hated getting to the last page.'
Roberta Ashley, Executive Editor, *Cosmopolitan*

A SELF-MADE WOMAN

Ruth Harris

NEW ENGLISH LIBRARY

The author wishes to thank Hollis Acker for anecdotes and kitchen time.

First published in the USA in 1983 by Macmillan Publishing Co. Inc.

First published in Great Britain in 1983 by New English Library

First NEL Paperback Edition June 1985

NEL Books are published by
New English Library,
Mill Road, Dunton Green,
Sevenoaks, Kent.
Editorial office: 47 Bedford Square, London WC1B 3DP

Printed and bound in Great Britain by
Cox & Wyman Ltd, Reading

British Library C.I.P.

Harris, Ruth
   A self made woman.
   I. Title
   823'.914[F]   PR6058.A/

ISBN 0 050 05735 6

*To Michael,
with love*

A SELF-MADE WOMAN

~~~~~~

ELLEN AND BRENDA/
MOTHER AND DAUGHTER

ELLEN GREW UP IN A MAN'S WORLD. BRENDA CAME OF AGE in the generation of women.

Ellen had defined herself as Frank Kendle's daughter, Phil Durban's wife, Brenda and Danny's mother. Brenda had always been—and would always think of herself as—Brenda Durban.

Ellen's heroines were the ladylike Grace Kelly and Ingrid Bergman (*before* her romance with Rosselini); Brenda's were Jane Fonda and Gloria Steinem.

Ellen's image of her ideal self had been shaped by *McCall's* and *The Ladies' Home Journal*; Brenda's reflection of her ideal self came from *Ms.* and *Self* and *Savvy*.

Ellen had been a virgin when she married Phil; Brenda had been living with Jeff since she'd been eighteen.

Ellen believed in breast-feeding; Brenda put her faith in the pill.

1

Ellen went to work because she had to; Brenda took it for granted she'd have a rewarding career.

Ellen's success had been hard-earned—day by day, dollar by dollar—and it had cost her the personal life she craved. Brenda assumed she'd have it all—marriage, career, children.

Ellen tried to make Brenda understand it wasn't as easy as the magazines made it look; Brenda saw her future as limitless and wanted to do things *her* way.

~~~~~~

THE NEW YEAR/1970

"JEFF PROPOSED!" BRENDA'S FIRST WORDS ON THE FIRST DAY of the new year bubbled out of her. Her beautiful, cat-shaped blue-green eyes—eyes just like Ellen's—danced with happiness over a late mother-and-daughter New Year's Day breakfast. "Right on the stroke of midnight! Isn't it romantic! I thought he was just going to kiss me. Instead, he proposed. Oh, Mom, I'm so happy!"

"And what are you going to do?" Ellen asked, surprised at such a starry-eyed Brenda. Brenda and Jeff had been living together since Brenda's sophomore year, and Ellen had assumed that, for Brenda's generation, marriage was irrelevant.

"Marry him, of course!"

"Right away?" Ellen asked. She drained poached eggs on paper towels, slid them onto freshly buttered English muffins covered with grilled ham slices, and ladled on the waiting hollandaise.

"Not this second," Brenda answered with the dopey sarcasm

3

of the young. "Right after graduation." Brenda would graduate from Brown this year. "In June."

"Why do you want to get married so soon? Why don't you and Jeff just go on living together until you get established in your career?" Ellen asked. Jeff—gentle, altruistic, idealistic—was nice enough. But was *nice* enough? And what about a career? Hadn't Brenda learned *anything* from *her* experience, Ellen wondered, bringing the two plates to the big antique harvest table. "Make sure you have a good, solid career. *Then* get married."

"I'm getting married first!" Brenda said adamantly. "Marriage means more to me than it does to you."

"Having a career comes first," Ellen insisted. "If you can support yourself, you have *choices*. You can take care of yourself—and your children. You won't be dependent, helpless, a victim. Believe me! I know."

"You think being independent is so hot. Look at you! No thanks!" Brenda said. "Anyway, I'm going to have a career, too."

Ellen raised an eyebrow. "So you're going to be a superwoman?"

"Just because you couldn't do both doesn't mean I can't." Brenda's hostility toward her mother was never very far from the surface.

"Brenda! Back off!"

"Work! Work! Work! Career! Career! Career! That's all I've ever heard from you. Well, I want more out of life than you have," Brenda went on, ignoring her mother's warning. "I want a career *and* I want a decent marriage *and* I want a family. I don't want my children to grow up the way I did without a father. With a mother who was always exhausted, always 'too tired.' And I don't want to have to share a man the way you share Lew Swann with his wife!"

"Brenda!" Ellen cautioned, angry, her patience gone.

"And it's your fault about Daddy!" Brenda accused, finally saying the words she had buried for so long.

Ellen felt herself go white. Was *that* what Brenda really thought? Was *that* beneath Brenda's barely concealed resentment? Did Brenda really blame her for Phil's . . . ? It was unspeakable. And with a rage that came from deep within her, Ellen slapped her daughter across the face, shocking them both.

"Don't *ever* say that again! Don't ever *think* it! And let me tell you a few things about your father . . . the father you've put on such a pedestal all these years—"

"No!" Brenda howled, putting her hands to her ears, trying— but failing—to shut out her mother's words. Words about money . . . words about debt . . . words Ellen had never spoken until now . . . words Brenda had never heard until now. "No!"

Brenda fled from the table, threw her clothes into her back- pack, and went back to Providence and the apartment she shared with Jeff. Her mother, she thought bitterly, was more liberated than she was. So liberated she thought love and marriage were millstones around a woman's neck. Well, Brenda knew better. *She* would never be *that* liberated.

Ellen cleared the untouched *eggs* benedict from the table and, as she began her hectic day, remembered the terrible arguments she'd had with *her* parents when she told them she was going to marry Phil. They had told her she was too young. They had urged her to finish her education.

But Ellen had been in love. She wanted to get married. Getting married was the most important thing in the whole world.

Her parents had lost, too.

I

A MAN'S
WORLD

1

Once upon a time it was a man's world. And, back then, there were three kinds of heroines—men's images of women. Virgins: icy and alluring like Grace Kelly, or pert and wholesome like Doris Day. Sex traps: ripely luscious and avidly insatiable like Marilyn Monroe or Brigitte Bardot, with wet, glistening mouths and pneumatic, comforting breasts. Or the more approachable, anxious-to-please girl-next-door types like Debbie Reynolds, who tried to hold her marriage together with diaper pins, or Janet Leigh, who gave up her career for her new husband, Tony Curtis.

For ordinary women, there was only one image: the happy housewife, adoring wife, and loving mother—the woman who lived in and through her family. Ellen, who had always been a good girl, adored her husband and loved her children and counted herself a happy woman.

But late one Saturday night in March 1959, she was considerably less than happy.

It was a typical Saturday night party in the era of Togetherness. The women talked to the women about recipes and children. The men talked to the men about sports and the stock market,

9

except Phil Durban, who talked to Carol Mattison. And looked
deep into her eyes. And smiled at some private joke. And
allowed her hand to rest intimately on his sleeve.

Ellen Durban watched, going crazy, until she finally—almost physically—pushed Phil out the Whittiers' front door.

"What do you want me to do? Wear a stop watch?" Phil
asked sarcastically. The tires on the brand-new yellow Buick
convertible that Phil had bought with his Christmas bonus
squealed as he backed out of Sam and Alice Whittier's driveway, made the turn, and started the half-mile down Dogwood
Lane to the Durbans' own split-level.

It was almost one. Ellen had been after Phil to leave the
party since quarter to twelve. Six-year-old Danny and nine-
year-old Brenda were home with Mrs. Blake, whose prices
doubled after midnight.

"How long am I allowed to talk to people at a party?" Phil
asked, his sarcasm an impregnable weapon. "Five minutes?
Two minutes? Or is it five for men and two for women?"

"You spent over an hour with Carol," Ellen said, trying to
keep the whine of accusation out of her voice, trying but, as
she well knew, failing.

"Jesus Christ! We were talking about gypsy moths!" Phil
sputtered.

"It didn't look that way! She couldn't keep her hands off
you!" Unconsciously, Ellen stroked the luscious red fox jacket
Phil had given her for Christmas—also bought with the bonus.
"She looked like she wanted to make love to you on Alice's
living room floor!"

"It's more than *you'd* ever do!"

"That's right! I'm not some floozy. I'm your wife!"

"It wouldn't hurt if you acted like a floozy once in a while,"
Phil snapped and made a sharp left into the short, downhill
driveway at Number 76, bringing the Buick to a fast, jolting
stop.

He slammed the car door and stalked through the garage to
the kitchen, leaving Ellen to pay Mrs. Blake and drive her
home.

"Get over here, Sweetcakes," Phil said, his voice Sunday-
morning-thick, sleepy-husky, sweet and sexy. He moved in
bed, reached out for Ellen, and his fingers grazed her breast.
Without a word, Ellen moved away from his touch and slipped

out of bed. She stalked into the bathroom, shut the door, and, still angry from the night before, turned on the water full blast.

Every Sunday morning, with Brenda as *sous-chef*, a term Ellen had learned in college French, she made two breakfasts: french toast from thick slices of homemade bread for the children; and for her and Phil something ultra-super-deluxe special because Sunday morning sex and Sunday morning breakfast were what kept the romance in the Durbans' marriage. This week: orange crêpes stuffed with orange segments topped with sugar and blanched peel glazed under the broiler. Fight or no fight, Ellen would cook for Phil.

"Need anything from the deli?" he asked as he passed through the kitchen on his way to the garage. Ellen could smell his tangy aftershave even through the sweetly aromatic cooking odors. She could have used some more butter but she tightened her mouth and pretended she hadn't heard.

Hurt, Phil shrugged a little, then tried to give her a little hug to tell her that he'd already forgotten their spat, but Ellen moved away in stony silence. A moment later, she heard the Buick's engine start.

Silently, Brenda broke *eggs* into a mixing bowl for the french toast, aware that Mommy was mad at Daddy but that Daddy was trying to make up. She *hated* it when her parents fought.

While Phil went out for the Sunday papers, Brenda and Ellen cooked, Danny set the table, and Irving got in the way. Irving was the Durbans' big, floppy golden retriever, the only dog in the history of Westchester County ever to flunk obedience school.

"Dammit, Irving! *Move!*" Ellen cursed, tripping over the dog as she opened the refrigerator to get eggs. "Brenda!" she snapped. "Aren't you done with that whisk yet?" Brenda was using the whisk to make the batter for the french toast; Ellen needed it for the crêpes.

"Keep your tights on!" Brenda snapped back, finishing the batter and handing the rinsed-off whisk to her mother.

"Sorry," Ellen apologized, realizing how she'd sounded. "I guess I got up on the wrong side of the bed."

You *bet!* Brenda thought but didn't say a word.

Ellen sensed her annoyance and kissed her lovely, naturally

wavy hair and watched as Danny, still baby-pudgy, arranged the knives and forks and bright yellow napkins, standing back now and then to survey his handiwork.

Why was I so jealous of Carol Mattison? In the sunny, almost balmy March morning, Ellen was embarrassed by her jealous outburst. *Carol Mattison!*

Carol Mattison was a tall, busty, ripely overweight blonde (natural, Carol liked to brag, part of her Scandinavian heritage but, as anyone with eyes could see, definitely helped along with a peroxide bottle) who saw herself as Westchester's answer to Marilyn Monroe. A suburban Jayne Mansfield. A split-level Diana Dors. In her too-tight clothes, pushup bras, and see-through blouses, Carol draped herself all over any man in sight, from everyone's husband, brother, or father to the kids who helped carry grocery bags out of the New Rochelle A & P. Everyone, including Phil and Ellen, laughed at Carol's sex-goddess delusions behind her back. Jealous of Carol Mattison!

In the clear light of morning it was ludicrous. Maybe, Ellen thought, it was the lateness of the hour. Or perhaps the un-accustomed brandy she had tasted after dinner.

"Your french toast smells out of this world," Ellen told Brenda as Brenda carefully took the crusty slices out of the pan, put them on two warm dishes, and spread pale amber Vermont honey on top.

"Mom's over her snit!" Brenda announced to Danny, who was on the floor playing with Irving.

"Snit," Danny repeated daringly, recalling the punishment he had received the week before for using a word ne had heard on the playground that sounded suspiciously similar. When no reprimand came, Danny, now bold, said in a loud and clear voice, "Mom's over her snit!" And dissolved into laughter.

Even Ellen smiled.

Inside, she suffered. She hadn't spoken to Phil since last night, had rejected his lovemaking, had not even deigned to respond to his offer to get her something from the deli. Shame burned at Ellen as she made the topping of sugar and glazed orange peel for the crêpes.

Who am I hurting anyway? I'm hurting myself, that's who! She hurt herself when she hurt Phil. She hurt herself when she refused his lovemaking. This morning had been one of the

handful of times in their ten-year marriage that they hadn't
made love—sensational, thrilling-to-the-toes love—first thing
Sunday morning. She hurt herself when she gave him the silent
treatment. She hurt herself when she deprived herself of his
love and company. She thought she must have been slightly
crazy last night and this morning to behave as she had. She
had ruined almost twelve hours of the weekend with her jealous
accusations and childish behavior.

Well, twelve hours is enough to waste! Ellen thought as she
sprinkled the grated peel and sugar over the rolled crêpes and
dotted them with butter. Right after breakfast she'd take the
kids over to Phil's parents. She'd apologize to Phil and take
him to bed, where she would show him just how much she
loved him and just how much she regretted her childish behavior. She would be aggressive in bed, which she knew he
liked but which she rarely was because she was too shy, too
well brought up . . . too something.

Not today.

Today she'd undress him, slowly and lovingly, and kiss
each part of him as the clothing came off. She would hold him
in her hands and in her mouth, exciting him and exciting herself
with her boldness, not allowing him into her until they could
barely wait a moment longer.

Ellen indulged her fantasy as she slid the *gratin* dish into
the oven to brown and glaze the orange-sugar-butter topping
and warm the opulently flavored crêpes when she heard the
car turn into the short, steep drive that led down to the house.

Ellen couldn't suppress the smile that curved her mouth and
rose to her eyes in sweet, sexy anticipation as she turned up
the flame under the asbestos pad that kept the Chemex hot.

She first sensed something was wrong when the front doorbell
rang.

No one ever used the front door. Phil always came in through
the kitchen door. Was he playing some kind of game with her?
Worrying her by changing the routine? Trying to get even by
scaring her? A peculiar warning bell went off in Ellen even
before she opened the front door.

Two uniformed policemen stood there. One white, one black.

"Mrs. Durban?"

She nodded, her mouth dry.

"Your husband's car was stopped for a red light on Route

forty-two. A school bus was on its way to the repair yard...
brakes failed... crashed head-on... bus empty except for the
driver..."

The taller of the two policemen, a sandy-haired man in his
early thirties, did the talking. His tired eyes were evasive,
moving from the floor to Ellen to an indefinite point just behind
her.

"Both men were killed instantly. I'm sorry... your husband
is dead."

Ellen's mind shut away the word. D-e-a-d. She refused to
accept the word that now ricocheted hollowly around inside
her. *Dead*.

She could swear she heard them tell her that Phil was in
the White Plains Hospital, in the emergency room. She was
suddenly aware that the tall, pale policeman was looking at
her, expecting her to say something.

"Thank you," Ellen said in a voice that didn't sound like
her own. *White Plains Hospital*, she was thinking. *She'd have
to get Phil's Blue Cross card from his wallet*. On Sunday
mornings Phil left the house with only a five-dollar bill, his
license, and the registration. The hospital would ask for the
Blue Cross number. Irrelevantly, Ellen remembered the Ni-
chols-May routine. It would be her responsibility to provide
the number.

Then they'd let her see him. Touch him. Hold him. Promise
she'd never be jealous again. *Never!* Just let her see him.

"Mommy, is everything all right?" Brenda asked, half hiding behind the dining ell entrance, afraid to come out, her face
serious, scared.

"Yes," Ellen said, trying to make her voice normal. "Everything's fine. Go eat your breakfast. Make sure Danny finishes
his milk."

Brenda looked questioningly at her mother, then at the two
uniformed policemen, and obediently left the room.

The two policemen glanced at each other, realizing that this
Mrs. Durban wanted to tell her children later, in private. Some
parents preferred to handle it that way.

Ellen stood rigidly silent, her face ashen, her eyes staring
straight ahead, glazed, unfocused. "Are you all right, ma'am?"
asked the shorter, stocky man.

"Would you like some coffee?" she responded, suddenly
remembering the Chemex, wanting to be polite.

"No, thanks," both men answered at once. Gently, they told her that the body was at the morgue, that she would have to identify it—purely a formality—and let them know which funeral home she wanted to use. One of them would take Ellen to the morgue; the other would stay with the children until a relative or a neighbor could come.

Ellen nodded.

She smelled the crêpes. They were burning. Dizzily, she thought she turned to go into the kitchen. Later, Ellen was not able to remember fainting, although that was what they told her she had done.

2

LATER, TOO, SHE WOULD HAVE NO MEMORY OF THE TWO DAYS that followed. Caroline and Tommy Durban, Phil's parents, made all the arrangements. And it was they who told Brenda and Danny that their Daddy had gone to heaven.

"When is he coming back?" Danny wanted to know, still too young to understand.

"It's Mommy's fault!" Brenda had blurted. "It's Mommy's fault! If Mommy hadn't been so mean to Daddy when he tried to hug and kiss her, Daddy wouldn't have been in that accident. Daddy would have come home the way he did every Sunday."

"Brenda, you don't mean that!" Caroline had said, shocked. "You mustn't say that. You mustn't even think it!"

"I'm sorry," Brenda said immediately. "I didn't mean it." Brenda was scared by what she had said, by what she had thought, by what it meant. She pushed the horrible thoughts out of her mind as soon as they surfaced. But the unremembered memory would cast its furious shadow over Brenda's love for her mother for years . . .

And what Brenda wouldn't let herself remember, Ellen couldn't forget. The argument had upset Phil. He was upset because

16

Ellen had pushed him away in bed and later in the kitchen. Upset, he was distracted, unable to concentrate. Unable to concentrate, he wasn't paying enough attention to the red light, to the oncoming traffic. If he hadn't been upset, distracted, he would have been able to do something, would have gotten out of the way of the bus, would have walked away from the accident—would now be alive.

Ellen tormented herself with the illogical guilt of the survivor. If she had loved him enough, he would be alive. But she hadn't—and he was dead. And it was her fault.

All Ellen could remember about the funeral was wishing that she were the one who was dead.

Zombie-like, she stood with Brenda and Danny at the church door mechanically accepting condolences. After the service, at the cemetery as she watched them shovel dirt on Phil's coffin, she vomited behind a gravestone and was too hysterical even to be ashamed. Phil had been her life, her whole world. And now he was gone. Without him, she was nothing.

And Ellen wondered whether, if she and Phil had made love that morning, she might have gotten pregnant. She was almost thirty—old to have a baby. Ancient. But lately she had found herself thinking about it more and more, had found herself "forgetting" her diaphragm, had dreamed of having another baby. She'd dreamed of being a mother again, of being someone. When her period came, right on schedule, she had cried. There would never be another chance for her.

Another *never*.

Then Ellen surprised herself. In the days and weeks immediately following Phil's accident, she became her usual calm and competent self. Weeping but composed, she handwrote acknowledgments to every condolence card. She telephoned the people to whom she felt especially close.

"Phil had an accident Sunday morning," Ellen told Lewis Swann, president of Decor Paints and Phil's boss. Phil had been Decor's sales manager for six years. "A school bus plowed into his car." She had a compulsion to talk about Phil's accident, to go over its details, to tell people about how she had burned the crêpes. The best cook in Westchester County, and she had burned the crêpes! She needed to make it all real to herself. "He's gone. Phil's gone . . ."

"We're going to miss him," Lew said, meaning it. Phil Durban had been a man in a gray flannel suit with golden dreams. A go-getter, an aggressive, ambitious, hard-working young-man-on-the-make. The kind of executive Lew, who was not threatened by excellence in others, liked to have at Decor.

"I'd like to come to Phil's office," Ellen said, clearing her throat. Her tentative tone made the statement a request. "I'd like to go through his things myself. It's one last thing I can do for him. Would it be all right?"

"Of course it's all right." For a moment Lew was impatient with Ellen for being so self-effacing. Of course she could go through his desk. She was his wife.

But as soon as Lew hung up, he went into Phil's office and closed the door behind him. He went directly to the top left-hand drawer and took out a manila envelope.

"If anything ever happens to me," Phil had said, half-joking but meaning it, "get rid of it. There are things Ellen doesn't need to know. Wives don't need to know *everything* about their husbands!" And he'd winked conspiratorially at Lew.

Lew considered the envelope for a moment, unsure about what to do with it. Then he taped it shut, marked it *Phil Durban: Personal*, and took it into the empty office next to his—the office his father had occupied until a year ago. Lew put the envelope on the top shelf of the coat closet, not knowing what else to do with it. He didn't think he should destroy it because, technically, it belonged to Ellen. But, obviously, now was not the time to give it to her, especially since he had no idea what the envelope contained. Lew thought for a moment about opening the envelope and looking through its contents, then pushed the thought aside. There was something snoopily offensive about looking through a dead man's property. It was better, Lew decided, to let a man's secrets be buried with him, and he shut the door—and Phil Durban's past—firmly behind him.

"When can you come into the city?" Al Sheldrock asked Ellen on the telephone. Al was Phil's accountant, and he was paying the bills until Ellen could open a checking account of her own. She had been slightly surprised to find that she could not sign on Phil's checking account.

"Would two weeks from now be all right?" Ellen asked, wanting to put it off as far as she dared. She dreaded meeting Phil's accountant, dreaded having to think about money, because when Phil was alive, he had handled the finances and paid all the bills. Ellen had not had a checking account of her own since college. She did not know a thing about the details of the mortgage, had signed the joint tax returns without even looking at them, and had never bought anything more expensive than a winter coat—and when she'd done that, she had always checked with Phil to see how much they could afford. Phil had always said that Ellen didn't need to know anything about money, and she had agreed with him. Everyone knew that women weren't good with money, that they didn't understand it. Besides, it wasn't feminine.

"Two weeks would be fine," Al said, and Ellen promptly put it out of her mind, because money was the one thing she'd never have to worry about. Phil had left a fortune in life insurance.

You'll never have to worry, Phil had told her when he bought the hundred-thousand-dollar policy. In 1959, when a designer dress cost $49.95, a pound of sirloin 75¢, and the minimum wage was a dollar an hour, $100,000 was a fortune.

You'll never have to worry if anything ever happens to me, Phil had said. At the time it had been inconceivable that "anything" would happen to Phil. But it had. And now Ellen remembered his words exactly: *Never have to worry*.

One hundred thousand dollars! Why, one hundred thousand dollars was more than a fortune! One hundred thousand dollars was all the money in the world!

3

PHIL'S OFFICE *WAS* PHIL.

On his desk stood a silver-framed portrait of Ellen, taken on her twenty-fifth birthday. Tucked into its corner was a snapshot that Phil had taken of her in Vermont. They had skied all that morning. That day, at noon, she wore Phil's bulky hand-knit Irish sweater, a blue ski cap pulled down to her eyebrows. Her skin looked polished, glowing from the cold and the exercise, and her dazzling smile almost eclipsed her remarkable eyes. Ellen remembered that afternoon. A blizzard moved in. Phil bought a bottle of red wine, and they spent the afternoon in their room at the lodge, in front of the fireplace, drinking wine and making love. They had slept through dinner and, at eleven, had awakened, ravenous. Almost ten inches of new snow had fallen. They couldn't even open the door to their cabin, so they had dined at midnight on what they found in the room: a chocolate bar, an apple, and a jar of homemade corn relish Ellen had bought in a souvenir shop. They had made love again and, snowbound, their weekend had stretched into a four-day capsule of tender joyousness.

Ellen put the framed picture and the snapshot into the shopping bag she had brought with her and tried not to remember.

She wanted to save her memories, to hoard them for future use. She didn't want to use them up too soon or wear them out by overuse. She swept the pictures of the children and the snapshot of Irving into the shopping bag without even looking at them.

The Day-at-a-Glance desk diary was still opened to the Monday after the Sunday Phil had had his accident. Neatly noted in Phil's bold block printing were Phil's lunch date for the day, a sales department meeting at three, a reminder to himself to make a dentist's appointment, and a note to pull together the quarterly sales figures.

Ellen wondered who had canceled the lunch date and what had happened at the sales department meeting and if anyone had gathered the first quarter's sales figures. Ellen didn't have the faintest idea. Men's worlds with their lunch dates, meetings, and sales figures were lightyears away from women's worlds with their car pools, toilet training, and washer-drier combinations. Although she had been married for ten years, Ellen realized that she didn't have the faintest idea what Phil did all day long to earn the money that supported them.

She put the desk diary into the shopping bag and then reconsidered: she put it into the trash can under the desk. A week later she would regret it, wishing she had kept the desk diary, thinking she should have saved it for Danny.

The desk drawers yielded half-empty rolls of peppermint Life Savers; a box of Instant-Shine tissues; a box of Kleenex; the Yankees' schedule for the 1959 season; boxes of business cards, and note pads printed with the legend: "From the desk of Phil Durban"; and a crayoned picture of a grinning bright blue alligator captioned in childish letters: "See you later, alligator"—a present from Danny to his father.

Ellen threw everything away except for Danny's picture, wondering briefly why the upper-left-hand drawer was empty. Had Phil cleaned it out for some reason? Or did he never use it?

Ellen swallowed hard, hoping to save her tears until she got home.

The closet was empty except for a broken umbrella, which Ellen threw away, and a white shirt of Phil's worn once, which she put into the shopping bag. On the closet floor stood an F.A.O. Schwarz shopping bag. It contained a junior chemistry set and a bottle of Miss Dior. The chemistry set was obviously

intended for Brenda's birthday coming up on April 20. The
Miss Dior was for her—Phil always gave her presents on each
of the children's birthdays—a way of thanking her every year
for them and the pleasure they brought him. Ellen decided to
give the chemistry set to Brenda just as Phil would have wanted.
A last, loving gift from a proud father to a talented daughter.
And she opened the Miss Dior, dabbing a little on her wrist.
She was reminded by its sophisticated fragrance of the image
Phil insisted she maintain—that of a sophisticated, worldly,
alluring woman—an image completely at odds with her own.
But, as Phil always said, he was the romantic one. Her senses
reeling, Ellen inhaled the opulent fragrance, the last, loving
gift from a romantic husband to a cherished wife.

Ellen had come to the office to find Phil, and she had found
him. Yankee fan. Sales executive. Proud father. Loving husband. And, even after ten years of marriage, romantic lover.
Ellen blinked back her tears and turned to leave the office.

"Can I see you for a moment?" Lew Swann's voice interrupted Ellen's emotional memories. Lew's voice was just like
Lew: used to taking charge, used to getting what he wanted.
Yet, with it all, there was a light, wry tone to it, too, as if to
say he knew that it all had been handed to him on a silver
platter. All he had to do was to keep the platter polished, a
task not always as easy as it looked.

"Of course," Ellen said, smiling as best she could. The last
thing she wanted to do was make polite conversation. She
wanted to go home and cry alone.

"It's a bitch about Phil. A real bitch," Lew said when they had
settled in his surprisingly modest office.

Ellen didn't have to say anything and didn't.

Phil's age, Lew Swann had the clean-cut, Princeton-Har-
vard-Yale look: impeccably cut hair the color of burnished
butterscotch and a compact, athletically fit body that made him
seem a good half-dozen years younger than he was.

"A car crash." Lew shook his head. "That's a hell of a way
to go..."

"Is there a 'good way' to go?" Ellen asked. Something about
Lew made it easy for her to say what was on her mind.

"No, I suppose not." To her surprise, Ellen found herself
noting that Lew Swann had the sexiest voice she had ever heard.
It was all velvet and steel, tender and strong.

"A neighbor told me Phil was lucky," Ellen said. "He said that at least it was fast. That Phil hadn't felt a thing." Ellen shrugged. "I guess he meant it as consolation."

"Are you going to be all right? You and the kids?" Lew asked.

"I guess so," Ellen said wanly. "Eventually. Danny still thinks his Daddy is away on a business trip. He keeps asking when Daddy is coming home. Brenda seems to understand. But she's very quiet. She keeps everything inside."

"And you?" Lew asked. "How about you?"

"How about me?" Ellen repeated. Her voice cracked, and she found herself in tears. Huge, wet, hot tears. They ran out of her eyes and down her face, trails of pain. Blindly, she groped in her handbag for a tissue. Gratefully, she accepted the big linen handkerchief Lew handed her across the desk and blew her nose and wiped her eyes.

"I'm sorry," she said when she could talk again. "I didn't mean to break down like this." She felt splotchy and ugly and forced a smile she didn't feel. "I guess I'm not exactly the merry widow."

"Jesus Christ!" Lew shook his head. "What do you expect of yourself. Ellen? It's not going to be a picnic for you. Alone with two kids."

"I console myself by thinking that things can only get better," Ellen said, smoothing the soggy handkerchief across her lap and then burying her face in it when she broke down and began to cry again.

Except for the immediate family, Lew Swann was the first person who seemed really nice, really concerned. Ellen had the feeling—maybe a little paranoid, maybe not—that other people sought a little emotional juice from Phil's tragedy, a little jolt of feeling lucky and maybe even slightly superior that they had escaped. That *it* hadn't happened to them.

Ellen blew her nose again, wiped away the tears, sniffled, and swallowed hard. Bravely, she forced her red-rimmed eyes up into Lew's and exposed her now makeup-innocent and blotchy face to him. She forced another phony smile, thinking she was getting good at it, at phony smiles. "Things have *got* to get better," she said. "They certainly can't get worse."

Lew swallowed. *I can't do it*, he thought. *I can't tell her. I can't tell her about the money Phil borrowed. Not now. Later. The five thousand will have to wait until later.*

After a moment, he cleared his throat.

"Look, I want you to have this." He reached into his desk, pulled out a checkbook, and scrawled on it. "It's Phil's," he said, tearing out a check and pushing it across the desk to Ellen. "Phil's bonus for the quarter. Figures were up eight percent. Phil did a hell of a job."

As he spoke, Lew wondered what he thought he was doing. He had planned to apply the bonus money against the loan, but now he was giving the widow the money.

"I can't take it!" Ellen wrapped her arms around herself and shuddered. "Money from the grave . . ."

"Take it!" Lew urged. "Phil earned it. It's yours now!" Turning down money! She was crazy!

"He left a hundred thousand dollars! I don't need *money*, Mr. Swann!" Ellen said, her voice shockingly loud in the quiet office. "I'm rich! I'm a rich widow! I don't need money! I need a husband!"

Ellen got up abruptly and, in doing so, overturned the chair she'd been sitting in. Tears of rage and loss and fury and hopelessness scalded her face. Ellen stood there, sobbing, unable even to see the door to leave Lew's office.

Suddenly, there was warmth and comfort. She felt strong arms around her, and she remembered how Phil used to hold her when she needed love and comfort, and how Phil could make everything better. She closed her eyes, and for a confused moment she thought the arms around her were Phil's. Lew held Ellen close as she leaned against him, her head on his shoulder. He spoke softly to her, and Ellen realized that it wasn't Phil who was holding her. It was Lew.

She pushed him away so suddenly and so violently that he tripped over the fallen chair and almost fell. She fled from his office, fled from his comfort, fled from his warmth, fled from her feelings.

It was disgusting, Ellen thought as she got on the train in Grand Central. Phil had been dead for barely two weeks, and she was already in another man's arms—allowing him to hold her, allowing him to comfort her.

How could she *do* such a thing? Feel such a thing? What kind of woman was she anyway?

Because what she had remembered as she sat in Lew's office

and talked to him was the way Phil used to tease her and tell her that Lew had eyes for her . . . that Lew had the hots for her.

"Stop it!" Ellen used to tell Phil. "He doesn't, and you know it!"

She had meant what she said, but she was also, deep down, flattered and flustered. Lewis Swann was a very attractive man.

He was also married.

Until the last few months, Lew's marriage had been a good one: sexy, warm, and close. But it hadn't started out that way.

Lew Swann and Reenie Elliot had had a big church wedding—at the Episcopalian church in Syosset where Reenie's family were Socially Registered and had registered socially for three generations. The Elliots had been against the marriage because, although richer than Reenie's family, Lew's family had zero social status.

Lew's father, Max, ran a paint factory. Lew's grandfather had been a German immigrant, a man who wore white overalls and painted other people's living rooms. The Elliots were appalled at their daughter's choice of husband, but when they found out that Lew's mother was a Carrington—a Locust Valley/Palm Beach/Dark Harbor Carrington—the bitter pill was sweetened just enough for them to relent and give their lukewarm approval to the marriage.

On the way from the church to the reception, Reenie, who had threatened everything from suicide to elopement if her parents didn't let her marry Lew Swann, turned to her brand-new husband and said, "I wonder why we did *that*?"

Reenie spent her wedding night crying, and two weeks later, on the last night of their Bermuda honeymoon, Reenie drank almost half a bottle of Gordon's gin and finally let Lew make love to her.

Reenie—and the marriage—seemed to settle down. In the next three years she gave birth to two daughters (much to Max's disappointment; he wanted *boys*) and divided her time between them and the horses that had been the real passion of her life since she'd been nine years old. If Lew's marriage wasn't ecstatic, he accepted its tepid pleasures, valuing them for more than they were worth, comparing them always to the battlefield of his own parents' marriage.

During the first eleven years of marriage, Lew had never touched another woman. It wasn't such a moral triumph, he reminded himself, because, for one thing, he had sublimated his energies in the tricky task of dealing with the difficult, demanding, infuriating, capricious, but endearing Max.

But, within the past eighteen months, two major changes had occurred in Lew's life.

The first was that Max, who had been dabbling in real estate on the Island, got into the construction business. He built a housing development on the scrub land outside the once-fashionable, now-commercial town of Huntington and made a bundle. Max immediately began to assemble acreage for a second housing development, this one to be built on the equally unalluring land outside Melville. Consumed by his new passion, Max turned Decor over to Lew. "You run the goddamn thing," he had said unceremoniously, dumping the company into Lew's lap without warning.

Getting out from under Max's shadow was one kind of liberation. The second change was in his marriage. At the age of thirty-two, Reenie suddenly seemed to have awakened sexually. She wanted Lew. She wanted him often. And she made it flatteringly clear to him just how *much* she wanted him. She even seemed to be interested in Decor—asking Lew what had happened at the office and how business was going—something she'd never expressed the slightest interest in before.

The dual liberation seemed to Lew to be just reward for the years of patience and forbearance, and life seemed finally to be settling into a happy groove. Lew hoped it would go on forever.

Not quite. It lasted for a year and a half. Then, without warning, without apparent reason, Reenie turned as cold as ice, behaving as if the months of her passionate sexuality had simply never happened. Confused and hurt, Lew admitted to himself that he didn't understand his wife.

As he picked up the chair Ellen had overturned, he wondered how long he could continue to be a faithful husband to a woman whose emotions ran hot and cold. He wondered how long he could continue to be, apparently, the only monogamous man he knew.

In a selfish way, he was glad Phil had died owing him money. That way, he had a tie to Ellen, a reason to see her again.

*   *   *

Ellen was haunted by loss. She was terrified that her children would die, that she would lose them as she had lost Phil. She awakened in the middle of the night, seized by the icy, heart-stopping terror that Brenda and Danny were gone. She got up and ran through the house to their rooms to see if they were there, touching them to reassure herself that they were still warm, still alive, still breathing.

Danny, who was six, acted like he was four. He was babyish, whiny, weepy, clingy, inconsolable. He kept asking her when Daddy was coming home.

No matter how Ellen answered, no matter what she said, no matter how many times she tried to explain, Danny didn't understand. All he knew was that he missed his Daddy and wanted to know when he was coming home.

Unlike Danny, who wore his heart on his sleeve, Brenda hid her feelings. Ellen had heard Brenda tell her friends in an eerily matter-of-fact way that her father was dead and would be gone forever. But Brenda constantly questioned Ellen about how long forever really was. Did it have a beginning? How was it measured? Was there a special calendar for forever? If not, why not? What if forever stopped? Why couldn't it stop? Who said so?

Ellen tried to answer Brenda's questions. The unsatisfied look in Brenda's eyes told Ellen she had failed. She remembered how she and Phil used to joke in exasperation that, unlike other kids whose first words were "Mommy" and "Daddy," Brenda's first word was "why." Only now it wasn't funny.

Brenda became moody and suspicious. She told Ellen that she was afraid Danny would die; she was afraid that Ellen would die. Ellen, who shared the same ominous fears, did not know how to calm Brenda's anxieties.

"Something terrible is going to happen," Brenda said.

"All that's going to happen is your birthday," Ellen said, trying her best to give Brenda something cheerful to look forward to. "Aren't you excited about your party?"

"I suppose so," Brenda said half-heartedly. She had invited all twenty-five boys and girls in her class. "Do you want to know who else I invited?"

"Sure," smiled Ellen. "Who?"

"Daddy," said Brenda. "I mailed an invitation to his office. Just in case."

4

AL SHELDROCK KNEW EXACTLY WHAT PEOPLE THOUGHT OF accountants. That they were boring people in a boring profession, adding up boring numbers. Unimaginative. Uncreative. Dull. Cloddish. Plodding. Cautious. Drones. Those were the words that came to people's minds when they thought about CPAs, and no one knew it better than Al. Except that Al had a secret: not one of those words applied to him. But, although he knew it, the world didn't. Not yet.

Al's parents, who were musicians, were appalled by his choice of profession and so embarrassed that they didn't even tell their friends what their son did for a living. They usually said that Al was a band manager.

Al's parents were what are called in the trade studio musicians. His father played the saxophone and, unlike many musicians, worked steadily as a backup man for commercials and pop recording artists. Al's mother, who had met Al's father during a recording session for a mouthwash commercial, was a singer. And *she* worked steadily doing commercials and backup, and once had dubbed the theme song for an early Tony Curtis costume epic. Al's parents made plenty of money—and never had a dime. Al grew up on a bologna-caviar seesaw, and

28

his parents' loud, bitter arguments about money gave Al the idea of going into accounting.

Good financial planning, Al realized, could spare his parents—and people like them—financial misery by allowing for the peaks and valleys in their earnings. But accounting, Al soon discovered, told him only part of what he needed to know. Law, he realized, would tell him the rest. Contract law, to be specific. In the entertainment business, getting a job was one thing, getting paid for it was often quite another.

So while Al crunched numbers by day at one of the nation's biggest accounting firms, he cracked the law books by night. The circles under his eyes were getting down to his knees, and the day Ellen Durban walked into his office, Al had survived the last three days on four hours' sleep a night.

"It's nice to meet you finally," Al said, getting up and shaking Ellen's hand. "I'm sorry the circumstances are . . . what they are."

Ellen smiled wanly. "It's nice to meet you, too. Phil spoke about you so much."

Al blinked and tried not to be obvious about it. Knowing Phil, Al had expected Ellen to be on the flashy side. A pretty, curvaceous blonde maybe, or a sultry smoky brunette. He'd expected tight clothes, heavy makeup, dragon-lady nails, jungle gardenia perfume—a real mantrap. Instead, she was pure Tiffany. Everything about her was classy: the ecru linen dress and string-knit cardigan, pearl earrings and slim gold bracelet, softly waved coppery hair, the understated makeup, and blue-green eyes to die from. . . .

"Sit down," he said, indicating the visitor's chair. Then, noticing the strained expression around her mouth, he smiled. "I know what you're thinking. An accountant. Yuck!"

Ellen had to smile. She nodded. Al had read her mind.

From everything Phil had said about Al Sheldrock, Ellen had imagined her version of a typical accountant. A middle-aged Albert Einstein, small, wispy, slightly stooped. Instead, Al was tall—six feet two—well built, dark-haired, and even-featured. He was saved from blandness by an intriguing nose that looked as if it had been broken—maybe more than once.

But what stood between Al and real attractiveness were fifteen pounds—a bachelor, he lived on doughnuts and pizza snatched on the run—and unflattering bookworm glasses. Al—unlike Phil, unlike Lew—was the kind of steady, unexciting, reliable man Ellen had always felt comfortable with. He was about as sexy as the cluttered, depressing cubicle he occupied in the vast offices of Cooley & Heiser on East Thirty-fourth Street and the gray-bound copies of the IRS tax codes that lined the bookshelves of the cubicle.

"I brought everything that was in the safe," Ellen said, handing Al the manila envelope. She felt anxious. She had never been in an accountant's office. She felt intimidated and, although she didn't know why, defensive. "Except for the cash. There was a thousand dollars in the drawer where he kept the financial records. I left it there. Is that okay?"

"Fine," said Al as he riffled through the papers. He had a deep, reassuring voice that made Ellen feel calmer. "I'll make an analysis of your finances," he said. "It'll take a few days or so. Can you come in again? Say two weeks from now?"

"Yes," Ellen said and got up, anxious to leave. She felt out of her depth, out of place here. "I'll see you then."

"By the way, do you know where Phil got the cash? What it was for?" Al asked.

"No," said Ellen. "I wondered myself. It was marked PPG. Do you know who PPG is?"

"I don't know," Al shrugged. "But people don't usually keep that much money around in cash."

"Phil wasn't just 'people,'" Ellen reminded Al. "He was different . . . larger than life . . ."

"I know it's difficult," Al said in gentle warning. "But try not to romanticize Phil too much."

"I wasn't romanticizing him," Ellen denied. "He was wonderful," she said, and her eyes misted.

When Ellen was gone, Al buzzed for Gail Berger. Gail was Al's assistant, an excellent bookkeeper who was taking night courses at NYU, cramming for the CPA exam. "*Something to fall back on*," her mother said. Leaving unsaid: *if you don't get married*.

Gail was dark and small-boned, handsome rather than pretty, with glossy walnut hair, amber eyes, and a narrow, elegantly boned face. Her makeup was subtly flattering, emphasizing her eyes and long lashes. She wore a smart tawny dress that set off her petite figure perfectly. She was one of those wonderfully turned-out New York working women featured in fashion magazines.

Gail and Al had gone out three times, and they were still in that early nervous stage of courtship when *she* wonders if she's going to be asked again and *he* wonders if he's going to be accepted or rejected. Al and Gail danced around each other cautiously, moths around a flame, playing with danger and desire.

"There's no way he could afford a new car, a fur jacket for his wife, and all those Brooks Brothers clothes on his salary," Gail commented a week later when she and Al had finished going through Phil's finances. "Not even including his bonus."

"Perhaps he had a source of income we don't know about," Al said, well aware of how secretive people tended to be about money, of how much they distorted, exaggerated, lied, or concealed about their finances, depending on their personalities. "Maybe he had a trust fund, a private income, or a rich uncle."

"Maybe he was a gambler," Gail grinned. "A lucky gambler."

At that, the telephone on Al's desk rang. It was Lewis Swann. He wanted to talk about a loan he had made . . . a loan to Phil Durban.

Al covered the receiver and looked at Gail. He raised his eyebrows. "I hope Phil Durban *did* have a source of income we don't know about—for Ellen's sake."

Everyone who knew Ellen remarked on how brave, how strong she was. Some people were unexpectedly nice, others incredibly insensitive. Three different women actually told Ellen she was lucky to be so young when Phil died; it would be so much easier for her to find another husband. More than a few men made it clear that their sexual services were available for the asking.

A few weeks after Phil's accident, Carol Mattison's husband, Jimmy, appeared one afternoon. He got to the subject on his mind with almost no preliminaries.

"You look terrible, Ellen," he said, and put his arm around her. "You know what's wrong with you? Your problem is that you need sex. It's tough on women to get along without it once they're used to it."

"For your information, I'm not interested in sex," Ellen said. "And I'm especially not interested in sex with you. Just get out of here!"

He shrugged, showing what a good sport he was. "You'd be in a better mood if you were getting it regularly," he advised, and, on the way out, he left his card on the dining table. Penciled in under his office number was his home number. Suppose she *did* call? Didn't he care if Carol answered? Incredible.

Ellen threw the card into the garbage with the coffee grounds and the orange peels where she thought it belonged.

And Andy, who ran the lawn service and played in the same Saturday afternoon softball game Phil had, came in one afternoon and asked for ice water, something he did now and then. When Ellen turned to get ice cubes from the freezer, she suddenly felt Andy's arm around her.

"I've always liked you," he said, his face close to hers.

"Andy! Please!" Ellen tried to push him away, embarrassed for herself and for him. She could smell the oil he used on the mowers.

"Most of the women here, they're housewives. Dull as dishwater. But not you. You're different. You walk sexy, Mrs. Durban. I mean it. All the boys say so, too..."

Ellen was humiliated at the thought of being discussed by the kids who mowed the lawn and weeded the roses. Andy was strong and his arm pinned her. She felt suddenly afraid. The thought that he might rape her crossed her mind like some terrible, dark nightmare, and she struggled to be free of him.

Just then there was a banging on the kitchen door.

"Hey, Andy?" It was one of the kids. "I got a stone caught in the edger, and it broke. Now what do I do?"

"Shit!" Andy muttered as the banging continued. "Hold on, for Chrissake's!" He went out to tend to the edger, leaving Ellen limp with fear.

When she fired him, he was furious. "You're not getting rid of me so easily," he threatened. "I know where you keep the keys. I'll be back, and the next time no one's going to interrupt."

Ellen changed the hiding place of the keys from under the mat to under the third flowerpot in the row that sat on the windowsill. Still uneasy, she spent seventy-five dollars to have new locks put on the doors.

Ellen's next-door neighbor, Len Dessault, got into the habit of "dropping over." He never made a direct pass at Ellen, but his fingers always seemed to accidentally touch hers when she handed him a cup of coffee, and his arm would settle casually over her shoulders when they stood at the kitchen window watching Brenda and Danny play catch. If Ellen gave him the slightest encouragement, she knew he'd be all too happy to offer his services, and she walked a tightrope with Len: fearing equally to encourage him or offend him. She wanted—she needed—the safety of a man living nearby.

Ellen tried to blank them all out of her mind and usually succeeded. And, deep down, she hoped the women who told her it would be easy for her to find another husband were right. She missed Phil in a thousand ways a thousand times a day. When he had been alive, she had felt important. Now that he was dead, she felt invisible. Even to herself.

In a crisis, the most unexpected people can turn out to be rescuers. In Ellen's crisis, the unexpected rescuer turned out, time after time, to be her mother-in-law.

Ellen had never considered Caroline Durban as a natural ally. In fact, Ellen could not imagine two women more different than Caroline and herself.

Ellen, at twenty-nine, still carried remnants of the tomboy-ishness her mother thought she'd never outgrow. Her wavy hair would never submit to hairdresser or hairspray. Her snappy stride was more suited to loafers than spike heels. Her slim, tidy body looked better in sweaters and skirts than frills and ruffles.

Caroline, with her perfect, every-strand-in-place bouffant coiffeur and faultless manicure, was the picture of a lady's lady. Caroline was always beautifully dressed. Her shoes and handbags always matched. Her voice was modulated, her lip-stick never smeared, compacts never spilled powder in her purse, and her stockings simply did not run. She appeared to live for her facials and beauty treatments (which certainly seemed to work, since, at fifty-six, Caroline looked barely forty); the endless parade of Bonwit's, Bergdorf's, Saks', and Bloom-ingdale's shopping bags; her living room decor, charity boards, bridge parties, and benefit luncheons. Her husband, Tommy, a corporate lawyer, was the prototype of the successful exec-utive in an affluent society. He adored his wife, functioning as a gray velvet background for her vivid color in the fore-ground. Caroline and Phil—who was an only child—had been a closed corporation—Ellen always the outsider—and she was

therefore surprised and pleased when Caroline complimented
her on how well she had been coping since Phil's accident.

"Phil always said you were the strong one," Caroline said
in her wispy, feminine voice. "You've been wonderful since
the accident. And you've been marvelous with the children. I
know it can't be easy."

"Thank you." Ellen was warmed by the two compliments:
Phil's and Caroline's. "But I'm not nearly as strong as I look . . ."
she continued, and then stopped herself before she admitted to
Caroline that she wore Phil's pajamas to bed every night because they smelled like him. And she did not want to admit
that she woke in the night terrified that because she had lost
Phil she would lose the children, too. And, further, Ellen was
not in the habit of confiding in anyone. Except in Phil. And,
in a man's world, certainly not in women. Women were the
enemy; women were the competition.

"Do you have enough money?" Caroline asked cautiously,
not wanting to offend Ellen but ready to offer help if it were
needed.

"Oh, yes," said Ellen. "More than enough. I found a thousand dollars in one of Phil's drawers. In cash! And then there's
the insurance! One hundred thousand dollars! I have an appointment to see the accountant about it next week. Could I
leave Brenda and Danny at your house while I'm gone?"

"Of course," said Caroline. "You don't even have to ask."

The week before Brenda's birthday, Lewis Swann called.

"Is everything all right?" he asked in his steel-and-velvet
voice. "I have an invitation Brenda sent to her father."

"Brenda seemed fine," Ellen said. "I heard her tell everyone
that her daddy was dead. And then she sent the invitation. I'm
worried about her."

"She's having trouble accepting it," Lew said gently. "But
what do you want me to do with the invitation?"

Ellen thought for a moment, weary from trying to answer
questions that had no answers.

"I guess," she finally said, "just throw it away."

"All right," Lew said, and then hesitated. "Ellen, have lunch
with me next time you're in the city?"

Lew told himself he'd discuss the loan with her. It would
be a business lunch. He was inviting her to lunch because he
had business to discuss with her . . . not because she had been

on his mind... not because he remembered what it was like to hold her in his arms... not because Reenie had refused to let him touch her since... since, come to think of it, the day of Phil Durban's funeral.

"No, Lew. I don't think so," Ellen said, still embarrassed by her behavior at their previous meeting. "I'm not very good company these days."

Lew almost said something about letting him decide whether or not she was good company, but he didn't. His own confused motives kept him silent.

Awkwardly, they said good-bye, and Lew wondered, when he hung up, how his father, Max, would have handled the situation. Max most definitely would not have hung up without setting a date. And Max most definitely would not have been conflicted about what he wanted....

Max Swann was a man's man astride a man's world. He was a short, compact man of uninhibited appetites: appetites for sex, food, drink, money, power, pleasure, control. He was possessed by passions rather than emotions; he was magnetic rather than handsome—a cross between Patton and Humphrey Bogart, with weathered skin, agate blue eyes, and dark blond hair brightened with silver. Women had never been known to resist him, nor vice versa.

He met Johanna Wycoff at that most potentially romantic of all encounters: the job interview.

Max had advertised for a secretary, and Johanna had answered the ad: nose by John Converse, skin by László, hair by Kenneth (Moonstruck Mink this month), body by Pilates, clothes by Bendel, and brains by IBM. Max took one look and decided he was going to get into her pants.

"You're no secretary!" Max said after reading her résumé. It listed her former job at the Wycoff Box and Carton Company as "executive assistant." "You're a rich girl whose old man gave you a job."

"I'm a rich girl whose old lady gave me a job, *and* I'm the best secretary you or anyone will ever have," Johanna retorted. Her *mother* had founded the family carton business and was its president. As Johanna spoke, she sized up Max and decided she liked what she saw: the blue-eyed, weatherbeaten, craggy, sunburned, crew-cut, rough-and-ready type. "I can do the work of *two* secretaries!"

"Like hell!" Max growled, the smile implicit if you knew where to look. And Johanna knew where to look.

"I'll prove it," she said. "Your ad said you'd pay a hundred dollars a week. Well, I'll work for you a week *free*. Then, if you decide to hire me, it'll cost you two hundred a week. Is that a deal?"

"It's a deal," Max agreed, even more turned on now that he knew she was a rich girl. Max preferred rich girls; after all, he'd married one. And he liked them not too thin, with good tits and sharp brains. He liked women who were a delight to the mind *and* the body. So what if he didn't need two secretaries.

By the time the interview was over, Max was ready to play around. And Johanna was ready to play for keeps.

Max Swann and Esme Carrington were a mismatch not made in heaven.

Esme was a Syosset debutante, used to country-club parties, horse shows, and boarding schools that taught table manners with the same seriousness with which they taught Latin and math.

Shortly after their first meeting, they married and Esme went straight from her father's big white house in Syosset to a big white house Max built on a hill in Locust Valley—a house, by the way, that Max couldn't quite afford at the time.

Esme had three babies in four years. "You were born six months after we got married!" Max had told Lew a thousand times. "Premature, your mother's parents called it. Hell, I called it a good time. Damn good! Your mother was one very good-looking girl."

Esme did what she had been brought up to do: she went to the club, organized horse-show balls, and served on hospital and library committees. Max devoted himself to business so that he could pay for the house, the babies, the live-in help, the stable fees, the vet's bills, and the country club dues—and also because he was dynastic and wanted to build an empire to leave to his children. All of whom had disappointed him—except for Lew. One brother, Max Junior, drove a truck for an asphalt company and actually—incredibly, according to Max Senior—liked it. The other kid was a girl: she would have made a good lawyer, according to Max's master plan, but she got married during Christmas vacation in her first year of college and dropped out. Max was philosophical about his daughter. "She's a girl," he commented to a friend. "What do you expect?" Despite his bluster, he really was disappointed. The idea of having a lawyer in the family had appealed to him.

As the years went by, Max became resentful because Esme wasn't a good cook and a full-time mother as his own mother had been, and Esme resented Max because he was not as socially adept as her father. Max did not exactly fit in with what he called Esme's lah-di-dah friends.

"Deb!" Max hurled at Esme during their (frequent) arguments, mad because the house was a mess despite servants and nothing was ready for dinner.

"Who do you think you married?" Esme retaliated. "The housekeeper?"

Inevitably, Max, with his robust appetites, began having affairs. At first, they weren't much more than a series of fast fucks, and Esme realized it and was smart enough not to make a fuss.

Inevitably, the girls-for-the-night wearied Max. He wanted something more and, being Max, found it.

Inevitably, it was his secretary.

Except that Johanna Wycoff was no ordinary secretary whiling her time away with a boring job until she dug up a husband. Johanna was, with ambition to motivate her, the best, most efficient secretary Max Swann or anyone had ever had—exactly as she had promised.

Max Swann had two interests: money and sex. Unusual, actually, because often men who are obsessed with money turn out to be not very interested in sex. Not so with Max. In any event, apart from his absorbing interest in sex, he wanted to be rich, richer, richest. And Johanna, who wanted to outdo the family that had ganged up on her, wanted him to be rich, richer, richest. And so she devoted herself to running the day-to-day details of the construction business Max was building, leaving him free to wheel and deal. The first housing development led to a second at a time when the house with the white picket fence was every American's (affordable) dream. To move from building houses to buying the land on which to build them was the logical second step. And so Max added a real estate empire to his construction empire. Max then added a chain of real estate brokerages to handle the sales (and make the commissions). It next made sense to sell people all the things they needed to put in the houses, so Max began building shopping centers, all of which, in four years, made him rich beyond even his most wildly abandoned greedy fantasies. All of which made him happier, more invincible, more self-confident, and more boisterous than ever. And much less interested in marriage.

All of which made Johanna—now minked, sabled, and Mercedesed—miserable. She had tried kindness. She had tried patience. She had promised to wait. She had drowned him in love and kisses and every kind of red-hot sex she could think of. Still, no dice.

Max hemmed and hawed around, promising to speak to Esme, promising to tell her he wanted a divorce, but somehow never getting around to it.

Max stayed married, and Johanna stayed determined.

"There's a special present for you from Daddy," Ellen said on the night before Brenda's birthday and gave her the big package from F.A.O. Schwarz. Brenda, with her usual impatience, pulled away the ribbons and the wrappings, tossed them aside, and oohed and aahed over the racks of test tubes, the bunsen burner, the vials of chemicals, the little slips of litmus paper, the instructions for the different experiments.

"*Daddy* gave me this?" Brenda asked carefully, wanting to make absolutely sure it was Daddy who had chosen it.

"Yes," said Ellen. "He bought it for you before he . . ." She stopped suddenly, like everyone else not wanting to use the next word. "Before his accident."

"Daddy didn't answer my invitation," Brenda said as if Ellen hadn't spoken. "I wrote RSVP on the bottom. Maybe he'll come anyway!"

"No, baby," Ellen answered softly.

There was, between mother and daughter, a moment of terrible silence. A mother who knew she could never, never replace a lost father; a daughter, furious at fate, with only a mother for a target.

"But he gave me a present," Brenda insisted. "That means he remembered. He didn't forget."

"He bought it *before* the accident," Ellen explained again, wondering if giving Brenda the chemistry set had been the right thing to do. How did you know what to do? How did you know what was right and what was wrong when you were in a situation you had never faced, a situation you had never dreamed of?

Brenda looked down at the chemistry set and ran her hands over it as if to convince herself that it really existed, and then she looked at Ellen.

"Well, you can't explain forever," Brenda said. "I bet you're wrong about Daddy coming to the party."

The party began beautifully, with the girls in party dresses and hair ribbons and the boys with carefully combed hair and blazers. Brenda had lovingly set out the chemistry set—its vials and beakers and petri dishes, its bunsen burner and litmus papers—in a shrine-like display. Ellen's present, a real telescope on a tripod, won Ellen a hug and a kiss and the biggest compliment of all: "That really sends me!" Brenda kept exclaiming, treating each of her guests to a peep through it.

And, as her guests oohed and aahed, Brenda kept glancing toward the door. Hoping it would open. Hoping Daddy would be there. Wanting the nightmare to be over. *That* was the birthday present she wanted.

Over the hamburgers and french fries, Brenda still looked toward the door, drawn as if by a powerful magnet. Hoping that her father wouldn't let her down, *knowing* that he would never let her be unhappy.

And when the ice cream and cake were served, Brenda just stared at the door, *willing* it to open, *willing* her father to be alive.

And when she blew out the candles and made a wish, she glanced once again at the door, and Ellen knew what her wish had been.

But the door didn't open.

And Brenda finally knew that it never would, that the nightmare wasn't a bad dream that the nightmare was real, and that Daddy was gone.

Suddenly Brenda snatched the poker from the fireplace and smashed the chemistry set, breaking the vials and the beakers and the petri dishes into a thousand useless shards, as sharp and dangerous as her now defeated hopes. And, as her classmates looked on in confused horror. Brenda fled into her room and slammed the door behind her, refusing to come out.

That night for the first time since Phil's accident Brenda allowed Ellen to comfort her. In tears, Brenda lay on her bed, howling her grief. Ellen held her, feeling her convulsive racking sobs, wondering how much pain anyone could absorb. She held Brenda in her arms until, finally, finally, her sobbing subsided enough to permit her to speak.

"Mommy, am I ever going to stop missing Daddy?"

Another unanswerable question, Ellen thought, but she tried to answer it anyway.

"Probably not," she said softly. "But it won't always hurt so much."

There was a long silence while Brenda thought over her mother's words and decided to accept them. Then she said, "I decided something today. I'm going to be a chemist."

"I thought you were going to be an executive," Ellen said, smiling. Brenda had loved going into Decor with Phil and playing "office."

Brenda thought for a moment. "I'm going to be both," she said. "Just like Daddy." Before going into sales, Phil had been a chemist, a specialist in the aniline dyes used in the manufacture of paint.

Ellen smiled silently at her daughter's impossible dream. Little girls didn't grow up to be chemists—or executives. They grew up to be wives and mothers. But Ellen didn't say anything to Brenda; Brenda had already had enough dreams shattered for one day.

Poor Brenda. She was a daddy's girl and now Daddy was gone.

From that day on, Brenda enshrined her father. He became a god, a hero, an idol, and she would not tolerate the slightest criticism of him. Brenda's room became a temple to her father's memory. Photographs of him lined the bulletin board. The silver picture frame Ellen had brought home from his office stood on Brenda's bureau and she polished it religiously. She went to sleep every night with one of Phil's sweaters clutched in her arms.

Ellen understood exactly how Brenda felt because now she felt the same way. She remembered only the good parts.

When Phil had been alive, the birthday parties had been fun.

When Phil had been alive, people had been interested in her.

When Phil had been alive, the telephone had never stopped ringing.

When Phil had been alive, the house had been full of life.

When Phil had been alive, the children had been happy.

When Phil had been alive, *she* had been happy.

When Phil had been alive, everything had been perfect.

Phil.

With a strong beak of a nose, satiny olive skin, flashing green eyes, and long, dark lashes, he had been the most popular man on campus at the University of Pennsylvania. A senior when Ellen had been a freshman, Phil had a white Oldsmobile convertible with red leather seats, a Brooks Brothers-J. Press wardrobe of tweed and cashmere and shetland, and a trail of girlfriends up and down the East Coast. He was science editor of the campus newspaper, president of his fraternity; he maintained a more than respectable B+ average and was ranked number three on the tennis team. People wanted to be with him, to be like him, to be liked *by* him; and while men liked him, women loved him. They petted him, mothered him, vamped him, adored him, best-friended him, and set their various traps for him.

Incredibly, he noticed Ellen. Incredibly, he asked her out. Incredibly, he asked her out again. And again. Incredibly, he proposed to her—and, incredibly, he married her.

And he took over her life. He taught her how to be the woman he wanted, how to dress and how to flirt, how to ski and how to watch a football game, how to order in a fancy French restaurant and how to look over the rim of a champagne glass deep into his eyes.

Because of him, Ellen felt pretty, she felt adored, she felt admired. Being the center of Phil's world was the same as being the center of the whole world.

He loved her. He wanted her to have his children. And she wanted what he wanted—even more than he did.

She never regretted it. Not for a minute. And she never realized that in becoming his, she had given up, without realizing it, what was hers.

Ellen had thought only millionaires had estates. Astors and Vanderbilts. She found out she was wrong the day she dragged herself into Al Sheldrock's small office. Phil had—as Al explained—an estate. His will was simple: Ellen was to inherit everything: the new yellow Buick, the house on Dogwood Lane, $1,551.42 in a savings account, $722.30 in a checking account, a $25.00 War Bond. Everything even included the old Ford Phil used to go to and from the station.

"That rattletrap?" Ellen asked.

"Yes," Al said, "that rattletrap." He smiled for the first time since Ellen had entered his office. She had noticed that he wasn't exactly animated. Well, he was an accountant. What did she expect? Errol Flynn?

"So I'm an heiress," Ellen said, trying to muster one of her phony smiles. "I guess I'm rich."

"Not really," Al said, reverting to his careful, idiot-proof accountant's voice. "I'm afraid you're also going to inherit Phil's debts."

"Debts?"

"There's the mortgage—twenty-four thousand dollars is still due. Twenty months of payments left on the yellow Buick—Phil just bought it this past winter. And, of course, the loan."

"Loan?" Ellen asked, blank. A loan? What loan?

"Phil borrowed five thousand dollars from Lewis Swann in January."

"Five thousand dollars! From Lew Swann!" Ellen almost choked. No wonder Lew had seemed so interested in her! He must have wondered when she'd repay Phil's debt.

"Five thousand dollars!" Ellen repeated. "What did he need five thousand dollars for?"

"Overdue bills," Al said. "Clothes, restaurants, the down payment on the Buick, a fur jacket—"

"But he said he used his bonus to buy them."

"His bonus wasn't *that* big. Between the mortgage, the car payments, and the loan, the estate's debts add up to just over thirty thousand dollars."

"Thirty thousand dollars," Ellen repeated Al's words for the third time, shell-shocked. "I didn't know. I had no idea."

She didn't know. Hadn't known. *Oh, yes, you did*, a little voice said. Phil Durban never let anyone else pick up a check. His sweaters were always cashmere, his suits from Brooks Brothers. Ellen's red fox jacket had come in a Bergdorf Goodman box, and Phil drove a jaunty yellow Buick convertible while everyone else on Dogwood Lane drove Fords and Chevies. Whenever Ellen had said anything to Phil about his extravagance, he had always hushed her. *Don't worry, Sweetcakes. We can afford it. I'm the best. You know that.* And Ellen had always let him persuade her. Then she remembered something else he had said: *You'll never have to worry. Never have to worry.*

"Thirty thousand dollars is over one-fourth of the insurance," Ellen said, doing the instant subtraction. "Can I afford to send the kids to college when the time comes? Can I stretch the seventy thousand dollars far enough?" Suddenly, the one hundred thousand dollars didn't seem like all the money in the world.

"Ellen," Al said slowly, "I'm afraid there's a problem."

Ellen had not lived in a man's world long enough to know that when an accountant said "problem," he meant "catastrophe."

"A problem?" Ellen's voice sounded as if it were coming far away from her, from some place beyond her.

She heard Al tell her that Phil had borrowed against his insurance—"to the hilt"—with the same bizarre dissociated feeling she had had when the policeman had come to her door on the morning of March 29. Al was telling her that Phil's estate was thirty thousand dollars in debt. That *she*, as his survivor and heir, was thirty thousand dollars in debt. And, finally, that there was not one cent in insurance with which to pay it. Not one cent of insurance on which to support herself and to bring up her children.

"Now what?" Ellen asked, swallowing back a stab of nausea that suddenly twisted her stomach.

"Can your parents help out?" Al asked.

Ellen shook her head. "They're dead."

"Phil's parents?"

Ellen sighed. "They have their own problems." Tommy Durban's brother had had a stroke at the age of thirty-four and had never recovered. He lived in a rehabilitation facility near Baltimore, and Tommy had for years supported him, his wife, and his children.

There was a long silence in the crammed, depressing office. Al had cautioned Phil about his wild spending and constant borrowing, but Phil had always brushed Al's warnings aside. *I like being in debt*, Phil used to tell Al. *It motivates me. It makes me work harder.* Now Al wondered what was going to happen to Phil's widow.

"Well," Ellen said bravely, still in shock, "I grew up poor. I guess I'll get used to it again. I'll get a job. I'll get along somehow." All she could think of was the expensive telescope she had bought Brenda for her birthday. The bill hadn't come yet. And Brenda hadn't touched it since the day of her party.

"I'm sorry," Ellen heard Al say. "You don't deserve this."

Ellen stood at the door of Al's office, an ugly door, varnished brown, with an ugly frosted, pebbled-glass insert. She made a sad, helpless gesture with her hand, a gesture of goodbye. She wanted to say something but didn't know what. She turned to the door when a sudden thought occurred to her. She turned back to Al.

"You've been paying the bills ever since Phil died," she said suddenly. "What have you been using for money?"

"Lewis Swann sent a check over. He said it was Phil's bonus for the last quarter."

As soon as Ellen got home, she wrote Lew a note asking him to be patient but promising to repay the loan. And she thanked him for sending Phil's bonus check along to Al.

She signed the note with a formal "sincerely yours."

The minute she mailed it she wished she had been more personal, less formal. But it was too late.

5

No, SHE COULDN'T TYPE AND NO, SHE COULDN'T TAKE SHORT-hand, she told the interviewer, a blonde who looked like Jayne Mansfield and had the charm of Adolf Hitler, at the first personnel agency she went to in White Plains. No, she knew nothing about bookkeeping and no, she had never had any office experience.

To Ellen, there was nothing remotely romantic about a job interview, and even as she answered the questions Jayne/Adolf pushed the button on her intercom to tell her secretary to send in the next applicant.

Ellen was happy to get out of there alive. She decided that if she wanted to get a job—and she *had* to get a job—she would have to be more aggressive at her next interview. Instead of waiting to be asked questions, Ellen would let the interviewer know that she had job experience—not much, but some.

"I worked at a French restaurant on the Cape for two summers," Ellen told the one man at the one-man agency. He was tall and heavy and consumed an entire roll of Tums and half an onion bagel during the interview. "And in college I worked in a country inn. I waited tables at first. Then I subbed in the kitchen. I ended up as an assistant sauce chef."

An exaggeration. But, under the circumstances, forgivable. The fact was that Ellen had filled in when the sauce chef disappeared on his periodic three-day drunks. The owner of the restaurant told Ellen her sauces were better than the sauce chef's sauces and, from then on, Ellen did most of the sauce making. Without the title—or salary, of course.

"I'm sorry, but we don't have any openings at a French restaurant," he said, sounding genuinely sorry. "Don't think we ever have, either, come to think of it. But how about a caterer? Do you think you might be interested in working for a caterer?" He belched discreetly (he thought) behind a surprisingly dainty hand.

"Yes, I would," Ellen said, thinking that anything having to do with food really appealed to her. She was always happiest in the kitchen, all the burners lit, stirring and tasting and adjusting seasonings. In fact, she liked to cook much more than she liked to eat.

"You'd be the boss's assistant.. You'd do some cooking. Answer the phone. Talk to the customers," he said, consulting a card from the card file. "Thirty-five dollars a week. You want to go over and see about it? It's in Scarsdale."

Thirty-five dollars a week! That was nothing! But Ellen said she'd talk to the caterer. At least it was a possibility. She had been job hunting for a week and had found nothing. She had been told over and over at the agencies that she had no skills. She was told to go to secretarial school and learn to type. She was told to study bookkeeping. She was advised to get a beautician's license. But no one told her how she was supposed to support herself and her children while she got the job training she lacked.

Thirty-five dollars a week? It occurred to Ellen, as she drove to Scarsdale, that maybe the job was part-time and the interviewer had forgotten to mention it.

Countess Tamara was Russian. She was six feet tall and wore a black Balenciaga suit with a white silk blouse. She had long, scarlet-lacquered fingernails and smoked thin black cigarettes from a long gold holder. Her interview consisted of asking Ellen who her parents were, who her husband's parents were, where she had gone to school, what clubs she belonged to, and where she bought her clothes. None of Ellen's answers pleased her.

"I'm looking for an assistant who can bring in business. Someone with social connections," she told Ellen in a voice pickled in Lapsang Souchong.

"I'm a wonderful cook," Ellen said, looking around the elegant shop, which was in the nicest part of Scarsdale. Tins of truffles, boxes of elegantly wrapped chocolates, a side of pale smoked salmon, loaves of rich-looking pâtés, and a tub of pearly black caviar were gorgeously displayed in the small, handsomely decorated shop. It was, thought Ellen, like being inside a jewel box where the jewels were edible.

"Yes, well . . ." the Countess said dubiously, considering.

"You wouldn't be sorry," said Ellen. "I'd like very much to work for you." She had never met anyone with a title, and she was extremely impressed by Countess Tamara—by her accent, her clothes (Ellen recognized the Balenciaga from *Vogue*), and even by her height. Other women would have been bothered by being so tall, but the Countess seemed to consider her height an asset. In fact, Ellen noticed, she went so far as to wear three-inch spike heels. No wonder her business seemed so successful—the customers must have been just as bowled over as Ellen was.

"On a trial basis . . ." the Countess hedged. "Just to be sure how you work out."

"Of course," Ellen agreed hastily. "On a trial basis."

"Good! *Haroshó!*" said the Countess. "You'll start tomorrow. The hours are eight to six, Monday through Saturday. The salary is twenty-five dollars a week."

Ellen's mouth dropped open. "The agency said thirty-five." She spoke as firmly and deliberately as she could.

"Twenty-seven?" countered the Countess, sipping Lapsang Souchong from a glass in a silver filigree holder. "My grandmother's," she said, indicating the glass and its holder. "From the Petersburg palace."

"Twenty-seven! That's outrageous!" Ellen exclaimed, furious. "The minimum wage is a dollar an hour!"

The Countess's sharp blue eyes, crayoned in kohl, actually managed for a moment to look hurt at Ellen's insinuation. "Twenty-eight fifty," cajoled the Countess, purring seductively. "But that's my final offer."

"I can't afford to work for twenty-eight fifty!" Ellen said. She was upset and disappointed, and she hadn't even gotten around to mentioning that she considered Monday to Friday a normal work week. "I'm not a society girl working for the fun of it. I'm a widow. I have children to support."

"What a pity," said the Countess in genuine sympathy, thinking she'd have to hire one of those high school kids. They knew from nothing, but they'd work for $28.50—$27.00 if she paid in cash. "And so young. Poor thing."

She put down the glass of tea and went over to the refrigerated case and extracted a single portion of chocolate mousse. She gave it to Ellen. "If you reconsider, you'll let me know?"

"All right," said Ellen, terribly let down. She thanked the Countess for the mousse. "But I won't reconsider. Not unless you reconsider the salary. I expect thirty-five dollars a week. That's the salary you listed at the agency."

"I told you. Twenty-eight fifty." The Countess lowered her voice a little. "Cash. Off the books. It's my last offer." Countess Tamara's *r*'s were Russian, straight from the palace in Petersburg, as far as Ellen knew. Her bargaining techniques came straight from the souks of the Middle East.

"Countess, this is Scarsdale," Ellen reminded her.

The Countess shook her head and sighed. "Yes. So they keep reminding me. I keep trying to forget."

Ellen left the elegant shop and, despite the fact that it had been a waste of time, realized that she rather liked the old pirate. Not, she reminded herself, that her amusing experience was going to help support her and the children. She had not thought that finding a job would be so hard and so discouraging. She was beginning to get a little scared.

When she got home, she tasted the mousse. Her own was better.

She put her house on the market.

"Ask thirty-five." The first broker, henna-haired, raspberry-lipsticked, a cigarette jammed in the corner of her mouth, advised in a gravel voice. "But settle for thirty-two."

"I thought I'd ask thirty-five," Ellen began when she spoke to the second broker, who wore a gray flannel suit with a canary yellow vest and who was as graceful and elegant as Fred Astaire.

"Don't undersell yourself," he counseled. "It's bad psychologically. I'll list it at thirty-eight. We can take it from there."

The third broker, a disheveled housewife whose executive husband was battling the bottle—not too successfully—and who didn't seem to know the first thing about anything, said, "How should I know what you ought to ask? It's your home. *You* price it."

Ellen paused, then plunged. "Thirty-eight," she said. "I'm asking thirty-eight."

Who knows? Maybe she'd get it. Then she could afford an extra bedroom in the apartment she planned to rent as soon as the house was sold. The house she had so lovingly decorated, the house she had lived in with Phil, the house in which they had dreamed they would watch their children grow up. Ellen tried not to think about it, tried not to cry, told herself that necessity was necessity.

The morning after her meeting with Al, Ellen drove the yellow Buick to a used-car lot in White Plains. The five hundred dollars she got was less than book value, but, as the dealer was quick to point out, convertibles were a pain in the ass, a drug on the market. These days everyone wanted air conditioning. Ellen was too intimidated to argue. She accepted the five hundred dollars and slunk away, feeling soiled and diminished.

Five hundred plus the thousand she had found in the file drawer was fifteen hundred. If she were *very* careful, they could live on it for five months.

Meanwhile, she continued her job hunt.

Methodically, she registered at every employment agency in Westchester County and answered every single classified help wanted ad, no matter how impossible-sounding. And every morning, after she got the kids off to school and before she started her own job hunt, she thoroughly cleaned the house, leaving it sparkling, just in case any potential buyers came to look at it.

Ellen wasn't aware of it yet, but the energy was beginning to seep out of her, little by little, day by day, as the reality of her situation began to sink in on her.

For the next few months, Ellen bounced from hope to despair and back to hope.

"The paint on the baseboards is chipped," said the would-be buyer, an anorectically thin mother of three. "And that stain in the bathtub is disgusting! I wouldn't even consider asking my husband to live here." She spoke as if Ellen weren't present, in a tone of voice that indicated the queen of England was a close relative.

"Orange wallpaper in a boy's room! How god-awful!" The woman was referring to the paper with football pennants Danny had picked out—and loved. She, too, spoke as if Ellen weren't there, were deaf and/or retarded, or just possibly paying for her opinions.

"I just love it! It's so clean and so airy! And I love the view of the woods behind the house!" exclaimed a young wife. "And I know Jack's just going to love it, too!"

Jack came to see the house the next morning.

"I love it!" he told Ellen. "It's just perfect. Exactly what we've been looking for!"

The day after that, he called with his offer: twenty-eight thousand.

"No," Ellen told the housewife/broker who was desperate for the sale. "I won't sell for that. See if Jack will make a better offer."

"Forget it," Jack said and was never heard from again.

There were more.

People who said they'd "definitely" make an offer disappeared off the face of the earth; people who asked to see it a second time never showed up for their appointments; once, contracts were drawn, but at the last minute, the wife backed out.

Ellen hated every minute of trying to sell her house. And she began to hate the way brokers inevitably referred to it as a "home."

The petty pretension annoyed Ellen beyond all reason.

It was a house. Period.

Progress on the job front was the same draining roller coaster of hope and disappointment.

Ellen was offered a job by a Larchmont divorce lawyer who wanted a receptionist and—he made perfectly clear with his hands and his eyes—a bedmate as well. She answered an ad for a job selling lots of land outside Phoenix via telephone, a job she accepted with soaring hopes—it paid a commission on top of the hourly salary—until she was told she would have to be at her telephone twelve hours a day. She applied for a job as a waitress but found that the restaurant's peak cocktail and dinner hours conflicted with the time her children needed her most. She was almost hired as a dentist's receptionist but lost the job to a younger girl who would work for less. She actually found a job proofreading for a printer of classified telephone books that sounded ideal, but the company went bankrupt three days before Ellen was to begin.

Ellen wondered how women without men survived. Women like herself. But, as far as she could see, there weren't other women like herself. Or if there were, they were as invisible as she was because all the women she knew were married, busy with houses and husbands and children. And all the women on television and in the movies and in public life had someone. A man. Lucy had Desi, Mamie had Ike, and Simone Signoret, older and alone in *Room at the Top*, had Laurence Harvey. The only heroine Ellen could think of who had been by herself, without money, was Scarlett. And she had Rhett.

Reluctantly, Ellen resigned herself to the fact that she would have to go into the city. There were more jobs in New York, and Manhattan wages were higher than Westchester wages. The most likely possibility she turned up was as a filing clerk in an insurance company. The salary started at forty-five dollars a week, with an automatic raise at the end of six months as well as extremely good benefits such as health coverage, life insurance, and vacations.

Ellen hesitated. She would have to leave home at seven-thirty; she wouldn't be back until six-thirty. What was going to happen to her children? Who would take care of them? She'd never see them.

"You'll have to make up your mind by ten tomorrow," the supervisor said. He was spongily plump, sour, unpleasant, and smelled of bananas. "Otherwise, it goes to someone else. We can't afford to wait around while you girls take the time to make up your so-called minds."

"Forty-five dollars a week?" Al said when Ellen told him about her job. She had gone into his office to sign forms: insurance releases, the estate accounting, federal and state tax returns. Ellen had spent ten years as Phil's wife signing nothing except Christmas cards. Now that he was dead, the world seemed blanketed with forms requiring her signature.

"Forty-five a week!" Gail exclaimed. "That's shocking!" Gail herself was earning ninety-five a week—less than the men who had the same job she did at Cooley & Heiser, but more than most women she knew who worked—and she was proud of it.

Ellen shrugged. "I know. It's pitiful, but it was the best I could find. You're lucky you know bookkeeping. I envy you."

"Gail's going to take the CPA exam this fall," Al said proudly. He glanced at Gail, and Ellen realized he was in love with her. She felt, suddenly, more abandoned, more bereft than ever.

"I hear it's a real killer," Gail said, looking worried. "Tougher than the bar exam, even." The fact was that Gail dreaded the exam. She'd be happy being a bookkeeper until she got married and had children, and she hoped—cross her fingers!—that Al would propose soon.

"It's certainly hard," Al admitted. "But you got the second highest grades in your class, Gail. I'm sure you'll have no problem."

Gail didn't look convinced and seemed relieved when Al turned to Ellen.

"Ellen, if you take that job, you'll be in a higher tax bracket," Al said, looking up from some calculation he had been making. "Given what Phil's already earned this year, it's going to cost you money to go to work."

Ellen suddenly realized why Countess Tamara had stressed "off the books." "But I already told them I'd take the job," Ellen said.

"Tell them you'll untake it," Al said.

That evening, ten minutes before she would have dinner on the table, Danny appeared in the kitchen wearing one of Phil's cardigan sweaters, a camel-colored cashmere with leather-covered buttons, its hem dragging unevenly on the floor. Brenda was aghast.

"That's *Daddy's*!" she screamed at her brother. "How dare you wear it! You'll get it dirty! Take it off this second!"

Brenda pulled at the sweater, trying forcibly to take it off Danny.

"Leave me alone!" he cried in retaliation and punched her to keep her away from him.

"Children!" Ellen warned, trying to separate them.

"He can't wear it! It's Daddy's!" Brenda cried.

"I can too. Can too!" And they pummeled each other.

Irving, thinking it was a game, began to tug at the hem of the sweater.

"Irving! Stop it! Stop it this instant!" Brenda yelled.

Irving, egged on by hearing his name, only tugged harder, and suddenly Brenda saw that he had unraveled the stitches.

"Irving! Stop!" she screamed at him, and when he tugged even harder, Brenda hit Irving, surprising him.

Irving, shocked at the assault, growled at Brenda and showed his teeth. It all happened in a split second, and Ellen, frightened at the thought of Brenda being bitten, opened the front door.

"Come here, Irving!" she called, holding the lead. She'd take him out into the yard and hook his lead to the iron ring Phil had sunk into the big oak tree that stood at the southwest corner of the house. Irving, scared by Brenda's attack and responding to Ellen's call, fled out the door and up the rise to the road before Ellen could get the lead on him.

Brenda, up in a flash, ran out the door yelling Irving's name. Dinner was forgotten.

First they reported him lost to the police department. Then they spent the evening combing the neighborhood trying to find Irving, calling his name, knocking on all the nearby doors. Ellen got into the car and drove up and down every road in New Rochelle while Brenda and Danny called Irving! Irving!

It's my fault, Ellen kept telling herself. *If only I hadn't opened the door so wide. If only I'd been quicker with the lead.*

They were awake all night long. And Irving did not come home.

The next day Ellen called the insurance company and told the supervisor she'd decided not to take the job after all.

"At least you called," he said. "Most of you cunts don't even have the brains to do that."

Irving did not come home that day, either. Or the next day. Or the day after that.

6

PHIL'S BIRTHDAY, FOLLOWED BY IRVING'S DISAPPEARANCE, was the trigger that catapulted Ellen out of her self-protective numbness and drove the fact home to her that Phil was dead. Period. He would never come back. Period. She could never apologize. Period. She was twenty-nine, a widow, and alone. All alone. Unimportant. Unwanted—even by herself.

The stark realization that her husband was dead hit Ellen like a punch in the stomach, leaving her reeling, sick, afraid, empty, unable to think, unable to function. She began to resent Brenda and Danny, to resent their endless, unanswerable questions, their tears, their needs, and condemned herself for resenting them.

She could remember the funeral now. She had wished she were dead then. She began to wish she were dead now.

Phil had been dead five months.

"Would you and Tommy take care of Brenda and Danny?" Ellen asked Caroline on a lethally hot and humid day in late August. "If anything happened to me?"

"Don't be morbid!" Caroline exclaimed. "Nothing's going to happen to you."

"That's what I thought about Phil," Ellen said with deadly logic. "Would you, Caroline? Would you?" She was intense, desperate, for Caroline's reassurance.

"Of course we would," Caroline said, noticing that Ellen seemed to be getting worse, sadder, more depressed as time went on rather than better. "It's time you began to think about the future and stopped dwelling on the past. You have Brenda and Danny to think about. And, first, you have yourself to think about."

"But that's so selfish," Ellen protested. For years she had put Phil first, Brenda and Danny first, herself last, if at all.

"Like hell!" Caroline exclaimed, startling Ellen. "If you don't take care of yourself, you can't take care of your children. You used to be such a go-getter. Phil told me you were one of the prettiest, most popular girls at college. He was so proud of you. He said you could do anything!"

"Really?" asked Ellen wanly. College seemed centuries ago. The Dark Ages. She could barely remember it, barely remember herself at that age.

"Really!" Caroline said briskly.

Ellen tried to smile—unconvincingly. The Ellen that Caroline was talking about was a stranger to today's Ellen, a girl she didn't remember, didn't recognize.

Ellen had gone to the University of Pennsylvania on a partial scholarship, had majored in home economics, minored in French, gotten straight A's, held a part-time waitressing job at an elegant country inn, and looked forward to an exciting job like the one her Aunt Sally had as assistant to the head of food services for a company that ran cruise ships.

Sally, her mother's younger sister, planned the menus, helped with the purchasing of huge quantities of ingredients, and always seemed to be coming back, loaded with presents, from exotic ports in South America, Europe, the Caribbean, and the Far East. Sally, who wore bold gold earrings and necklaces of large colored beads, and who laughed with her entire body, shaking until the tears ran out of the corners of her eyes, had been Ellen's idol, although her father had always called Sally a nut.

Sally, who paid part of Ellen's tuition, had encouraged her to go to college in the first place, while her father declared that education was wasted on a girl. Sally had convinced Ellen

that she could do anything she set her mind to. There were
worlds to conquer, and Ellen had been on fire, sure she'd
conquer them—until she met Phil.

Phil . . . handsome Phil, popular Phil, magnetic Phil. Phil,
the center of attention. Phil, most likely to succeed. Phil, everyone's dream man, had fallen in love with her. And Ellen was
filled with a sense of incredulous disbelief that Big-Man-On-
Campus Phil Durban had been attracted to shy and mousy little
her—except that wasn't really the way it had been, it was how
she had come to think of herself during the last few years of
her marriage.

It wasn't what she—or anyone—had thought of her at the
time.

Because, at the time, when Phil had been most popular man
on campus, Ellen had been one of the most popular girls in
the freshman class. Not conventionally pretty, she had shining
coppery hair that blazed in the light and those exotic wide-set
cat-shaped eyes that made her stand out. *Mademoiselle* magazine had photographed her in a cashmere sweater set and
bermuda shorts for the annual August college issue, and she
even got a letter from a Madison Avenue modeling agency
asking her if she were interested in a modeling career. Which
she wasn't.

Busy as she was, burning as she was with her ambitions,
Ellen had more dates than she knew what to do with. The
phone in her dorm rang for her constantly. Her letter box was
filled with love notes and requests for dates from boys on and
off campus. Her bulletin board was crammed with mementos:
corsage ribbons, restaurant menus, dance cards, football ticket
stubs, swizzle sticks from nightclubs, and romantic poetry written for her by boyfriends with poetic leanings.

As Phil had said the night he proposed, "When I found you,
I found Somebody."

He had been so proud of her.

What had happened between then and the night before Phil
died? The night he accused her of not being a real woman? An
accusation Ellen had not even denied.

What had happened during her ten years of marriage?

What had marriage done to her?

What had Phil done to her?

Why had she rewritten her own history?

Why had she turned herself from a Somebody into a No-body?

The hot weather dragged on. And on.

In early September, Ellen reduced the asking price of the house from thirty-eight to thirty-four. Fewer people seemed interested at thirty-four than had seemed interested at thirty-eight. The "lookers" had dwindled to a thin trickle. The brokers who, in the beginning, had called frequently, now called rarely. The house had been on the market for a while, and the brokers, turned off, focused their energies on newer listings.

Just after Labor Day, the Fred Astaire look-alike broker called with an offer of twenty-eight and advised Ellen to accept it.

"It's probably the last offer you'll get until spring," he said. "I know it's a big disappointment. I had thought we'd do better, much better, but fall is slow for sales, and winter is a dead loss."

Twenty-eight thousand. It was crushingly little. Still, twenty-eight thousand was twenty-eight thousand. It would be money for Brenda and Danny if she . . . A sudden, shocking thought of suicide came into her mind, and Ellen pushed it away, appalled.

She told the broker she'd think about it.

By mid-September the last of the fifteen hundred dollars was gone, spent on the new shoes and new clothes the children needed for school. Caroline "lent" Ellen money. Ellen accepted. She had no choice. She was so preoccupied with her own problems that she never stopped to wonder where Caroline got so much money.

Ellen re-registered at all the employment agencies where she'd been interviewed right after Phil's death. Nobody had a thing for her. She tried some agencies she hadn't tried before. At the fifth one, the interviewer, who was a few years older than Ellen—and looked it—took pity on her.

"Mrs. Durban, let me be honest. You're just not going to find a job. The reality is that you have no experience. You have no office skills. The most you could hope for is drudge work at the lowest hourly salary—namely, the legal minimum of one dollar an hour. The reality is that we—and every other agency—are flooded with new graduates this time of year.

They're all dying for a job, and they'll put up with anything to get one. They're young, they're unattached, they're willing to put everything they've got into their job. You're a widow, you have children. Your loyalties are divided. You're not attractive to employers who know that children get sick, mothers worry, and their work suffers, and that children have accidents and mothers have to rush home from the office in the middle of the day. Mrs. Durban, I'd like to help. Believe me, I would. But the fact is that you have nothing to offer."

Ellen swallowed and nodded. She said nothing; there was nothing to say. *Nothing to offer.* Three words that summed up the way she felt about herself. *Nothing to offer.* Not to an employer, not to the world, not to her children, not to anybody or to anything.

She got on the train for New Rochelle, crushed by still another failure in an unending chain of failures, devastated by hopelessness and helplessness.

Automatically, without thinking, she picked Danny up at the Durbans'. He got into the car, silent, subdued, the way he'd been since Irving had run away. Forlornly, he stared out the window, not speaking, a heavy and accusing presence.

As she turned into Dogwood Lane, the school bus, a few minutes ahead of schedule, was just stopping, and Brenda stepped off. Ellen slowed down and opened the car door. Brenda got in.

"Hi, Mom," she said. "How come you're not at home?"

"I went into the city," Ellen said, irritated. "You know perfectly well I've been going into the city to look for a job."

"Oh," Brenda said sulkily. "Well, it's a good thing you got back. I don't like it if you're not home when I get there."

Something else I can't do right, Ellen thought, but she said nothing, and Brenda, like Danny, subsided into depressed silence. At 76 Dogwood Lane, Ellen turned right and drove down the short driveway. She wondered in an indifferent way what she would do about the Ford. The shocks were shot, the brakes were going. Where would she get the money to have it repaired? Once again, and even more shockingly than the first time, the thought of suicide came unbidden into Ellen's mind, *What if*, she asked herself. But before she could continue the thought, Brenda shrieked, "Look! Look!"

The exclamation broke through Ellen's distraction, and, startled, she jumped a little. And then she blinked. She didn't believe what she was seeing. She literally didn't believe her own eyes.

"Irving! Irving!" Danny cried, scrambling over his sister in his frenzy to get out of the car. Irving bounded across the lawn from the thicket of trees behind the house.

"Irving!" Brenda yelled, opening the car door before Ellen could bring it to a complete stop. The children tumbled out of the car and threw themselves on Irving, whose tail wagged so furiously that the entire rear half of his body gyrated.

"I'll never hit you again! Never!" swore Brenda, hugging him and kissing him. "Never!"

"Irving!" Ellen exclaimed, finally getting out of the car. "Where were you? Where were you?"

Irving lunged over to Ellen, dragging the kids along with him, and as Ellen threw her arms around the dog and the kids, her eyes brimmed over with tears.

"Oh, my God!" Ellen kept exclaiming over and over as she hugged her children close to her, squeezing them hard, unable to believe that she had actually been able to even think of suicide. From now on it would be the three of them against the world!

"Goddammit! I'm sick of feeling sorry for myself," Ellen told Caroline the next morning. "I'm sick of being turned down for jobs I don't even want in the first place. Sick of being sad, miserable, weepy. And, most of all, I'm sick of myself!"

"Good!" said Caroline, her light, feminine voice surprisingly emphatic. "It's about time!"

"I'm going to take care of my children—*and* myself. I've been thinking about what you said. I *did* used to think I could do anything. I don't know what happened to me. I got less competent, less energetic. But that's over with! The trouble is I can't find a job. Anywhere! Being a good housewife doesn't seem to be worth very much in the job market," Ellen said, trying to keep the resignation out of her voice.

"The hell with a job!" Caroline said. "Why don't you do what you do best? You're the best cook in the world. Everyone says so!"

"You mean be a cook for some millionaire?" Ellen asked uncertainly, unable to imagine it.

"I mean, start your own business," Caroline said impatiently. "Start a—"

"Catering service!" Ellen said, finishing Caroline's sentence for her. "I love it! I'll start a catering service. What will I call it? I know. À La Carte. That's what I'll call it!" Ellen ran on as though a dam had burst within her. "Oh, Caroline, what a brilliant idea! You're a genius! What would I do without you?"

"Struggle and starve," Caroline said bluntly, and she and Ellen began to laugh.

It was the first time Ellen had laughed in a very long time. Since March . . . since Phil's death. It was the best feeling in the whole world!

7

"ELLEN'S À LA CARTE! WHAT A BRILLIANT IDEA! AND WHAT brilliant timing!" Alice Whittier said. Alice, who had been a frequent dinner guest and was a great fan of Ellen's cooking, was the first person Ellen called. "Sam's boss is coming to dinner a week from Saturday, and I want to impress the pants off him. What's the fanciest dinner you can make?"

Fancy meant French.

"I could make some *pâté de compagne* to start with," Ellen suggested, thrilled with Alice's encouraging response. "Then I could make *coq au vin* and a watercress-and-endive salad, and follow that with a cheese course of Brie. And, for dessert, I could do a baked alaska."

"Sounds divine! Let's do it!"

"It'll be quite expensive," Ellen said tentatively. She didn't know how to talk about money—she had never had any practice in talking about money—and, feeling uncomfortable, not sure of what to say next, she let the sentence trail off uncertainly.

"Don't worry about it," Alice said breezily. "Whatever it costs, it costs. Sam can put it on his swindle sheet. His boss will end up paying for it and never know the difference."

Ellen was slightly shocked at the petty dishonesty Alice

admitted so openly. Phil would never have done anything like that . . . or would he?

"And, Ellen . . ." Alice was saying.

"Yes?"

"Would you mind staying in the kitchen? I'll do all the serving. I want Sam's boss to think I did it all myself."

"Of course," Ellen said, startled at the two tacky little secrets she had learned in one conversation. The way the world really worked, she began to see right from the very beginning, was quite a bit different from the way she had *thought* it worked.

But she was so thrilled with her first order that she plunged right into a second call, dialing the Dessaults' number. The moment she hung up, the phone rang. It was Al, telling her that the IRS had approved the estate's tax return.

"Gail and I are having an engagement party in two weeks," he said when Ellen told him about À La Carte. "What kind of cake can you make?"

"Chocolate, vanilla, or mocha," Ellen reeled off after congratulating Al. "Orange, caramel, lemon, butterscotch, Grand Marnier—"

"Stop right there," Al said, laughing. "You pick. Anything." Then he paused a perfect beat, "As long as it's Grand Marnier."

Laughing, Ellen accepted the order, promising to deliver the cake to Gail's Murray Hill apartment. And she felt very good when she hung up, happy to have the second order and pleasantly surprised to discover that Al had a sense of humor. She hadn't thought that accountants *ever* laughed.

"Dollink! It's the best chocolate mousse I ever tasted," Tamara raved after sampling the mousse Ellen had brought over to her shop. "The best! It's absolutely the best chocolate mousse I've ever tasted! Except for mine, of course."

"Of course," Ellen agreed drily. What Ellen wanted to know was whether Countess Tamara ever needed extra cooking help.

"Dollink! You're an angel from heaven!" The Countess had four dinner parties, a birthday party for sixty, and a retirement dinner for two dozen booked for the coming weekend. Booked? Overbooked. The Countess tended to run her business like an airline. "Eight quarts of borscht, chicken kiev for sixty, and coulibiac for two dozen. I'll need everything by Saturday noon. Can you handle it?"

"Certainly," Ellen promised recklessly, knowing that one

of her cookbooks had a recipe for chicken kiev because she remembered having read it and wanting to try it. She hoped she'd be able to find a recipe for coulibiac. Whatever it was. Ellen had never heard of it. The borscht was no problem because it had been one of Phil's favorites, and Ellen made it all the time. For a moment Ellen wondered where on earth her confidence came from. Desperation, she would eventually decide.

Sheer desperation.

Only Carol Mattison had something bitchy to contribute.

"Cooking? For money?" she exclaimed as if Ellen had told her she was planning to clean toilets for a living. "Phil always told me you were constantly in the kitchen. No wonder he flirted with everything in skirts! What man wants a *hausfrau*?"

Ellen, wounded, taken off guard, had no answer, and she hung up feeling defeated, wishing she knew how to defend herself.

But Carol's bitchiness was forgotten two days later when Ellen made a *filet* of beef with Madeira sauce along with wild rice and Bibb lettuce salad, Orange Bavarian cream, and *palmiers* for a dinner party for Esther Simpson, a woman who played bridge with Caroline. She came home after midnight with a hundred dollar check in her purse and woke Brenda and Danny.

"Look!" she said, thrilled, showing them the check. "Mommy earned a hundred dollars tonight!"

"A hundred dollars!" Danny exclaimed, touching the check in awe.

"Wow!"

"Wow!" Brenda echoed. "When I grow up I want to be just like you!"

Ellen hugged her and thought it was the nicest compliment she had ever received.

Countess T. accepted the borscht, chicken kiev, and coulibiac (Ellen had had to go to the White Plains library to look up a recipe) with exclamations of ecstasy.

"*Dollink!* Mah-vellous! You saved my life! How can I ever repay you?"

"You owe me forty dollars," Ellen said.

"*Dollink!* After! After!" the Countess said. "*After* the food has been served. *After* it has been eaten. *After* the guests have approved. We have Countess Tamara's reputation to think of!"

Ellen did not know how to be tough. She did not know how to insist. She left without her money.

A week later, Ellen got a panic call. The Countess was hopelessly overbooked.

"*Dollink!* Can you possibly rescue me?" Tamara needed beef stroganoff and kasha for twenty-four—*that* afternoon.

"First pay me the forty dollars you owe me," Ellen demanded, outraged at the Countess's *chutzpah*. "And then I'll rescue you."

"Of course *dollink*! Of course!" Tamara replied unperturbed. "That's exactly what I was planning to do."

Even when she was in the wrong, the old crook managed to get in the last word. Ellen had to hand it to her.

Gail Berger paid Ellen when the Grand Marnier cake was delivered.

"Don't tell Al," Gail confided when Ellen asked how she had done on the CPA exam, "but I didn't take it. I never really planned to, only Al doesn't know it. Everyone says the CPA exam is much tougher than the bar exam. I was positive I'd fail, so I figured why bother?"

"But Al said you were second in your class!" Ellen said. She was impressed by Gail's achievement—impressed and envious.

"I was," Gail said in an indifferent tone that dismissed her accomplishment, "but so what? I was also the only woman in that class of sixty-five," Gail said, her amber eyes becoming intense. "I felt like a freak. Anyway, Al and I are getting married. I'm going to get pregnant just as soon as I can."

Ellen smiled.

"I know how you feel," she said, remembering how badly she had wanted her children. "I was pregnant three months after Phil and I got married."

"That's just what I'm planning," Gail confided. "Just remember, though. Don't tell Al about the exam. I told him I'd failed. He'd kill me if he knew I never took it. He thinks I ought to get my CPA certificate even if I don't practice."

"I promise," Ellen said, and she didn't know whose side she was on. Half of her agreed with Gail, understood Gail, *was* Gail. Half of her wondered whether Al wasn't right. A professional degree was worth its weight in gold, and Gail apparently was terrific at her job. Al had even said something about wanting to go into independent practice one day with Gail as his partner. And if anything ever happened to Al, and Gail had children to bring up alone...

The dinner for Sam Whittier's boss was such a great success that Alice Whittier ordered the identical dinner a second time— for Sam's parents' thirty-fifth wedding anniversary. Esther Simpson's sister ordered carrot cake for the Jewish holidays, and Vera Dessault asked Ellen to cater Lori Dessault's sweet sixteen party.

Ellen's reputation spread, literally, by word of mouth, and at the end of October she took an advertisement in the *Westchester Record*:

ELLEN'S À LA CARTE

PARTY TIME/HOLIDAY TIME/ANYTIME

It cost seventeen dollars and did its job. All through November, Ellen's phone rang with orders for turkeys and cranberry-orange Grand Marnier relish, pumpkin and mince pies, curried nuts and cheddar cheese straws, braised chestnuts and sausage-sage stuffing.

Ellen made three hundred fifty dollars that Thanksgiving and thought she had fallen into a gold mine. She sent Lew Swann a check for fifty dollars as Christmas orders began to top the Thanksgiving orders.

8

CHRISTMAS BEGAN THE DAY AFTER THANKSGIVING. ELLEN TOOK orders for three turkeys, two geese, and two hams, and for almost double the quantities of cranberry-orange Grand Marnier relish and sausage-sage stuffing as at Thanksgiving. Orders poured in for dozens and dozens of cookies and pies and gingerbread men, for dozens more chocolate truffles, curried nuts, glazed onions, and candied sweet potatoes. She had agreed to cook and serve three entire Christmas dinners and provide a bartender for one of them.

"Brenda, how would you like to be a professional *sous-chef*?" Ellen asked in the beginning of December. She had been working eighteen-hour days, and she needed help, needed it badly. "I'll pay you fifty cents an hour, but you'll have to promise me you'll work every day after school."

"Okay," said Brenda, who had been helping out now and then. "There's a dress I want for the holidays. It's deep green velvet, and it has a white lace collar. I'd wear it with patent leather shoes. If I work, I'll be able to earn enough to pay for it."

And Ellen made the same offer to Danny.

"I wonder how much money I can make," he said, thinking out loud. "I can ask Grandma to recommend some stocks."

"You're going to ask *Grandma* to recommend some stocks?" Ellen asked, thinking she had misheard Danny.

"She's very bullish now that Kennedy's been elected. She says the market always goes up when the Democrats are in," Danny quoted.

Ellen blinked. The thought of asking Caroline about the stock market was like asking Miss America to play linebacker for the Green Bay Packers.

Ellen got up at four-thirty on Christmas morning and turned the oven on in the kitchen even before she went to the bathroom. When the kids got up, Ellen gave Danny the bike he'd wanted and Brenda the vanity table with the frilly skirt she'd wanted, proud to be able to buy the gifts with money she'd earned herself. Out of her holiday earnings she had been able to send Lew Swann another check for fifty dollars and had sent it along with two dozen of her own chocolate truffles.

She spent the morning in the kitchen with Brenda and Danny helping. As she cooked and packed the food, she was aware of feeling optimistic for the first time since Phil's accident. The worse, she thought, was behind her. What lay ahead was making a life for herself and her children. She knew there'd be ups and downs, but she felt sure now that she'd make it.

The children surprised Ellen with their own Christmas present for her, bought with their earnings: a gift certificate to have her hair done at the beauty parlor.

"You haven't had your hair done since Daddy died," Brenda said earnestly. "I liked it when you used to look pretty."

"Don't you think I look pretty anymore?" Ellen asked, perfectly aware that she hadn't had her hair cut or professionally set since the Friday before that Sunday in March. She hadn't wanted to waste the money on herself.

"Not as pretty as you used to be when Daddy was alive," Danny said, trying to be diplomatic.

Well, thought Ellen, count on kids for bluntness.

Touched, she thanked them for their gift and was surprised at just how much she meant it. Since Phil's death, she and the children had become much, much closer—that was the good that had come out of the bad, the good Ellen had never even remotely anticipated.

At noon, she dropped Brenda and Danny off at their grand-parents' and went to pick up the three helpers she'd hired. With their help, Ellen cooked and served three Christmas dinners: one at one-thirty, one at three, and one at five-thirty.

People, in happy holiday moods, showered Ellen with compliments on her delicious food and her pleasant helpers. One of the husbands took Ellen aside as she was about to leave and gave her a twenty-dollar tip. Ellen refused, but the man absolutely insisted, thrusting it at her.

"It's the first Christmas since we've been married that didn't end up with my wife exhausted, the kids fighting, and me getting drunk. Please take it, Ellen. Think of yourself as a marriage and family saver."

Ellen joined the children at the Durbans' for the fourth Christmas dinner she had cooked and served that day, and she and Brenda and Danny found they couldn't face another turkey, even if this time it was theirs to eat. Exhausted, they left early and on the way home stopped off for pizza.

"What are you smiling at, Mom?" Danny asked when they were back in the car.

She was smiling because getting pizza for Christmas dinner was something Phil would have done, enjoying it all in high spirits. But she didn't tell Danny what she was thinking; she didn't want to upset him by bringing up Phil's name. Instead, she said, "I'm smiling because I cooked for sixty-five people today. I earned almost a thousand dollars."

"Wow!" was Danny's only response.

"A thousand dollars!" Brenda exclaimed. "I thought you said we'd have to be careful with money now that..." she stopped, near tears.

"We *do* have to be careful with money," Ellen said. She had not quite known what to tell the children about their financial predicament. She had not wanted to frighten them, and she had not wanted to burden them with insecurity and anxiety about money when they were too young to handle it or to do anything about it. But she had known that she had to tell them that she couldn't be as free with money as Phil had been, that she couldn't buy them everything they wanted or provide the generous supplements to their allowances as their father had.

"But a thousand dollars is a lot of money!" Brenda protested.

"Yes, it is," Ellen agreed. "But we have quite a few bills. We have to be careful."

"Oh." Brenda's tone indicated only a very reluctant acceptance of what her mother was saying.

Ellen, uncomfortable with the subject of money, let it drop. She was unhappily aware that to earn the thousand dollars she had had to cheat Brenda and Danny out of a real family Christmas, unhappily aware that Phil had been the invisible presence that had hovered throughout the day, although his name had never been mentioned.

But the last thing Danny said Christmas night when Ellen tucked him in was in a quiet little voice, "Did Daddy have a Christmas tree in heaven?"

Ellen said yes and went back to her room exhausted and in tears. Perhaps it was the crushing fatigue, perhaps it was the emotional vulnerability the holidays always evoked that caused Ellen, tossing and turning, to fall into an abyss of self-pity. She had helped other people's families to celebrate and enjoy Christmas, but there had been no time for her own children's celebration. Ellen wondered if she would ever have a real Christmas again, if she would be able to give her children the happy memories they should have. At three A.M., she finally got up and took a Miltown, her Christmas present, she told herself bleakly.

Brenda couldn't sleep either. She remembered the Christmas before, and the one before that, and all the Christmases in her life—the tree and the wreath, the excitement and the secrecy of the days before Christmas. This year all she could remember was work. She'd made trays and trays of hors d'oeuvres, quarts of stuffing and relish, and decorated hundreds of cookies. But none of what she had done had been for them. It had all been for strangers.

There hadn't been one second of fun the way there'd been when Daddy had been there. This year, Mommy hadn't done any of the things she had done every year for as long as Brenda could remember. And she hadn't once talked about Daddy or even mentioned his name.

Had Mommy forgotten him already?

Well, she wouldn't. Not ever.

* * *

New Year's Eve was even worse than Christmas.

The entire week before, Ellen worked in the kitchen. She made enough pâté to stock every restaurant on the East Coast and made so many cheese straws, mushroom tarts, and smoked salmon rolls, she couldn't stand the sight of them anymore. She baked hams and roast geese, and she made so many chocolate truffles, chocolate mousse cakes, *crèmes brûlées*, and *croquembouches* that she feared a diabetes epidemic. All for other people and other people's parties.

Ellen didn't receive a single invitation. When Phil had been alive, they went from party to party, staying up all night, drinking champagne, laughing, enjoying themselves.

As 1960 chimed, Ellen opened a bottle of wine left over from Phil's holiday loot from the year before. She drank every bit of it all by herself, reflecting bitterly on the difference between being half a popular couple and a widow.

9

In January, Ellen sobered up in more ways than one. Business came to a grinding halt. The phone, which had rung constantly, now hung on the wall like a dead flounder. People who had paid their Thanksgiving bills promptly did not pay their Christmas bills promptly. The pile of bills on Ellen's desk, which had begun to diminish, now began to pile up again.

Toward the end of January, she went into Village Hardware to buy aluminum foil. She wanted to charge it.

"I'm sorry, Mrs. Durban," said Mike Zacker, the owner, "but I'm going to have to ask you for cash. You still owe me eighty-five dollars from November."

"I understand." Ellen flushed and reached into her bag for the money. She wouldn't be able to pay Mike until her customers paid her. "I'll send you a check just as soon as I can." She handed him a five-dollar bill.

"It's nothing personal," Mike said apologetically as he rang up the sale, "but I've got a store to run."

Ellen had bought all her supplies from Village Hardware ever since she and Phil had moved to New Rochelle and she was pregnant with Brenda. She liked Mike and his wife, Mary Ann, who helped out in the store. And the Zackers' daughter,

Christine, was in Brenda's class. Both Ellen and Mike were embarrassed, and when the transaction was over, Ellen almost ran out of the store.

Bernie Arkin, who owned the best butcher shop in New Rochelle, wasn't as nice as Mike. When Ellen went in to pick up hamburger for the family, he waved her unpaid bill in her face.

"Two hundred and twenty-five dollars," he said, his face redder than usual, his eyes mean. The three customers at the counter turned and stared. One of them Ellen knew by sight—she had a daughter in Danny's class. "Pay it by the end of the month, or I'm getting my lawyer after you."

"Just as soon as I can, Mr. Arkin," Ellen mumbled, painfully aware of being stared at.

"It had better be 'as soon as you can,'" he mimicked. "What do you think this is? A goddamn charity?"

Ten years of being a good wife and a good mother had taught Ellen how to be loving but not overprotective toward her children; how to greet her husband, tired at the end of a rough day at the office, with a freshly made-up face, a pleasant smile, and a cold martini; how to have gleaming floors, spot-free glasses, odor-free bathrooms, and twenty-five ways to make hamburger; how to organize a car pool, what to say at a PTA meeting, how to make curtains out of the new printed sheets, and how not to let petty domestic concerns like a broken washer interfere with a good sex life with her husband. It had not taught her a damn thing about the world outside the four walls of her own house. A house that remained unsold and whose mortgage bill came from the bank promptly on the first of each month. It had not taught her how to run a business, how to support her children, how to fend off creditors, how to take a bank loan, what kind of insurance was best, and, above all, it had taught her absolutely nothing about money—making it, using it, budgeting it, managing it.

In the months following Phil's death Ellen got plenty of practice deciding which bills could be put off and which had to be paid. If she let the telephone bill go, she could pay something toward Danny's pediatrician's bill and Brenda's ear specialist, who had been treating a stubborn ear infection. If she paid Macy's a little on account for the new clothes Danny needed, then she could pay the drugstore for the antibiotics that still hadn't cleared up Brenda's infection. The insurance on the car could wait, but the Westchester Light and Power couldn't. The bank would wait for the mortgage payment, but the A & P took only cash. An unexpected bill from the garage when the Ford needed a new fan belt reduced Ellen to tears.

Whole days went by when Ellen didn't think of Phil once. She lay awake at night filled with financial dread. In a perverse way, she thanked her father for his harsh training in doing without.

Don't owe anyone anything, and don't let anyone owe you anything. That had been her father's favorite sentence: it summed up what he had learned from life.

Frank Kendle's hardware store went bankrupt during the Depression. Because his customers could not pay what they owed, Frank could not meet his bank notes. He had never recovered from the shame. For the rest of his life he worked, faceless and timid, as an expediting clerk in a freight-shipping office in Scranton. He hated and feared his boss, lived in terror of losing his job the way he had lost the store, and, at home, was a petty tyrant taking his fear, shame, and bitterness out on his wife and children.

Ellen's father never spent a dime he didn't have to spend. He doled out grocery money to Ellen's mother only after she told him exactly what she needed to buy to put food on the table and how much it would cost. He never owned a house, never bought a car, had two suits he wore to work, which he took off the instant he came home, exchanging them for a pair of stained and threadbare trousers and a darned sweater to save the wear on his suits. Ellen's memories of childhood were colored by a sense of harsh material deprivation, a deprivation her mother always said was unnecessarily severe, the result of her father's irrational terror of running out of money. When Phil had proposed to Ellen, her mother had been happy.

"Phil's going to be successful," she had told Ellen. "You'll have a much better life than I did."

Ellen's father had been sourly suspicious. "I don't trust him," Frank Kendle had said when Phil came to visit in an MG sports car. "All show and no substance. You'll see," he had warned. "One day you'll be sorry. One day you'll pay the piper."

Ellen remembered how much she had resented her father's

distrust of the man she loved and wanted to marry. Her poor father. He had lived a poor life. He was dead now, had been for years. He would have smiled his bitter, beaten smile to find out that he had been right about Phil. His words—*Don't owe anyone anything, and don't let anyone owe you anything*—beat relentlessly in her ears.

As she turned thirty, Ellen lived the way she had lived when she had been ten. Meat only twice a week and lots of casseroles; darned socks and mended underwear (Phil, fastidious about himself and the people around him, would have ripped the darning egg out of her hands); powdered milk and margarine (except for the things she made for sale—then she used only the best of everything); no trips in the car that weren't absolutely necessary; no clothes bought except on sale. All the little economies came back to Ellen automatically and instinctively. And when the children complained—they were used to Phil's generous ways—Ellen told them that mommies weren't as rich as daddies.

"That's not fair!" Danny exploded.

Brenda agreed. "There's no reason daddies should be rich and mommies poor. *I'm* going to be rich!"

Ellen doubted it, but she kept her opinion to herself.

It seemed, in January and February, that no one entertained, no one had birthdays, no one got engaged or married or promoted or had anything whatever to celebrate. People seemed to have forgotten that Ellen was alive, and her telephone was ominously silent.

In early February, she found a part-time job in a stationer's—a gloomy, dusty-smelling shop that sold newspapers, magazines, paperbacks, candy, greeting cards, wrapping paper, and school supplies—that allowed her to get the children off to school in the morning and be back home when they returned in the afternoon. She took home twenty-two dollars a week.

"Mommy, what's going to happen to us?" Brenda asked in March, her face clouded with worry, almost at the point of tears.

"What do you mean?" was Ellen's alarmed response. Although she tried to sound assured, she felt an echoing stab of Brenda's worry.

"Christine Zacker says you can't pay your bills. Her father says we don't have any money."

Ellen reassured Brenda as best she could and held her close, filled with love and pain.

And rage. Ellen no longer felt guilty about the last fight she had had with Phil, about her accusations. She no longer was annihilated by regret because she had refused to speak to him, had refused his touch, had stonily and silently pushed him away that last morning. Oh, no. She was *glad*. Happy that she had punished him, happy that he had died without her last touch, her last kiss, her last word. He had earned her anger. It served him right. He deserved to die hurt and unloved.

Phil had lied to her. Not about women, the way she had feared, but about their *life*. About its entire fabric, its tiniest detail. About the car they drove that wasn't theirs. The house they lived in that wasn't paid for. The fox jacket that was way above their means. The pretty Christmas dresses he had to borrow to buy and that she had no *right* to wear and that he had no *right* to buy. Lies. The lavish presents and restaurant dinners and evenings at the theater, and all the nights that they paid Mrs. Blake so that they could go out and have fun. Lies. Every single bit of daily reality, things that had once seemed so secure and so tangible Ellen had never given them a second thought, turned out to be lies, supported only by papers and promises, as insubstantial as the wind.

You'll never have to worry, he had said. *Never have to worry*. The biggest lie of all.

Rage. Impotent rage ate her up, gnawed at her and consumed her. How could he have done this to her?

How *could* he?

It was in this mood that Ellen finally cleared out Phil's personal belongings. She sold the expensive suits and cashmere sweaters and fine pigskin luggage, the Egyptian cotton shirts and heavy silk ties and imported overcoats. The razor and toothbrush, the hairbrush and aftershave went into a black plastic garbage bag and out into the rubbish.

Gone. All traces of him. Except for anger and resentment. On the anniversary of Phil's death, Ellen sold her beautiful fox jacket to put food on the table.

Over the next two years, a pattern emerged. January and February were disastrous. Business suddenly picked up at Easter, and Passover was even better than Easter. Summers shook. Ellen catered pool parties; graduation, engagement, and wedding parties; picnics, barbecues, back-from-camp and off-to-school parties. Thanksgivings were a godsend, and Christmas the biggest money-maker of all.

Even the weeks had a pattern: Mondays, Tuesdays, and Wednesdays were fairly quiet; Thursdays—the weekend on everyone's mind—picked up; and Fridays, Saturdays, and Sundays were frantic.

Even though she knew the pattern of the weeks and the seasons, and followed Al's advice about getting a half-payment in advance and pushing higher-profit items like chicken, starches, and sweets, Ellen made just enough to break even.

Every month as the mortgage payment came due, Ellen lay awake at night wondering if her clients would pay soon enough, if their checks would clear, if she'd get more orders. She worried about Brenda's orthodontist bills, Danny's tutor—his grades had fallen off terribly since Phil's death—gas and repairs for the car, food for the table, and new clothes for her rapidly growing children.

She spent not a dime on herself. She stopped wearing skirts, except when she met someone for the first time to plan a party, because she didn't want to spend money on stockings that ran so easily. She cut her hair herself, though not very well, and she had not bought a new blouse or even a new lipstick since Phil's accident.

By scrimping and saving, by serving the cheapest cuts to her children while she cooked luxuries for others, Ellen scraped through. But it was exhausting to the soul, and the strain showed on her face. She was thirty-two; she thought she looked fifty-two. She wondered how long she would have to go on; how long this constant financial insecurity would be endurable; how many parties she could cater before she collapsed; how many mornings she could get up at five to begin cooking for a party that would be served at eight and cleaned up by two, fall in bed at three, and rise again at five to start all over again. She wondered, two and a half years after Phil died, if she would ever meet another man.

And the Christmas of 1962 passed, like the other Christmases since Phil died, in an ache of fatigue. Ellen had no time to trim a tree or to entertain. For yet another year, the Christmas decorations stayed packed in their cartons in the garage, and the children spent the day with Caroline and Tommy while Ellen worked.

"Do you think we'll ever have a real Christmas again?" Danny asked that night.

"I hope so," said Ellen.

"Of course we will," said Brenda. "As soon as Mom gets married again."

10

"ELLEN DURBAN? DELIGHTED TO SEE YOU." WILSON HOBACK introduced himself and checked Ellen's name off a list. He was tall and broad-shouldered, with thick sandy hair prematurely sparkled with gray and alert brown eyes behind distinguished horn-rimmed glasses. He projected a very specific kind of haute Manhattan glamour, composed of nine-tenths confidence and one-tenth galloping anxiety. "It's your first time at one of our seminars, isn't it?"

Ellen nodded. "I've been looking forward to it for months." At first meeting, all Ellen saw was his vast self-confidence. She wondered suddenly how badly windblown her hair had gotten in the four-block walk in April weather from her car on Seventy-first Street to the Cuisine Concepts kitchens on Seventy-fourth. Wilson Hoback's high-octane magnetism captivated her—as it was intended to—and, dazzled, she barely heard him say that she could take any seat she wished.

The four-week cooking course for professionals only—a gift from Caroline—was being taught by four of Ellen's greatest heroes: James Beard was demonstrating ways with fish and seafood; Julia Child was doing a session on pastry; Craig Claiborne was devoting an evening to chili and variations thereof;

and Michael Field was offering a sampling of desserts. It was very heady stuff, and Ellen was fascinated, impressed, and awed. She was also preoccupied with Wilson Hoback's smile. As she watched Beard poach and sauce fish, his hands amazingly graceful and precise, she was aware of Wilson Hoback in a way she hadn't been aware of a man—not even Lewis Swann—since she had first met Phil Durban. She suddenly remembered what it was like to feel nervous about her hair, to be excited by a glance, to fear that her thoughts were so transparent that they could be read across the room.

When Beard was finished, everyone was invited to sample the dishes he had made and to try the Italian wines that were being offered with them. As she sampled, Ellen chatted with the other students. They included the author of an Indian cookbook Ellen used frequently, two other caterers—one from northern New Jersey and the other from Manhattan—the food editor of a Chicago newspaper, the recipe editor of a gourmet magazine Ellen subscribed to, and several restaurant chefs anxious to improve their knowledge and techniques.

Not for the first time, Ellen realized how isolated her life had become since Phil's death. Except for her clients, her life revolved around the Durbans and the children. She had forgotten about the outside world and the interesting people in it. Without Phil, she had not known how to go about meeting people. And she realized that her isolation had been increased by the fact that, other than Countess Tamara, she was the only woman she knew who was in business for herself. It was interesting, encouraging, and exciting to compare notes with the other caterers, one of whom, the one from Manhattan, was also a woman. Divorced, Laney Wells struggled with the same things Ellen had struggled with: learning to deal with money on a nonemotional basis, feeling confident enough to say no to irrationally demanding clients, summoning the courage to charge enough for her work. But the whole time Ellen talked with other people, she was conscious of Wilson Hoback's eyes on her, and when she went to get her coat, she was surprised-but-not-surprised to find him there ready to help her on with it.

"What would you think about having a nightcap with a stranger?" he asked.

"I think"—Ellen paused, weighing the lateness of the hour

against her interest in the stranger, and made up her mind—
"that I'd like it."

"If business goes bad, I could always get Kennedy to recognize Cuba," Wilson said, after telling Ellen a hilarious story
about the trials and tribulations of coordinating the hectic
schedule—and large egos—of the four superstars in the cooking seminars he was sponsoring.

"From what you say, the Cubans would be a rest cure,"
Ellen said, enthralled at Wilson's inside gossip about the petty
jealousies and not-so-petty egos of the Food Establishment.
"But if you think food people are impossible, let me tell you
what it's like to cater engagement parties exactly a year apart
for sisters hell-bent on outdoing each other." Ellen went on
with *her* hilarious description of sibling competitiveness expressed in terms of French wine versus domestic; caviar versus
smoked salmon; bands versus strolling strings; dishes, tablecloths, and the number of flowers at each table. As she spoke,
Ellen realized for the first time that there was a highly humorous
element to her business. Until now, she had seen only the grim
necessity of work, work, and more work.

The conversation turned to their personal lives. Wilson spoke
regretfully of his divorce. "I never thought it would happen,"
he said, explaining that he had been brought up a Catholic.
"The problem was that Mary Lou didn't grow with me." And
he told Ellen how much he missed the children, now thirteen
and eleven, who were living with their mother and stepfather
in rural Maryland.

Ellen told Wilson about Phil, about her early struggle to
support herself and her children, and the insoluble conflicts
between raising children and running a business. She was quite
aware that she made À La Carte sound a little more successful
than it really was. She sensed that Wilson wanted her to be
successful, and she wanted to please. As always.

The nightcap stretched into four hours of nonstop conversation, and it was three-thirty when Ellen finally let herself into
the house—not that unusual an hour for her, since the cleanup
after a big party might take that long—but it was the first time
she'd gotten home that late from a rendezvous with an attractive
man since the very early days with Phil.

As Ellen turned out the light, the phone rang. It was Wilson.
"I just want to tell you I can't get your cat-shaped eyes out

of my mind," he said. "Will you have dinner with me tomorrow?"

Ellen wanted to but couldn't. She had a dinner party for ten the next night. The night after, a cocktail party for thirty-five, and the night after that—Saturday night—a cocktail party and a dinner party.

"Then what about Sunday?" Wilson asked.

"It's the one night I can spend with my children," Ellen said. "I promised them I'd take them to see *The Music Man*." Although she knew she was being naive, Ellen half-hoped Wilson would suggest going along with them.

"Then I'll call you," he said, "next week."

Ellen believed him.

Yes, the catering business was seasonal. But, no, she did not have to be its helpless victim. Ellen's conversation with Laney Wells about Laney's commercial clients gave Ellen an idea.

Using the commercial listings in the Yellow Pages and the advertisements in the local newspapers, Ellen made a list of every company that seemed a likely candidate for catering services: the office supply company that sold to the stationery store she had worked in, dental and medical supply companies, fashion boutiques, florists, lawyers, accountants, stock brokers, magazine and paperback-book distributors, bookstores, gift shops, and jewelers. Most businesses, Ellen learned from her conversation with Laney, had occasion to entertain: to give cocktail parties, receptions, breakfasts, sales conferences, and parties to introduce new executives or new products. And businesses, unlike private clients, entertained all year. If she could develop a list of commercial clients, Ellen reasoned, she might not be so vulnerable to the busy holiday periods and the droughts in between. Ellen composed a brief letter outlining her services and mailed it to every company on her list.

She couldn't wait until Tuesday's class to tell Wilson how well the idea she had gotten as a result of his cooking seminar had turned out. The expression in his eyes was her reward. And even though she never consciously articulated the thought, what she said to herself, deep inside, was: If you want me to be successful, I'll be successful.

* * *

Wilson Hoback considered himself a romantic. Not, to be sure, an old-fashioned romantic, but a new-fashioned, up-to-the-minute romantic.

He sent Ellen flowers. Not old-fashioned bouquets of violets or *démodé* dozens of red roses, but dazzlingly new-fashioned sprays of ravishing cymbidium orchids from the "in" florist of the moment.

He sent books. Not the traditional slim volumes of verse. Instead, he sent bound galleys, autographed, of the about-to-be-published Julia Child.

He wined her and dined her. But not in dimly lit, red-checked-tableclothed, and candles-stuck-in-Chianti-bottles restaurants in the Village. It was Table 15—and nothing less—at Twenty-One, or poolside at the Four Seasons, where steamed fiddle-ferns flown in from Canada were presented like rare opals.

He held her hand in the movies. Not at movie theaters showing current blockbusters to lines-around-the-block waiting crowds, but at cushy, luxurious studio screening rooms tucked into glittering skyscrapers where films are previewed before their release to the general public.

He took her to Broadway plays, where they sat in house seats; to dinner parties in penthouses where startling-to-the-eye pop art—Jim Dine's paintings of bathrobes and Andy Warhol's of Campbell Soup cans—hung next to Renoir's flowers and Degas's dancing girls; to cocktail parties written up the next day on the *Times*'s Style page.

But it was not the glitter nor the electric "with it" buzz that pervaded every room, every event, that most impressed Ellen. It was the women she met. A dinner party on East Sixty-eighth Street was typical.

Wally Nestor was a financial reporter for *The Wall Street Journal*. Beth Kouros was the head of her own PR firm specializing in fragrance and cosmetic company accounts. Wally and Beth were husband and wife.

Steve Reinberg was a bankruptcy lawyer. Barbara Climbe edited a newsletter for the travel industry. They were married (to other people) but lived together.

Bruce Rich was an assistant district attorney in the Bronx. Lynne Farland was a theatrical costume designer. Bruce and Lynne were divorced (from each other) but lived together.

Michael Stein was a precious metals broker. Sharon Hertz

was vice-president of a heating and air-conditioning company. Michael and Sharon were married (to each other) but maintained separate apartments.

"Do you realize," Wilson asked Ellen as he drove her back to New Rochelle, "that none of the women have the same last name as their husbands?"

Ellen nodded. "Also I noticed that they all have a career. Isn't anyone in New York just a housewife?"

"If they are, they hide in shame," Wilson said definitely. "Or else their husbands hide them."

Ellen smiled because she knew it was the response Wilson wanted. "I feel like I visited a brave new world," she said. "I'm the only woman I know in Westchester who works." She did not count Tamara, who was an exception—to everything.

"Just shows you're ahead of everyone else," Wilson said. "I like that . . . being on the cutting edge."

His tone made Ellen feel warm and wanted, and so did his hand as it covered hers. He kissed her good-night, lingeringly, passionately, hotly, invading her mouth and her emotions.

"This is just the beginning for us," he murmured. "Just think what it's *going* to be. We have a future, Ellen. A long, long future."

Ellen melted, her knees weakened, wanting him, wanting to love, and wanting to be loved.

She thought, as she got into bed, that Wilson might call. The way he had the first night they'd met . . . wanting to say good-night, wanting to wish her sweet dreams . . . dreams of him. When he didn't, when the phone didn't ring, she felt oddly empty, somewhat cheated.

And yet . . .

When she saw him next—he took her to a screening of a pilot for a new TV series—he held her hand in the dark screening room, pressing its back and its palm to his lips, sometimes running his tongue lightly along her skin, sending shivers up and down her spine.

And when he introduced her to his friends at the buffet afterward, he proudly said—as he always did—that she owned her own business: À La Carte. He looked at her and beamed, as if she were a prize he'd won after great effort.

"You might be the lucky one," a beauty-with-brains told Ellen after the screening, her lion's-mane hair and rich, hippie, layered-bangled-and-spangled outfit camouflaging her six-figure success as a commercial real estate broker. "Every woman in the city is after him."

And Ellen suddenly remembered what a junior at the University of Pennsylvania had told her after she'd begun dating Phil: "He's the one. Everyone wants him. I think you'll get him." Ellen had only smiled then; she only smiled now.

Everything about Wilson seemed like a dream come true—except for his rhythm. A month would go by between telephone calls, six weeks between dates. Ellen never knew when—or even if—she would hear from him again. When he was with her, he acted as if he were madly in love with her holding her hand, looking into her eyes, kissing her passionately. She'd be sure she'd hear from him the next day. And then another six weeks would pass before he called again.

"I'll call you," he always said.

Ellen no longer let herself believe it.

Although he had spoken of a future—their future—he had never tried to make love to Ellen, had never tried to get her into bed. He was passionate with his kisses and embraces but seemed content to leave their physical relationship right there. But Ellen didn't know why and didn't know what to say. And so she said nothing . . . nothing about his sexless passion and nothing about his puzzling rhythm.

But, because of Wilson, Ellen felt attractive again. She felt sexually aroused—and sexually suspended.

"You're making a mistake," Jak Busch said as Ellen put the twelve-inch skillet on the counter. His tone was gruff, impatient, authoritative. "I sell 'em because people want 'em, but they're no goddamn good. They rust, they warp, the handle doesn't fit the hand. What you want is this one."

He left the counter and moved to the back of Jak's Kitchen Supply, a huge hangarlike structure behind a shopping center on Route 42. He took another skillet from a wall of steel racks jammed with skillets, sauté pans, griddles, chicken fryers, cast-iron pans, enameled *daubières*, a tin-lined copper *gratins*.

"This," he said, putting his choice on the counter next to Ellen's other purchases, "is heavy-gauge stainless steel. The bottom is aluminum, a superb conductor of heat. It is bonded to the steel and therefore warp-proof. The handle is modulated to fit the contours of your hand. I get 'em in Italy. I'm the only one in the United States who sells 'em. It costs fourteen dollars more than the one you picked out, and you will never have to buy another one as long as you live. This"—he took the skillet Ellen had chosen and threw it into a cardboard shipping carton used for a waste can next to the cash register—"is a piece of crap."

Ellen picked up the Italian-made skillet. It was heavy but beautifully balanced in her hand. She thought he was right; it was probably worth the extra fourteen dollars.

"You don't believe me?" Jak asked as Ellen stood there, considering. "Here, I don't need the money." He grabbed the pan back out of Ellen's hand. "Take the other one, if that's what you want. I'm only trying to sell you something that's worth your money. What do you plan to use it for anyway?"

"I'm a caterer," Ellen said. "It'll get very heavy use."

"A caterer? From where?" he asked. He sipped tea from a plain white restaurant-style cup. There were no other customers in the barnlike space jammed to the rafters with kitchen equipment.

"New Rochelle."

"You must know Tamara, that old faker," Jak said. He lounged back against the counter, prepared to chat. "She's a countess like I'm the king of England. She came here on a boat from Brazil just after World War Two. Who knows where she came from before she got to Brazil? Still, she makes the best coulibiac I ever tasted."

"*She* makes it?" Ellen was horrified.

"So she says. She says it has to have that Russian touch," Jak said, sipping his tea.

"Well, for your information, *I* make it, and it has that New Rochelle touch."

"No kidding! Well, it doesn't surprise me. She's a crock. A big liar. Always knew that. So you're a caterer? How come I never heard of you?"

"I've been in business just a few years," Ellen said. "Ellen's À La Carte."

Jak Busch exuded energy and masculinity in thousand-watt dosages. He was not more than five feet ten; he had the powerful chest and shoulders of an athlete, sandy hair cut in an old-fashioned brush cut, and intelligent, predatory pale blue eyes that were never still.

"If you're buying cooking equipment, I can help you," he said. "I used to cook on oil rigs. I was in Venezuela—the

fucking jungle sucked up men like a sand dredge. In New-
foundland. Freeze your ass off up there. And Saudi Arabia.

"God knows why they can't find oil in anyplace you'd want
to spend more than half an hour in. Anyway, that's to tell you
I know my way around a kitchen. I know what works and what
doesn't. I know what's worth buying and what's worth leaving.
Here, come here."

He then spent an hour and a half with Ellen, advising her
in enormous and knowledgeable detail on the differences between copper and aluminum and stainless steel; on how to tell
whether a handle was riveted in and would last or was screwed
on and would loosen after a few washings. He advised her on
carbon steel knives, the difference between maple and pine
cutting boards, on the best double boilers, roasting racks, and
basters.

Somewhere after the first hour, he asked Ellen if she'd like
a drink, and before she could answer, he thrust his cup at her.

"Have some," he said, and when Ellen hesitated, he pushed
it into her hand. "Don't be afraid. I haven't got any diseases."

The "tea" turned out to be bourbon, and the afternoon ended
in Jak's office in the rear of the cavernous space with Jak's
lips hungrily pressed on Ellen's. His powerful arms crushed
her, pinning her arms to her side.

"Please," she said, resisting, her mouth crushed by his.
"No."

His hands were all over her: on her hair, her face, her
breasts, her thighs, her belly, her thighs. She tried to squirm
away, and his arms only held her tighter.

"Don't fight it," he said. "You want it. And I want it, too,"
and his tongue was on her and in her. He was rough, he was
tender, and she no longer resisted, no longer wanted to.

Jak was right. She did want it, fiercely.

It was the first time Ellen had had sex since Phil's accident,
and she didn't even know whether or not she liked Jak Busch.
What she did know was that Wilson's stop-and-start courtship
alternately aroused and disappointed her. That she was starved
for the touch of a man and that Jak was an overpowering lover,
and that she was hypnotized by his aggressive masculinity.

When she left, hardly believing what had happened, Jak
said, "You're a real woman, Ellen. There are hardly any of
those around anymore. Come by next Tuesday, four-thirty."

A real woman . . . Ellen repeated the words silently, embracing the compliment.

When Tuesday came, Ellen had regained her sanity. She did not show up at Jak Busch's for their "date." Instead, she drove into Scarsdale.

"Ellen! How nice to see you! Have some tea!" The dry, smoky scent of the Lapsang Souchong wafted through the empty shop, and Tamara was in a particularly good mood. Within the past year she had opened a branch in Greenwich and bought the florist's shop next door in Scarsdale so that she could now provide the floral arrangements along with the food catering. It had added a good fourteen percent to her gross, a healthy eight percent to her net.

The assistant she had hired to run the shop, a former art teacher at Parsons named Claus Feiring, was working out very well. The customers liked him—he was tall, blond, the perfect Nordic type—and liked his elegant but unstudied floral arrangements inspired by the Flemish masters of the seventeenth century, a reference that always impressed the customers and allowed Tamara to raise her prices. Art was good business. But Tamara had always known that.

"I don't appreciate your telling people that *you* make the coulibiac," Ellen said, ignoring the tea. As she got the words out, she realized she was even angrier than she had thought. "People ought to know that *I* make it. That it comes from *my* kitchen. Not yours!"

"Ellen, don't be so upset!" Tamara said, knowing she'd have to make an offer. She couldn't afford to lose Ellen. She had called her Greenwich branch That Russian Touch, and business was sensational. "Look, I'll make a deal with you: I'll split part of the profits with you."

"Forget it," said Ellen. "Knowing you, I'd never get a straight story about how much you actually sold."

"Is that what you think of me?" Tamara looked hurt, but not terribly. Then she asked, "What *do* you want?"

"I want the credit, Tamara." Ellen took the pile of order forms from the counter. "*And* a split of the profits." The order forms, Ellen noticed, listed the specialties with That Russian Touch: kasha, chicken kiev, beef stroganoff, veal Orloff, cutlets Pojarsky, salmon coulibiac—all made by Ellen. The order forms listed Tamara's name, the addresses and phone numbers of the Scarsdale shop and the Greenwich shop. There was no mention of Ellen—and no prices. God knows, Tamara probably set the prices by her horoscope on any given day.

"What are you doing with those forms?" Tamara asked, and this time she was alarmed. She saw orders going out the door with Ellen's departing back. "You bring those back! I paid to have them printed!" Tamara yelled, her exotic Russian accent suddenly pure fishwife.

If Ellen heard, she gave no indication. She got into her car, turned the key in the ignition.

"Ellen! Ellen!" Tamara had followed her to the street and was rapping on the car window. "If you don't trust me, I'll put the prices on the order forms."

"*I'll* put the prices on the order forms!" Ellen yelled back, took her foot off the brake, and backed out of her parking space.

"How can you!" Tamara beseeched the heavens. "How can you do this to me?"

"Easily." Ellen smiled. "And with incredible pleasure!"

Claus Feiring had heard every word of Ellen's argument with Tamara, and afterward he spent all afternoon creating a lavish bouquet that he personally delivered to 76 Dogwood Lane.

11

"JOHANNA?" MAX SAID FROM THE DEPTHS OF POST-ORGASMIC bliss, his arms and legs splayed out on the king-sized bed in the Gramercy Park apartment he'd bought for Johanna.

"Yes?" she whispered, her hair (Medium Champagne Blonde) a curtain of silk on the pillow.

"Do it again."

"No." Flat. Just like that. A word of one syllable. No.

"What?" Max asked, startled, rising up on his elbow.

"No." Flat. Matter-of-fact. Take it or leave it.

"What do you mean 'no'?" Max was outraged. "No" was not exactly a word he heard a lot of.

"You heard me. No."

"Well, now what?" Max asked, confounded and perplexed.

"It's up to you."

"Up to me?"

"You want me to do it again?"

"For Christ's sake, that's what I said in the first place," Max said, relieved that she was finally thinking straight again.

Johanna moved slightly and, putting her mouth close to Max's ear, whispered six immortal, never-to-be-forgotten words that made her position crystal clear.

"You mean I've got no choice?" he asked.

"It means you've got no choice," Johanna confirmed.

"Shit," he said.

It was the closest Max Swann ever came to proposing.

"What do you know that I don't know?" Max asked Lew three weeks later. "Women send *you* money!" he said with his usual boisterous good humor. "*My* women only know two things: 'Gimme!' and 'Gimme more!'"

Max was slyly proud of the demands his women put on him—and his ability to satisfy those demands—financial and sexual.

"I'm a little surprised myself," Lew admitted. "Ellen's paid off almost half the loan," he said. Another check—this one for three hundred dollars—had come in the mail the same morning Max had come into the city with news for Lew. Lew was about to call Ellen to thank her and then invite her to lunch. Over the past year they had gotten into the habit of meeting for lunch every time Ellen made another payment on the loan, and neither of them admitted—yet—just how much they had begun to look forward to those lunches.

"Your mother and I are getting divorced," Max said, watching Lew for his reaction. "I hope you won't think I'm the bad guy."

"No, of course not," said Lew, who wasn't surprised by his father's news. "You and mother—" Lew broke off, indicating with a gesture that he understood, that he knew that Max and Esme hadn't gotten along for years.

"The divorce is going to cost me a fortune," Max told Lew ruefully. "Your mother is out for blood. Not that I blame her."

"What's going to happen to Decor?" Lew had worked for Decor for a dozen years; it felt like his life to him.

"No problem," Max said. "Your mother isn't interested in the business. She wants the house and cash. *Beaucoup* cash. You can keep on running Decor as usual. Hell, it's your baby," Max said, although, strictly speaking, he was only half-right. Decor was half Lew's baby, half Max's baby. Each owned 50 percent of the stock.

"I'd like to buy out your half," Lew said. "I'd feel better if Decor were all mine." The last thing he needed was for Max to sell out to a stranger to raise the cash for his divorce. Or, worse, to sell out to Johanna, who was, in Lew's opinion, a gold-plated, brass-balled bitch.

"Shit, Lew! You couldn't afford to buy me out," Max said with his characteristic good-natured sarcasm. "You've done too good a job at Decor. The stock is worth plenty now. You screwed yourself."

"If you decide to sell, I want you to offer it to me first. Is that a deal?" Lew was not going to give up easily. He had much too much of an investment—emotional and otherwise—in Decor.

"Sure," promised Max. "Hell, you run the goddamn thing!"

"I heard the goddamnest thing today!" Max told Johanna when he go back to the Island. "A woman paying a man! Remember Phil Durban? Did I ever mention him to you? Lew's sales manager? He owed Lew five thou when he croaked. Lew thought he'd never see it again. But, lo and behold, the little widow is paying it back, a hundred here, two hundred there." Max threw his head back and laughed in wonder and admiration.

"What does she look like?" Johanna asked, instantly wary. She was all too aware of Max's unquenchable appetite and constantly roving eye.

"How the hell should I know?" asked Max. "I've never laid eyes on her."

Johanna didn't know whether or not she believed *that* one but let it drop and got to the subject that really interested her. "What did Lew say? When you told him about the divorce?"

"He asked if Esme was going to get Decor in the settlement," Max said. "I told him not to worry. Esme's strictly interested in cash."

"Didn't he say anything about me?" Johanna asked. What did she care *what* Esme got in the settlement? Max was so rich that no matter what Esme got, there'd still be plenty left.

Max shook his head.

"I want him to like me," Johanna said, wondering what she could do to make Lew like her. Max's divorce was going to be a nasty one, and Johanna wanted allies, knew she would need allies. And Lew was more important to Max than anyone except herself. She wanted Lew to like her; she wanted Lew to be on her side. She decided she'd have to think of something really special to give Lew as a gift . . . something that would

make him see what a nice person she was... something that
would make him like her.

Max's divorce and Lew's surprised realization that he thought
it was the right thing to do finally jolted him out of his resigned
acceptance of the indifference of his own marriage. After her
cold, wintry spell, Reenie had once again reverted to the tepid
affection that had marked the earlier years of their marriage.
Tepid, Lew thought, envious of his father's bold pursuit of
happiness, was not enough. Lew was thirty-six and a passionate
man. Too young for merely tepid.

That afternoon Lew cashed the check Ellen had sent him
and used part of the money to send her flowers. On the card
he thanked her for her efforts in repaying the loan and, as was
his custom, invited her to lunch.

He had been thinking about her between lunches for a long
time. Now it was time to act.

12

"YOU NEVER CALL ME," WILSON SAID TO ELLEN ALMOST A year after they'd first met. He had taken her to the Carlyle Bar to hear Bobby Short. Baby Jane Holzer, whose abundant hair glistened like gold, was there with Andy Warhol, whose die-straight hair shone like silver. Mick Jagger, in a white satin suit with white soutache braid, was with a group of recording executive types, blowing smoke and dreams, and a whisper went around the room that David Bailey and Jean Shrimpton were on their way in.

"Is that good?" Ellen asked, joking to cover her confusion. She didn't understand. Was Wilson asking her to call? Hinting that she should? When he said *he'd* call, did he really mean that he expected *her* to call? Ellen remembered courtship from the days when Phil had courted her, when the man made all the moves and the woman waited, or, as they said at the time, "he chased her until she caught him." Ellen had never called a man in her life—and never would. "Or bad?"

"It's different," said Wilson, smiling enigmatically. He was as attractive as any of the celebs or mini-celebs (or micro-celebs) in the room. When he walked in, every head had swiv-eled, checked him out for a moment, and then reluctantly returned to the conversation at hand. Ellen was acutely conscious of the attention Wilson drew; proud to be with him, very aware that *she*—conservatively dressed—had been dismissed in a split second.

"Oh," said Ellen, not knowing what else to say. There was a brief, uncomfortable moment of silence. Ellen always felt slightly nervous with Wilson. Partly because she found him so attractive; partly because he seemed so polished and so sophisticated that she was constantly afraid of doing or saying the wrong thing (whatever that might be in the "in"-one-second "out"-the-next circles in which Wilson moved); and partly because of the sexual irresolution between them.

What she didn't know—what she couldn't know because Wilson didn't know it himself—was that he was a man in transition: partially governed by the way he'd grown up, which was the way Ellen had grown up; partially governed by the free-for-all society in which he found himself a particularly desirable and sought-after member. Wilson's life was a *Playboy* dream come true.

His phone rang so often he had had a second line installed in self-protection. Legions of bright, chic, enviably successful women—lonely and divorced, scared and single, married but available—deluged him with invitations to cocktail parties, dinner parties, publication parties, gallery openings, lunches, brunches, the theater, ballet, movie screenings, or, simply and in words of one syllable, to bed.

When Wilson got the flu, women lined up to bring him homemade soup and the latest magazines, to play two-handed gin, bring his mail from the office, rub his back, do his laundry, change his sheets, and pick up the groceries.

The weekends Wilson did not spend in someone's exquisitely converted Connecticut barn (part of a divorce settlement), he spent in someone else's rakishly modern house set on an East Hampton dune (built with money she'd earned herself).

Ellen wasn't like the other women Wilson knew.

She never telephoned him. She never sent him cute, wistful, why-haven't-I-heard-from-you-lately studio cards. She never mailed him a clipping relevant to a conversation they'd had at a cocktail party or just dropped him a note "to keep in touch." She never invited him anywhere—not to lunch, brunch, cocktails, or a party. She never "happened" to be waiting for a bus across the street from his apartment house when he left to go to work in the morning, and she never "happened" to be passing his office when he left work in the evening.

Wilson was used to being wanted; Ellen didn't seem to want him.

"You're driving me crazy," said Wilson. He was a Now-style lover: he came on strong and then waited to be wanted. Half the pursuer, half the pursued; half the boy he'd been, half the man he'd become.

"Nice-crazy, I hope," Ellen said. She was dazzled by Wilson and by Wilson's world. Dazzled and intimidated and flattered by his attention—and confused. Confused because he sent out confusing signals.

"Crazy-crazy," Wilson said, and the expression in his eyes was an expression Ellen had seen in Phil's eyes. The expression of a man who was a pursuer. It was just that Wilson was a little out of practice.

For a change, Wilson Hoback found himself the aggressor. For a change, he found himself picking up the phone to call a woman. For a change, he found himself thinking of ways to please a woman. For a change, he found that he was the pursuer and not the pursued. And, for a change, he wondered not when but if Ellen would go to bed with him.

When he kissed her, she returned his kiss, but that was all. When he embraced her, she returned his embrace, but that was all. When he licked her palm, she shivered, but that was all. He had become accustomed to women taking the next step, to making it clear that he would not be rejected.

But Ellen never took that next step.

So accustomed was Wilson to women making the step from the living room to the bedroom that he began to wonder what was the matter with Ellen. He wondered if she were a man-hater. He wondered what her game was. He wondered why she didn't act like every other woman he'd met since his divorce.

The one thing that absolutely, positively never even dawned on Wilson was that he might have competition.

Whole *filets* of beef, cartons of lemons and onions, bushels of potatoes, gallons of milk and quarts of heavy cream, plastic wrap and aluminum foil containers by the dozen, pots, pans, whisks, and cookie cutters—all bought at wholesale because À La Carte, Al told Ellen, was now doing enough business to buy at wholesale—jammed the garage which was now a storage room. A secondhand refrigerator stood in the dining ell; and during busy seasons, rented ovens were lined up on the butcher block table.

In the beginning, the quantities seemed overwhelming. But every single bit got used, and the savings began to add up—savings that went to pay the two high school students who now worked for Ellen almost every day after school and most weekends.

Ellen's idea of soliciting commercial accounts turned out to be the right idea at the right time because in 1963 the Dow shot from an opening of 646 to end the year at an all-time high of 767, and the economy was in its thirty-fifth straight month of expansion. The Dow and the GNP were the artifacts of men's worlds that still meant nothing to Ellen, and yet their effects affected her.

Within the first year after her mail solicitation, she catered the sales presentation of a new line of desk accessories for an office supply company in Armonk; a cocktail party for a new partner of the White Plains branch of Merrill, Lynch; two fashion shows (spring and fall) for the Youthquake Boutique in Scarsdale; an opening party for the Hartsdale branch of a New York savings bank; a dinner party for the partners in a Rye law firm; and the yearly Fourth of July picnic the *Westchester Record* gave for handicapped children.

But the commercial clients accounted for only part of the growth. Nineteen sixty-three was a year of firsts for Ellen's À La Carte.

She catered her first party for one hundred—an engagement party. It went so well that the mother of the bride-to-be asked Ellen to cater the wedding—for two hundred and fifty. Another first.

She got her first steady booking. Ellen had catered the monthly luncheon for the White Plains Library Committee three times when the chairman asked if she'd cater it on a regular basis, every other Tuesday.

And there was a crossover between private and commercial clients. Helena Branch, whose husband owned the *Westchester Record*, was so impressed with the Fourth of July picnic that she asked Ellen to cater her thirty-fifth wedding anniversary party, and Sam Whittier's boss liked the *coq au vin* and beef stroganoff dinners that Ellen produced every six months so much that he asked her to cater his division's presentation of a new line of home-repair kits to a trade press lunch.

When Ellen told Wilson how well À La Carte was doing, she wasn't exaggerating anymore.

And the year of firsts for Ellen was also the year of a last— the last payment on Phil's five-thousand-dollar debt.

"My treat today!" Ellen said as she walked into Lew's office with a picnic hamper—an elaborate wicker affair Phil had bought at Abercrombie & Fitch and which Ellen had not used since his accident. "We could go to the park." It was a perfect early May day, warm and tender green with pale wisps of clouds floating high in a fresh-paint-blue sky.

"I'd love to," Lew said, "but the architect I was to meet with on the twentieth floor at three-thirty just called to say that he's got to catch a four o'clock plane to Washington, so he'll be here in an hour."

"You finally decided to lease it?" Ellen asked.

Lew nodded. "We got the deal we wanted."

"So let's have our picnic on the twentieth floor," Ellen said.

"That's a deal," Lew said and got up. As they walked toward the elevators, Ellen noticed the drop cloths in Max's office.

"Johanna," Lew explained. "She's redecorating Max's office for him."

"I thought he never used it," Ellen said.

"He doesn't," said Lew.

"Then why is she redecorating it?"

Lew shrugged elaborately. "Who knows? It's a real nuisance, too. She's in my office every half-hour asking me about this paint sample, that paint sample, what kind of upholstery fabric I like, and how many cabinets the carpenter ought to make."

"Why doesn't she ask Max?"

"She says she wants it to be a surprise for him."

"That's nice of her," Ellen said.

"Yeah," said Lew. "I suppose so. I just wish she'd leave me out of it."

The twentieth floor was eerily empty. Sawhorses and power tools and sheets of plasterboard propped up against the walls were the only furnishings. Ellen spread the checkered tablecloth in a sunny corner and spread out the picnic: roast chicken with a mustard-tarragon coating, a new-potato salad, and sliced tomatoes with mozzarella cheese dressed with oil and minced basil; for dessert, sliced fruit with Kirsch and thin hazelnut *tuiles*. And a bottle of champagne.

"Champagne!" exclaimed Lew.

"It's a celebration," said Ellen, handing Lew the check she had brought. "Four hundred thirty-two dollars. I'm out of debt!"

"You're terrific, Ellen," Lew said, putting the folded check into his pocket.

"You thought you'd never see the money?"

"That's right," Lew said, eating the chicken with his hands in a way Ellen found earthy and appealing. She didn't like people who picked at their food or who were daintily detached from it. "I didn't think I'd see it and my father didn't think I'd see it. He still can't believe you're paying the loan back. He teases me about it all the time."

"I probably ruin his image of women," Ellen said, laughing.

"That's for sure!" Lew said. "He once told me women could only count to nine and that's because they're pregnant for nine months."

Ellen laughed again and shook her head in despair. It was so typically Max! And then she asked Lew to tell her how he had managed to lease the twentieth floor on the terms he wanted. As they ate the picnic and sipped the champagne, they began to admit to themselves just how important their lunches had become.

For Lew, Ellen was the only woman with whom he had ever been able to discuss business. She understood cash-flow problems, delivery holdups, temperamental employees, manufacturing errors, and crises—all the thousand and one details that were part of running a business. For the first time, Lew began to understand how compelling it was to be able to talk to a woman about what he cared about most. How compelling and how irresistible. For the first time, he could begin to understand the fascination Johanna held for Max from Max's point of view.

For Ellen, Lew was a link with a happy past, someone who had Phil's stamp of approval. She remembered how Phil used to tell her that Lew was attracted to her. Incredible as it seemed, it was as if Phil were encouraging Lew and her.

And unlike Al, whose interest in À La Carte was a professional one, and unlike Wilson, who considered À La Carte a status symbol—an essential status symbol—Lew had a personal stake in her success because her success had allowed her to repay the loan he had once made to Phil.

But now that the loan was paid off, she had no excuse to have lunch with him . . . and Lew had run out of reasons to have lunch with her. Both were acutely aware of this as they enjoyed the food and champagne.

"I increased Decor's line of credit to take over the floor and meet the startup costs of the new line. It's going to be called Eagle Paints," Lew was saying, his excitement obvious. "It'll be a premium-quality line featuring Early American colors. It'll have its own sales staff, ad department, and billing department." Eagle was Lew's idea, the first step in the realization of his dream of making Decor into a big company—a step he had been able to make since Max was now distracted by Johanna and his own empire and no longer had the time to second-guess every idea of Lew's. "I've borrowed a hundred thousand dollars to get Eagle properly launched."

"My God! A hundred thousand dollars!" Ellen said, thinking of how free, how relieved she felt to have the burden of Phil's five-thousand-dollar debt finally—finally!—lifted from her shoulders. *Never owe anyone money.* . . . Ellen put her hand on Lew's arm sympathetically. "How long will it take you to pay it back?"

"Eighteen months . . . two years," Lew said casually, electrically aware of her touch but not revealing it. "The point is that we can go ahead with the new line. We anticipate it will show a profit by the second year. Our research shows a market for quality paints in Early American colors. No manufacturer is hitting that market—yet. Decor will be in there first!" As the intensity in Lew's voice grew, he leaned closer to Ellen and covered her hand with his.

"You sure seem *happy* about starting something that will put you in debt!" Ellen said, thinking only of how crushingly depressing it would be to owe a hundred thousand dollars. "I'd shoot myself if I owed that much money."

"Well, I wouldn't let you have a gun!" Lew joked and opened her fingers as if to make sure no weapon was there. He—and she—smiled at each other to prove how light, how teasing their touch was, how casual, how unimportant. "Borrowing money is the name of the game, Ellen. It lets you *make* money."

"*You* see it as a way to make money," Ellen countered,

taking her hand from Lew's arm, removing her hand from his, suddenly a little too aware of his touch. "*I* see it as a debt . . . a burden."

Lew busied himself refilling both glasses, aware of how empty his hands felt without hers, and shook his head slightly. "Ellen, sometimes you think too much like a housewife."

"But I *am* a housewife," she said.

"Maybe," Lew said. "But you're also a businesswoman. You run a successful business. After all, the proof is that you paid off Phil's debt."

With that, Ellen put her hand on Lew's arm again. "I wonder if we'll ever see each other again now that I have . . ."

Lew was quiet. He was almost unbearably aware of Ellen's physical presence. Of the way the coppery lights played over the wave that fell across her cheek and the shadow of her lashes on her almost-transparent blue-green eyes. Her words made him feel, with a stab, just how much he would miss seeing her, being with her, talking to her. And, in the silence, Ellen memorized Lew: the texture, firm and fine, of his lightly tanned skin; the sun-touched thick dark blondness of his hair; the precise timbre of his voice, light yet authoritative, intelligent, humorous, and warm. For a long, tense moment they sat in rapt, nervous silence, afraid to break the spell.

Then, suddenly, Ellen was in his arms. He kissed her with enormous tenderness, his hands in her hair, his lips warm on hers, warm and then hot. Ellen lost herself in their kiss, a kiss that drifted into infinity as they lay on the floor wrapped in each other's arms, oblivious of everything except what they were feeling.

"I've been looking all over for you! Your secretary said you might be down here." Johanna Wycoff stood in the doorframe, swatches of fabric over her arm. "I have some samples I want you to see." Her voice sounded unnaturally loud in the empty suite of offices, echoing off the bare walls and bare floors. She looked from Lew to Ellen and back to Lew.

"If it's a bad time . . ." she said, standing her ground, not the least bit embarrassed, not the least bit awkward at the scene she had so obviously interrupted.

Lew and Ellen looked at each other, their eyes full of unspoken emotion. Ellen bent to gather up the picnic, the wine, the napkins, avoiding Lew's eye, Johanna's frank assessment.

"I'd better be going," she said, aware that her cheeks burned with emotion and embarrassment. "The kitchen's going to be busy this afternoon."

She packed the plates and the leftovers into the hamper, not looking at Lew, wishing that this woman—whoever she was— would disappear off the edge of the earth.

"I'm Johanna Wycoff," Johanna said and extended her hand to Ellen, as if they were meeting at a cocktail party.

Mussed hair, flushed cheeks, good body on the thin side, no boobs, short legs, great eyes, nothing clothes, Johanna registered, not missing a beat.

"Ellen Durban," Ellen said, wanting only to flee this sharp, rather strident, glossily well-groomed woman.

"Max thinks you're wonderful," Johanna said. She had strong hands and held Ellen's hand in her own for a moment. She turned to Lew provocatively. "Doesn't he?"

Lew looked away, wishing, as Ellen did, that Johanna would disappear, loathing her insensitivity. Meanwhile, Johanna blithely chatted away about fabric samples, holding up first one and then another, soliciting Lew's opinion, asking Ellen for hers. She did not say one word about the kiss she had interrupted. She just filed the episode away in her memory . . .

For future reference . . .

Along with the manila envelope of letters she had found tucked away on top of the closet in Max's office.

13

"I DON'T WANT TO LET THINGS END THE WAY THEY DID," LEW
said that afternoon on the telephone, his voice showering Ellen
like a waterfall of pleasure. He was referring to Johanna's
interruption; he was referring to their own unresolved feelings.
He wondered what would have happened if Johanna hadn't
walked in when she had. "Would you meet me for lunch next
week? Tuesday?"

Ellen agreed, her soaring heart leaping far above her doubts
and uncertainties.

Tuesday.

Her hair was freshly washed and set, nails manicured, rare
treats from her to herself. She wore a new peachy lipstick, her
prettiest, laciest underwear, a pale linen dress, and a strand of
pearls. And the Miss Dior she had worn since Phil's accident.
For once even the New York Central was on time.

Ellen stepped out of Grand Central at 12:02 and walked
uptown to the Coq Rouge between Second and Third on Fifty-
second Street where she was to meet Lew. She walked slowly,
savoring the day, the air, the brisk stride of passersby, aware
for the first time in a long time of feeling pretty, of being

desired and desirable. She noticed how many lovers there were on the streets of the city, couples holding hands, walking with arms around each other's waists, kissing passionately in the shadows of skyscrapers, whispering of love and the future, and she felt a secret bond with them. She felt *included*—not, as she had felt since Phil's accident, excluded, alone.

She remembered the kiss she had shared with Lew, imagined the kisses they would share in the future. Wondered about the texture of his skin, the strength of his arms, the circumference of his waist, the smell of his hair, the length of his legs, the caress of his hands, and, blinded by her inner visions, walked straight into Wilson, colliding with him on Forty-eighth Street.

"Ellen! You were a million miles away!" Wilson said, thinking he had never seen her looking so beautiful, so soft, so approachable.

"I guess I was," Ellen admitted, secretly thrilled to have run into Wilson—literally!—when she knew she looked her best. Strangers on the street had stared at her, remarked her passing with a flattering gaze, a provocative smile.

"Where are you going?" Wilson asked, looking at his watch. "Do you have time for lunch?"

Ellen shook her head. "I'm sorry."

"Heavy date?" Wilson teased, taking her by the arm and walking along with her.

"Just a friend," she mumbled, embarrassed to feel herself blushing.

"Just a friend!" Wilson mimicked. "Ellen, you're the worst liar I ever met!" Suddenly, he thought of all the people they had met together, all the men, married and single, and he had seen their response to Ellen. "Anyone I know?"

Ellen shook her head. "No," she said. "No one you know." They were at the corner of Fifty-second and Lexington. "This is my street," she said. "I have to leave you now."

"I wish you didn't," Wilson said in a tone Ellen had never heard before.

Wilson watched as she turned east on Fifty-second, watched until all he was left with was the faint memory of her perfume. Now he knew why she had been so cool with him, so maddeningly elusive. He wondered who she was meeting; he wondered who the competition was. Fifty-second Street was lined with elegant, high-profile restaurants; whoever he was, he wasn't hiding her under a bushel.

As Ellen walked east on Fifty-second Street, she could not summon back the romantic fantasy her meeting with Wilson had interrupted. All she could think was that Lew was married, happily married as far as she knew, and that she must be out of her mind to be meeting him now that there was no legitimate reason to do so.

When she got to the door of the Coq Rouge, she put her hand on the heavy brass door handle, about to open it, when she hesitated. Conflict held her momentarily suspended. Conflict between the irresistible attraction she felt toward Lew and the knowledge that he was another woman's husband. She wondered how *she* would have felt if the man waiting inside were Phil and she were at home, waiting for him, loving him, trusting him.

She shuddered and deliberately removed her hand from the brass knob and continued along toward Second Avenue, her heart pounding, until she was out of sight, out of danger.

She walked back down to Forty-second Street and boarded the 1:14 to New Rochelle, ashamed of her cowardice and cruelty to Lew, but at the same time proud of her willpower.

"Do you want me to stay away?" Lew asked that afternoon when Ellen telephoned him.

"Yes," said Ellen. "It would be better."

"I know you're right," Lew said. "It would be better."

Better for whom? he thought when they said good-bye. And he wondered whether he'd have the willpower to stay away. After all, he hadn't had the willpower not to touch her, not to kiss her at their picnic. . . .

Two weeks later, Ellen went to bed with Wilson for the first time.

"I told you," he said, his voice husky, his eyes devouring her, "you're driving me crazy. Crazy-crazy, nice-crazy, and oh-my-God-I've-got-to-have-you-crazy."

He was a warm and tender and strong lover, and Ellen abandoned herself to him, responsive, hungry, passionate. And how wonderful, she thought, as she surrendered, for it not to be complicated.

Wilson was attractive. Wilson was successful. Wilson was desirable. Wilson was available.

* * *

"Where did you get those funny glasses?" Danny asked belligerently the first time Ellen invited Wilson to dinner. "They make you look like a chipmunk." Ellen was transferring a rack of lamb onto its serving platter and thought she'd go through the floor in embarrassment, rack of lamb and all.

"In the city," Wilson said stiffly, pouring himself a glass of wine and taking a hefty swallow.

"What city?" Brenda chimed in. "The capital of Lower Slobovia?"

"Not the *capital*!" Danny said, pasting a leaf of lettuce over his upper lip like a mustache. "Somewhere out in the sticks. Even the capital of Lower Slobovia wouldn't sell glasses like those."

"Danny! Brenda!" Ellen cautioned, wanting to kill them both. "Mr. Hoback's a guest. Be polite."

"Some guest!" Danny said, draping another piece of lettuce around his chin like a beard, the dressing dripping down onto his neck and the collar of his shirt.

"Yeah," sneered Brenda. She turned to Danny. "That's no guest. That's Mommy's boyfriend."

"Charming children you have," Wilson said, grimly carving the lamb. Ellen could have kicked herself for inviting him home to dinner. She should never have introduced him to the children. Never.

But a week later she did it again. Wilson was an important part of her life, and her children would simply have to learn to adjust.

"What do you do, anyway?" Danny asked.

"I own a public relations firm," Wilson said.

"Are you successful?" Brenda asked.

"Do you make a lot of money?" Danny asked at the same moment.

Ellen gritted her teeth and glanced at Wilson.

"Yes," he said firmly. "Yes, I'm successful. And yes, I make a lot of money."

"Are you going to be around here a lot," Brenda asked, "hanging around Mommy?"

"Yes," said Wilson. "And you're going to have to learn to get along with me. *You*," he said, turning to Danny, "are going to have to be a little less obnoxious, and *you*"—he looked straight at Brenda—"are going to have to change your attitude.

For one thing, I expect you to be much more respectful toward your mother."

To Ellen's astonishment, Brenda nodded obediently. "Yeah," she said, abashed. "I know I can be a pain."

And Danny, for once, didn't have a wise remark.

Wilson apparently had said the magic words, and Ellen's admiration for him, already high, soared.

What they needed all along was a man in the house, someone to lay down standards and stick by them. Ellen was all too aware that she alternated between being too easy and too strict with Brenda and Danny. Too easy because she was guilty at how much her work took her away from them; too strict when they began to show signs of being spoiled by her easiness. Trying to raise her children at the same time she had to run a business, Ellen found herself on a precarious seesaw, and she incessantly accused herself of not balancing it better.

"If you married my mother, would you be my father?" Danny asked several weeks later. He wanted to know what to tell the kids in school.

"Stepfather," Wilson said, understanding exactly what Danny had in mind. His own son had asked the identical question when Mary Lou had remarried.

"Danny, Mr. Hoback came for dinner," Ellen heard herself say with surprising authority. "He came for dinner, not the third degree."

Danny began to laugh—his laugh so much like Phil's that it invariably startled Ellen. "Third degree" was an expression Danny had heard on television cop shows, and anytime Ellen asked the children what they'd done or where they'd been, they accused *her* of giving them the third degree.

Ellen glanced at Wilson, who winked. She sensed that a major hurdle had been met and overcome, and she allowed herself, finally, to relax.

Just as "dating" was hardly the word for the intense and passionate relationship Ellen was having with Wilson—entire evenings when they never left Wilson's bed, evenings when they were absolutely unable not to be touching each other every moment—Ellen had no word for Wilson himself.

"Boyfriend" seemed teenagey, more appropriate for the fifteen-year-old Brenda. "Lover" was too sophisticated, more appropriate for sophisticated Europeans like Sophia Loren and Brigitte Bardot. "Friend" was hardly appropriate. Al Sheldrock was a *friend*. "Fiancé" was inaccurate, although Ellen was beginning to let herself think that Wilson might propose. After all, when Danny had asked point-blank if he was going to marry Ellen, he hadn't said no, had he?

And the fact was that Ellen wanted to get married.

She told herself she wanted to get married because she was lonely. Because it would be better for Brenda and Danny. Because a happy marriage was the most important thing in life. Because she was drained and literally ill—she had become anemic and had the beginnings of an ulcer—from the double demands of running her business and bringing up her children, worn from constantly having to make unsatisfactory choices between them. Because the attraction and affection she felt for Wilson was turning to love.

What she did not tell herself—what she barely allowed herself to think about—was that she had renounced her feelings for Lew just before she finally went to bed with Wilson for the first time. The connection she did not allow herself to make was the connection between the impossibility of her feelings for Lew Swann leading to anything more than a clandestine affair, and the promise Wilson held out—the promise of availability.

14

ELLEN GREW UP AT THE SAME TIME AND IN THE SAME CULTURE Wilson had and shared his ideas about men and women. Women were supportive; men supported. Women were emotional; men were rational. A woman's place was in the home; a man's place was in the world.

The choice for women was narrow and the price was high: abandonment of all interests and ambitions that did not serve ideal domesticity and self-sacrificing wife-and-motherhood. The choice for men was just as narrow and the price just as high: suppression of all emotions that did not serve granite-like strength and complete invulnerability.

The circumstances of Ellen's life had begun to change—just a little—her view of women. And the circumstances of Wilson's life had begun to change—more than just a little—*his* view of women.

Wilson Hoback came to New York in the mid-1950s, a young man with big, if vague, dreams of success. Fresh out of state college in Maryland, Wilson, equipped with the obligatory B.A. and English major, landed a job in the press department of NBC promoting the actors and actresses who appeared on the soaps. He moved his wife, Mary Lou, and their brand-new baby into the best apartment he could afford: a fourth-floor walkup in a noncharming Greenwich Village brownstone.

The instant he could, Wilson left NBC and the soaps and went to work for Paramount, where he did the same thing for movies and movie stars for a bigger salary in the bigger leagues. Wilson told himself he was on the way to becoming successful; Mary Lou asked herself why she spent so much time alone.

After two years at Paramount, a second baby at home, Wilson opened his own public relations business. He struggled along with the struggling actors and actresses he'd met along the way. He hoped—like every press agent hoped—for the big break. For the long-run show with national touring companies, for the blockbuster movie that would put him on the map, for the star who would become a superstar. Mary Lou longed for a decent place to live, for a lawn and trees, for the day she would no longer have to push-pull-bump-and-thump a baby carriage and a stroller up and down four narrow, dark flights of stairs twice a day.

Wilson got his break—but it came out of left field in the person of the Italian wife of an Alabama-born theatrical producer who was one of Wilson's few really successful clients, a petite, brainy, ballsy con artist named Clive Lyonhart.

Adrianna Lyonhart's family owned vineyards in the hills of Tuscany, where they had for generations made a pleasant dry Frascati wine called Amiata. Adrianna wondered if there might be an American market for the easy-to-drink, easy-on-the-pocketbook family wine. She wanted to make some money on her own; she wanted to free herself from Clive's stranglehold on the family's finances.

"Make them come to you," Clive told her, sharing one of the secrets of his success.

"How?" asked Adrianna, a willing pupil at the master's size six feet. Clive was five five—in cowboy boots with two-inch heels.

"Publicity," Clive answered, and suggested his own rep, Wilson Hoback.

"The *right* publicity," Wilson amended and went to work.

He went to Romeo Salta's with a liter of Amiata—and a proposition. If Romeo liked the wine, Wilson would sell it to him on an exclusive basis in Manhattan in return for Romeo's featuring Amiata on the wine list.

Wilson then got busy on the phone, offering the best Italian restaurants in Los Angeles, San Francisco, Chicago, Miami, and Dallas the same proposition. At the same time, he planted column items linking other clients to the wine—Star A in Chicago appearing in Stage Hit B enjoyed a bottle of Amiata at Restaurant C—thus achieving the press agent's version of the hat trick: four plugs in one item.

People were curious about the Amiata wine they read about. They went to liquor stores and asked to buy it. The store owners asked their distributors for cases. Which no one had.

Soon, Adrianna had three importers vying with each other for the right to import Amiata, a wine that eight months before had not been heard of in the United States.

Wilson's strategy worked brilliantly. And Mary Lou got what she wanted: a house with trees and a lawn in a Long Island suburb. She had not foreseen how much time she would spend alone in it with two small children as her only company.

"You were right," Adrianna told Clive as the sales of Amiata rocketed, referring to an earlier pronouncement of his. "Wine is show biz."

"My dear," Clive said, lighting up a Dunhill and checking that week's grosses in *Variety*, "*everything* is show biz."

Clive was delighted, absolutely thrilled with his wife's financial success. His hustler's soul was already conniving a way to get her to back a musical he had optioned. A rock opera, *Psychedynamite!* had *beaucoup* noise, *beaucoup* four-letter words, and *beaucoup* frontal nudity. It was very Sixties.

Very, *very* Sixties.

The success of Adrianna's Amiata was not lost on the Italian Trade Commission, who went to Wilson to see what could be done with the wines of Sicily and Corsica. What could be done, Wilson told them, was to hold an Italian wine festival and invite the press.

As Wilson's world expanded, Mary Lou's world shrank to car pools, the Mouseketeers, and Little League baseball; to hairdos, recipes, and toaster ovens; to the drugstore/dry-cleaner/supermarket circuit and the mumps/measles/chicken-pox syndrome.

When Wilson came home, tensely talkative about the Person-to-Person feature he had pitched that day for a client, Mary

Lou, distracted with a feverish child or the clothes washer that had flooded the basement, was indifferent: "Why can't you just forget about the office when you come home?"

And when Mary Lou, who had spent the whole day at home waiting for a plumber who never showed up, complained, Wilson was bored with her trivial preoccupations: "So big deal. He'll fix the faucet tomorrow."

Mary Lou's and Wilson's conversation was limited to talk about things ("The lawn mower broke." "Would you get the car waxed?" "Do you want chicken or lamb for dinner?"); plans ("The Fairchilds invited us for dinner Saturday night. Do you want to go?"); and problems ("The school doctor says Buddy needs glasses."). Although Mary Lou and Wilson never realized it at the time, they never talked about anything important, and the reason they didn't realize it was that they were no different from most of the other young couples they knew in the suburbs. In separate worlds, husbands struggled with success while wives struggled with isolation.

The decision to divorce was mutual. Mary Lou wanted to go back to Maryland, where people lived comfortable, familiar lives. Wilson wanted to stay in New York, where he could enjoy the thrilling kiss of life on the fast track.

The success of the Italians aroused the chauvinism of the French. Not that it ever takes too much to arouse the chauvinism of the French. French growers, too, produced good, drinkable, non-chichi wines!

It was a grave error to think that French wines were only the haughty Burgundies, the elegant Sauternes, the velvety Bordeaux, the pricey champagnes. What about the pleasant, unpretentious wines of Provence? Of the Rhône and Loire valleys? Of Cahors? *Zut! Alors!* They were, after all, the very wines the French themselves drank day in, day out.

The French wine producers, naturally, went to the man who had done so much for the Italians.

Wine, inevitably, led to food, and within four years Wilson's business was almost exclusively devoted to promoting food and wine. Almost, that is, except for certain old clients like the foxy Clive, whose *Psychedynamite!* had broken record Broadway grosses, whose album was a chartbuster, whose touring companies had spread all over the country, whose London production's premiere had been attended by the queen herself, and whose film rights had been sold for over a million dollars.

How much over a million Clive's shrewd press agent never quite spelled out, of course, allowing the press to speculate wildly in a fever of greed and envy.

Wine became fashionable in the United States in the sixties and began to give scotch and the dry martini of earlier times a run for the money.

In Boston in 1962 a woman named Julia Child, just back from France, began a series of cooking lessons on the local educational station. The French Chef became an instant hit, and Mrs. Child became an instant celebrity.

And, at that time, cookbooks were regularly enormous best-sellers. Their authors—Julia Child and her partners in the *École des Trois Gourmandes*; Craig Claiborne, food writer of *The New York Times*; James Beard, considered the dean of the American food establishment—became stars. And, unlike stars in more evanescent fields like movies, television, and the theater, the star cooks were stars with lasting power.

Food and wine were "in." *Psychedynamite!* was beyond "in." And Wilson was "in."

But after a few years of being "in," Wilson realized that "in" wasn't enough. He lived for almost a year with a sexually relentless psychotherapist who was the most ambitious person Wilson had ever met in his life. Her book, *The Erotic Rights of Women*, sold an almost-instant two million copies, and she became a fixture on the talk-show circuit. When she told Wilson that she was leaving him for an underground porn star, he was actually relieved.

But he was lonely. He missed Mary Lou and his children. He wanted to share his success. He wanted to share his life.

Wilson had learned from his marriage that a wife was not enough. And, by the early years of the mid-sixties, he had realized that a man could expect more than just a wife. Wilson, like many men, was beginning to see women differently.

And women were beginning to see themselves differently. But the difference was slight, and the observer had to be attentive. Two books cast the new images of women into bold relief.

The Feminine Mystique, published in 1963, made public what many women already knew privately. Women who'd been quiet and domestic began to talk out loud about the way silence and domesticity made them feel: angry, used, ignored, insignificant, frustrated.

Sex and the Single Girl spelled out that there was indeed life beyond husbands, kids, and the house in the-suburbs. Being single—happily, vibrantly single—was an alternative. A glamorous alternative, in fact, with exciting horizons that included financial independence, absorbing work, and an adventuresome sex life.

Being married suddenly began to seem just a little narrow, just a little boring.

The movies were right in step. In 1964 the Oscar went to Julie Andrews, who portrayed Mary Poppins, the governess, the fantasy "good mother" altruistically devoted to her children. In 1965, only one year later, the same award went to another Julie, Julie Christie, for her portrayal of the successful fashion model in *Darling*, a woman whose glossy, sexually intense, emotionally complex life had nothing to do with husbands, babies, or domesticity.

And in San Francisco at the Republican National Convention, Margaret Chase Smith, the senator from Maine, was nominated for the presidency, the first woman ever to be nominated. Perhaps the nomination was only symbolic, but symbols, nevertheless, count, too.

The outward image—as well as the inner image—also changed. Skirts were shorter; panty hose—a liberating, one-piece garment—replaced armored girdles and cumbersome garters and stockings; wash-and-wear haircuts freed women from the weekly hairdresser's appointment or hours devoted to setting, drying, and styling their hair. Paper-doll prettiness— the June Allyson/Doris Day/Janet Leigh/girl-next-door look— seemed bland and unexciting. Barbra Streisand with a nose that movie producers would have bobbed only five years before and exotic, Nefertiti eyes, changed the idea of what was beautiful in a woman, of what *could* be beautiful.

These new images of women—the new possibilities for women—didn't replace the traditional image but were added to it as an overlay. As the essayist, playwright, columnist, and social commentator Marya Mannes wrote at the time (1964): "No one objects to a woman being a good writer as long as she manages also to be a good wife, mother, good-looking, good-tempered, well-dressed, well-groomed, and unaggressive..."

Wilson wanted the woman Marya Mannes described. He

wanted someone who was liberated and independent but not threatening.

Ellen wanted only to make him happy.

"The only thing that's not perfect about you is your address," Wilson teased Ellen one morning at five-thirty. He was putting on the underwear, shirt, tie, and socks, the suit he'd worn the day before, and finally his shoes. He'd drive back to New York, shower, change, pick up the *Times*, and head for his office. "Sneaking out of the house like a thief . . ."

"But the children," Ellen interrupted, still in bed, already missing Wilson. She was sure he was teasing, but she was unable not to take him seriously. She always took men—their feelings, their wishes, their slightest changes of mood—seriously. She had been brought up to. What she and her mother wanted was unimportant compared to what Frank Kendle wanted. "I wouldn't know what to tell the children."

"I guess you can't exactly tell them that their mother is entitled to a sex life," Wilson said, "no matter how liberated they think they are." Danny at twelve and Brenda at fifteen knew more about sex—or at least thought they did—than Ellen had at twenty.

He came over and sat down on the edge of the bed and took Ellen's hand. "But what would you say about telling them we're thinking about getting married?"

"Oh" was all Ellen could say at first. "Oh, Wilson . . ."

To Ellen, it was a proposal; to Wilson, it was a possibility.

15

In the autumn of 1964, five and a half years after Phil's death, Ellen was a woman torn—torn between her rediscovery of the part of her that was still the terrific kid she'd been in college who saw no limits to her ability and the woman who still wanted what she had been brought up to want: to love and be loved by a man, to devote herself to his happiness and the happiness of their children.

So there were, when Wilson moved into her life, two Ellens: Ellen the Conqueror and Ellen Who Wanted to Be Conquered. The two Ellens lived in an uneasy détente, and as Wilson became more important to her, the balance between the two Ellens began to shift.

That first season, the year before Brenda was to go off to college, the year Danny started high school, they talked about getting married, getting used to the idea. Wilson wanted to do it right away.

"Let's drive right over to city hall," he said, his eyes intense. "You'd better nail me before I realize how scared I am."

"City hall's so unromantic!" Ellen complained, not really hearing Wilson's words, not understanding that he meant them—

even more than *he* thought. Ellen wanted to wait. Fall, with Thanksgiving and Christmas, was absolutely her busiest season, and she wanted to enjoy her wedding, not go through it in a state of terminal exhaustion.

"I want a *real* wedding," she told Wilson, confiding her dream, remembering that she and Phil had been married in her parents' modest living room, and how she had always regretted settling for such a simple ceremony. "With music, a beautiful dress, a reception—catered by someone else!—the whole romantic works." Her beautiful, exotically shaped eyes focused on the dream wedding of her fantasies: herself as bride, romantic and eternally in love; Wilson as bridegroom, strong, protective, and endlessly adoring.

"I understand." Wilson held and kissed her. What he understood was that women had different feelings about things like weddings than men did. He and Mary Lou had had an enormous wedding, an extravaganza willingly produced and paid for by her family. Mary Lou had an album, covered in white satin, of their wedding photos, and when they were first married she looked at it constantly. When they divorced, he found she had abandoned it in a carton in the garage along with the children's baby clothes. "If that's what you want . . . Myself, I'd settle for the justice of the peace and a few grains of rice."

"You men!" Ellen exclaimed. "You're so unromantic!"

"I guess I'm more old-fashioned than I thought," Wilson said, six weeks after the first time he'd stayed to breakfast. Six weeks during which Brenda and Danny had grown used to—incredibly quickly—his almost-daily presence at breakfast, dinner, and on weekends. "I'm more or less living here," Wilson said. "But you're paying all the bills. I'm beginning to feel like a kept man, and I don't like it."

Ellen agreed, with an unexpectedly sharp sense of relief, to Wilson's suggestion that he pay the basic bills.

"But," she asked, instantly deferring to him, "what should I do with the money I earn?"

"Spend it on yourself," Wilson said, always most comfortable, most assured in the role of protector and adviser, a role he assumed as instantly as Ellen had deferred. "For one thing, you certainly owe yourself a new car."

* * *

As winter turned into spring, Ellen felt married in everything but name. Brenda, at sixteen, had outgrown her moody rebellious stage and was, willingly, Ellen's most competent, most intelligent assistant in the kitchen.

"We'll be partners one day," she said. A member of the Betty Friedan/Gloria Steinem generation, Brenda knew she would work—and knew that she would love it. "Ellen and Daughter! And if Danny's good, we'll let him into the company, too!"

"Don't be a female chauvinist!" Ellen warned, teasing. "You know how much you hate male chauvinists!"

About Wilson, Brenda was cautiously accepting. "He's sexy," she said in worldly assessment. "Just like Daddy was. But I only hope he marries you . . ."

With no father in the house, Brenda's ideas of what went on between men and women had been formed by *Cosmopolitan*'s advice to single women, by a new generation of movie stars who openly admitted to living with their boyfriends (without the hindrance of marriage), and by television's Peyton Place, which brought teenaged trauma and illicit sex into prime time. Her sophistication—or what passed for sophistication—never failed to astound Ellen.

"He will," Ellen assured her. "We just have to find some time when our schedules permit."

"I'll believe it when I see the ring," the youthful cynic said. But, Ellen had noticed, the gallery of Phil's pictures, except for the one on Brenda's bureau, had gradually been packed tenderly away. Wilson was now the man of the house, and his presence filled an emptiness in Brenda that had ached since her father's death.

Danny blossomed. The boys in Danny's school were sports crazy. Sports was the way to make it, to be popular, to be looked up to—and Danny struggled as a third-string pitcher on the baseball team, wanting as much—and as unsuccessfully—to be popular as to have a sizzling fastball. He was angry and frustrated until Wilson, whose own father had been a high school gym teacher, took Danny out into the backyard and became his personal pitching coach.

"If you can't beat them with speed," he told Danny, "beat them with your brains."

He taught Danny how—and when—to use the off-speed stuff, the slider, the sinker, the change-up. And Danny, who had been third-string when he had tried to be a fastballer, was first among equals when he became the fireman, the reliever the coach sent in late in the game to hold on to a slim lead.

"Your grades are improving," Ellen commented when Danny brought home a report card with marks in the high 80s—a big difference from his usual indifferent middling 70s.

Danny smiled his devilish, just-like-Phil smile, and winked. "Wilson told me the secret: beat 'em with your brains."

Brenda and Danny had totally shifted their allegiance to Wilson. They kept asking Ellen when they were going to get married. Young conservatives, they wanted things legal.

Having a man in the house again was like driving familiar roads, sleeping in the comfortable bed of protected childhood, swimming in a warm and friendly sea. Everything about it felt right to Ellen. She could not get over how much she must have missed having a man in her life without having ever been consciously aware of it.

But when Wilson's laundry was in the hamper, when he came home for dinner most every night, when she watched him talk to Brenda about boys and sex or check Danny out on his down-and-out now that football season was approaching, when she cooked special breakfasts for him on Sunday mornings no matter how late she'd worked the night before, Ellen remembered what it was like to feel feminine again.

And she loved sex with Wilson, loving, domesticated sex, the kind of sex she'd had with Phil. The lust following the starvation of the years after Phil's death that had led her into Jak Busch's back room embarrassed her; the tidal wave of erotic fantasy Lew had evoked terrified her with its intimations of the depth of her own sexual impulses.

Feeling loved and loving—a woman with a man—was wonderful, and Ellen hugged the feeling to her like a warm kitten. She felt, as the months went by, that after an unfair detour life had forced upon her, she had come home at last. With a man in the house, a man in her life, Ellen felt like a real woman again—and even recalled Phil's words during their final argument with bittersweet tenderness.

A real woman. Ellen sighed in relief.

"I'm so happy," she whispered to Wilson, cuddling against him in bed, the night her new station wagon—perfect for delivering large quantities of food to parties, a station wagon she would never have thought of buying without Wilson's suggestion—was parked for the first time in the garage. "The car is wonderful," she said. "Thank you."

"You deserve it," Wilson said, accepting her thanks as if he'd paid for it out of his own money. "The next time you make some money, why don't you get a pair of those new Courrèges boots?"

The next day, for the first time since she'd started À La Carte, Ellen turned down a job, a Saturday night dinner party for twenty-five. Why should she cook for twenty-five strangers when she could stay home and cook for the man she loved?

Autumn was Wilson's busiest season, and he wanted Ellen to go everywhere with him: to be available for dinners at James Beard's Village townhouse, wine tastings poolside at the Four Seasons, cheese samplings at the Waldorf. Ellen could not go out with Wilson four nights a week and accept every job offered to À La Carte.

She had to make a choice. And the choice was easy: with Wilson's agreement, she turned down jobs and chose Wilson.

But as Ellen gave up more and more for Wilson, Wilson paid less and less attention to her. Ellen didn't know why, and when he finally explained, she was relieved.

"The lease for the office is up," he told Ellen, glad he could talk to her in a way he had never been able to talk to Mary Lou, who understood nothing of business and business problems. "If I stay where I am, the rent will go up eighteen percent, and I won't have one more square foot of space—which I need. But if I move, it will cost me even more."

He did not add that he had received a letter from Mary Lou asking for more child support—everything had gone up: tuition, doctors' bills, clothes, books, piano lessons. Wilson had replied with a larger check.

He felt squeezed for money and worried that he couldn't live up to his obligations or to his image of himself as provider and protector. He needed to make more money—and to make more he needed to spend more. More than he had.

But Wilson couldn't admit it. His way of sharing his financial anxieties with Ellen was to deny they existed.

"Money isn't the problem," he had said impatiently when Ellen had asked. "Expansion is. I need more office space, more employees to serve more clients."

"Can't you borrow?" Ellen asked, recalling her conversations with Lew, accurately interpreting Wilson's denials, sensing that money *was* the problem.

"Of course I can borrow!" Wilson exclaimed as if she had said something totally idiotic.

"I just want you to know I'm with you, Wilson. That I'm on your side," she said, backing down.

All fall, Wilson was preoccupied, short-tempered, irritable. All fall, he denied absolutely that he was having financial difficulties.

"Would it help if I paid the mortgage?" Ellen asked in November as holiday business picked up.

"No!" Wilson snapped. "Absolutely not! You know how I feel about women paying the bills!"

His tone of voice closed the subject.

In 1965, À La Carte did more holiday business than ever, and when Ellen presented Wilson with a check for three months of the mortgage, he did not refuse it.

"Thanks," he mumbled, avoiding her eyes as if by doing so the transaction had not taken place. He never referred to it, not once. His pride simply would not allow him to live on an equal financial footing with a woman.

But Ellen was sympathetic, loved him even more for his show of vulnerability.

By the beginning of the new year, Wilson finally made his decision: he signed a lease for office space on Fifth Avenue— expensive space with a prestigious address. Over and over Wilson asked himself if he had bitten off more than he could chew.

Was he getting too ambitious for a kid from Maryland? Was the prestige of a Fifth Avenue address worth the sleepless nights? Had he made the right move at the right time? Could he afford it? Could he afford, at the same time, the increased child-support payments?

"Do you still love me?" Ellen asked, hating herself for asking, for not being more understanding of the pressures Wilson was obviously feeling but not able to help herself. She wanted reassurance; she *needed* reassurance.

"You know I do," he answered, resenting the pressure Ellen was putting on him. Once more pressure at a time he least needed it. "We just should have gone to city hall and gotten it over with."

His words were hardly romantic, but Ellen knew he was right. She had been a fool, had thought like a nineteen-year-old girl instead of a thirty-six-year-old woman.

It was her fault that she and Wilson weren't husband and wife. Her fault for being so stupidly romantic. And because New Rochelle was basically a small town, people talked. Danny had gotten into a fist fight at school over a nasty remark he'd overheard, and Ellen accused herself of being the reason her son was reprimanded for fighting.

Still, Wilson assured her that he loved her; he took care of her and her children. Ellen told herself that if she were just patient everything would turn out all right. It was important, she told herself, not to rock the boat.

16

JANUARY AND FEBRUARY WERE LIKE, WELL, JANUARY AND February. Ellen's commercial clients—a brokerage house that celebrated the elevation of three new partners at a champagne reception, a boutique that showed the spring collection over croissants and orange blossoms, an advertising agency that pitched a travel account over a soufflé lunch—and a big, private Valentine's dance paid most of the bills for the winter months.

Wilson's expenses ran higher than he had anticipated. The move itself cost more than the estimate. The costs of renovating and furnishing the new offices ran almost twenty percent over the estimates. To tighten the screws, one of Wilson's mainstay clients, an importer of English teas and biscuits, went out of business, reducing Wilson's billings.

Ellen let the one-day-a-week cleaning woman go and contentedly did the laundry and cleaning herself. She had the time to make the gingham tab-end curtains she had wanted for so long and started the summer's geraniums from slips and the petunias from seedlings. And she began an herb garden—the parsley, basil, thyme, oregano, and tarragon to be used in her catering.

122

"I'm really very domestic," she told Wilson. "I like making curtains and gardening. Besides, it saves a lot of money," she added proudly.

Ellen didn't mind being poor. She was used to it.

Wilson hated it, having struggled much too hard to escape it. He hated feeling poor, hated feeling out of control, hated feeling unsuccessful, hated depending on Ellen and the money Ellen earned. He tried to hide the way he felt; he could not hide the effects on their sex life, which shrunk to zero.

For Ellen, sharing the money struggles brought her closer to Wilson, gave her the feeling that they were in it together, deepened her commitment to him. For Wilson, even admitting to money problems was impossible. He felt ashamed and diminished, less like a lover, less like a man.

During this period, Ellen often slipped and called Wilson "Phil." She couldn't understand why. In the two years she had known Wilson, she had never made that mistake. She tried very, very hard not to do it, and mostly she succeeded.

In March, the same month, ironically, in which Phil had died, Wilson came home with a bottle of chilled champagne—Dom Perignon, no less. There was the old spring in his step, his eyes gleamed wickedly, sexily; even his hair seemed electric and vital with life and energy.

"Well, I did it! Three new clients in one day!" he exulted, taking Ellen into his arms and spinning her across the living room in a wild fandango. One was a prestigious importer of Iranian caviar; the second a nationally distributed line of gourmet frozen foods; and the third a restaurant consultant with an excellent name in the trade who had just signed a cookbook contract and wanted her name to be better known by the public. "Not one! Not two! But three!" he exclaimed, popping the cork.

"That's wonderful! Just wonderful!" Ellen bubbled, happier over Wilson's triumph than she had ever been over any of her own. She kissed him and got two champagne glasses down from the cupboard. "Oh, Wilson, I'm so happy for you!"

"The move turned out to be a stroke of genius," Wilson said. "Even if I say so myself. The Fifth Avenue address was what finally sold the importers. They said that Fifth Avenue was synonymous with the best, and they wanted the best."

"It's wonderful!" Ellen exclaimed. "You're wonderful!"

"It's a great opportunity for you, too! The importers are planning a huge party at the Plaza to introduce their caviar. They want to blow the Russians off the map! They're inviting caterers to bid the party. I put in your name. The sky's the limit, Ellen! Let your imagination run wild! The Plaza! With an unlimited budget!"

And the last thing he told Ellen that night after they'd made love—more hotly, more passionately than in months—was, "I won't need your help with the bills anymore. I want you to buy the prettiest dress Bergdorf's ever sold, and then we're going to show it off at the Four Seasons."

As summer turned into fall, life returned to an even keel. Wilson was working harder than ever and seemed to thrive on it. Ellen was working less than ever and thriving on *that*.

She now accepted only those parties she could handle without their interfering with her time with Wilson, Brenda, and Danny. She wanted to spend weekends with them, and so she no longer accepted weekend events. Now that Wilson's company was in high gear, his calendar was crammed with social events, dinner parties, cocktail parties, charity events, and tastings, and he wanted Ellen to be able to attend with him, so she no longer accepted many evening commitments.

She did continue with the afternoon bridge parties, the business breakfasts and luncheons, the afternoon cocktail parties, and the ladies' teas. When Wilson told her that the importers were holding a repeat of their last year's Plaza party and that she should bid it again, Ellen began to work up some figures, using her previous year's bid as a starting point. Everything seemed fearfully expensive to her, and, finally, without telling Wilson, she never entered her bid.

Caroline did not approve. Not at all.

"You were on the verge of building a really successful business," she told Ellen. "Why are you backing down now? A little more effort and À La Carte could really be something to be proud of . . . something to pass on to Brenda and Danny."

"I don't need the money," Ellen explained, thinking that Caroline sounded exactly like Phil. "There's enough for Brenda's and Danny's education, even enough for indulgences for me like an expensive Italian handbag or a really good haircut. What more do we need?"

Mostly Ellen reveled in not having to deal with the day-to-

day unpleasantness of running a business. She didn't miss reminding the hostess who called the day after a party demanding
her money back because her guests hadn't liked the food that
everyone had had seconds and some people thirds, hassling
with suppliers who sent less-than-impeccable-quality ingredients, or making a dozen phone calls before she could find a
plumber the days the sinks backed up. She felt no nostalgia
for the times her best help was out with the flu, or when three
hundred crêpes for a bar mitzvah had to be remade because
someone had mistakenly used salt instead of sugar in the batter.
She had always hated collecting late payments, firing insolent
bartenders, and hoping that people would somehow see how
nice she was underneath her businesswoman's façade.

She felt the way she had felt when Phil was alive: she had
gone back in time, to a time that was comfortable. She felt
feminine. Someone—a man—was there to take care of her.

She was even wondering if she'd close down À La Carte
one day. She wanted to build a life with Wilson; the idea of
having his baby occurred to her, although she was careful not
to mention it to him. She felt calm and happy and comfortable;
at night she slept deeply and dreamlessly, as if she'd been
tranquilized.

The only incident that marred that happy interim was when
Wilson found out that she hadn't put in a bid for the caviar
importer's second annual Plaza party.

"It's a prestige event!" he said angrily. "You can't *afford*
not to bid."

"But I lost last year," Ellen said defensively. "The estimates
were even higher this year than last. I knew I didn't have a
chance, so I didn't see why I should bother." What she didn't
say was that the party would be a tremendous amount of work,
and she didn't see any reason to work that hard when she didn't
have to.

"How do you know you didn't have a chance? Your prices
can't be much higher than anyone else's. Knowing you, they
were probably less! Do you think I get every client I want the
first time I meet with him? Do you think clients accept every
idea the first time I present it? What you do, Ellen, when you
run a business is try *again*!"

Wilson was annoyed and irritated, and for a week he kept

a cool distance between them, disdaining all Ellen's efforts to make up to him.

Wilson confused her. On the one hand, he wouldn't let her pay for anything except the kids' bills. Whenever she made some unexpected money, he told her to go buy some new clothes. She kept telling him she wasn't interested in new clothes. She was interested in *him*. And whenever there was a conflict between a cocktail party someone wanted Ellen to cater and a business event that Wilson wanted Ellen to attend with him, he expected her to turn down the party and go wherever he wanted her to go.

On the other hand, there were times when he seemed to think she should take her business as seriously as he took his. He wanted to be able to impress his friends and clients with her success. He wanted her to be an ornament after his own definition: financially independent, successful, a woman with an exciting career who devoted herself to him and put him first.

17

ELLEN AND WILSON HAD THEIR FIRST MAJOR FIGHT—AN UGLY, wounding, verbal free-for-all—Thanksgiving night. The bitter irony of it all was that the day had been perfect. Absolutely perfect.

Thanksgiving 1967 was the first "real" holiday Ellen and her children had had since Phil's death, the first family holiday with the whole family assembled, the first holiday that Ellen had not been either crippled with depression or haggard with overwork.

"Let's have a real old-fashioned Thanksgiving this year," Ellen had suggested when the first holiday orders began to come in, thinking of the old-fashioned holidays they'd been cheated out of the years before. "For us."

"Who deserves it more?" Wilson agreed. "My children will be here. It's time you met them."

"I'll invite them," Ellen said, already nervous about whether or not Wilson's children would like her. "And your parents, too," she said, knowing that Wilson tried to avoid them. "We'll be like a real family."

"I'd love that," Wilson said, to Ellen's surprise. She'd taken a calculated risk when she'd suggested inviting Wilson's parents, and she was thrilled that Wilson approved her suggestion; she wanted everyone to be happy. "It's been a long time since the kids have seen their grandparents. And a long time since I've had my family all together. Too long." Now that Wilson's business was more successful than ever, he was, in all respects, the man Ellen had first met: totally confident, his anxieties concealed. He wanted his family to see what a success he'd become.

And so Ellen had invited Wilson's parents, who drove up from Maryland along with his two children—now sixteen and eighteen. The Durbans—Tommy looking older than his age as time went on and Caroline looking younger than hers—came. Brenda was home from Brown with her best friend, Toni Reese, upon whom Danny had a tremendous crush.

"I'm going to marry you," Danny told Toni.

"I love you," Toni said. "But I'm an older woman."

"Only four years," Danny said. "Four years doesn't count."

Eighteen to Danny's fourteen, the four years seemed a century to Toni. She laughed fondly. "I don't want anyone to accuse me of being a cradle snatcher."

"Don't worry," Danny said seriously. "No one will!"

And Toni thought it was just terrific to have a fan. A woman with her eye on an M.B.A. needed all the fans she could get.

As usual, but this time for love not money, Ellen had been cooking for three days before the holiday. She had set the big harvest table with her best pewter, with vases of white daisies and yellow chrysanthemums, and shiny brass buckets stood on the brick floor, filled with brilliant red and yellow branches of autumn leaves. Across the pine serving table she had arranged the turkey and the relishes, the creamed onions and the gravy, the garlicky broccoli and honeyed acorn squash, the puréed potatoes, the chestnut stuffing, and the salted nuts, the pies— mince and pumpkin—flanked by pitchers of rich sweet whipped cream.

"It looks like a picture in a magazine," Danny said, echoing what everyone—even Wilson's hypercritical mother—was thinking.

While Danny said grace, Ellen prayed a silent prayer of thanks for herself and Wilson, for love, for the happiness she had been so unbelievably lucky to find not once but twice in one lifetime. She gave thanks for her blessings, moved beyond words at the gathered families, the happy faces of her children and Wilson's children, the bountifully laden table. Thanksgiving was a dream come true, and Ellen was its heroine.

She served dinner at four; by nine-thirty, replete, the guests had left. At eleven, when Ellen was finishing cleaning up, Wilson complimented her on the dinner. "It was wonderful," he said. "The best I've ever had."

Ellen smiled, warmed. "I left nothing to chance," she said. "I did every bit of it myself."

"When did you have the time?" Wilson asked.

"I turned down most of the Thanksgiving business," Ellen said, taking the large turkey platter to the vertical storage bins.

"You *what*?"

"I took only the pickup and takeout orders," Ellen said. "I turned everything else down. We agreed we'd have a real old-fashioned Thanksgiving this year. How do you think I could do it if I worked as hard as I did last year?"

"I don't believe you! Last year you were so thrilled at how good business was. At how many repeats you had. At how every year your holiday receipts have gone up, and this year you turn business *down*? What the hell's the matter with you?" He was incredulous.

"I thought having our own dinner was more important," Ellen said, as mystified by Wilson's outburst as he said he was by her turning down business.

"Couldn't you do both?" Wilson asked.

"How?"

"Your assistants can make the relishes and pies and vegetables just as well as you can. We could have eaten what the clients eat," Wilson said, annoyed that Ellen had done everything including the serving herself. Why hadn't she used one of the waitresses to serve and wash up?

"But I wanted it to be perfect. I didn't want us to eat things other people made. I wanted to do it all myself. I wanted it to be personal," Ellen said.

"What the hell difference does it make who cooked it as long as it's good? À La Carte would have had a better year than last year, and you threw it away!" Wilson, who never drank after dinner, poured himself a scotch, sipped it once, threw the contents of the glass into the sink, and put the glass into the dishwasher. "You threw it all away for a family holiday!"

"A family holiday's more important than some dumb dress I'd buy with the money I made," Ellen retorted heatedly. Why was he attacking her? He knew she'd been cooking for days. They'd agreed on a real Thanksgiving. And what had she done other than give him what he said he wanted?

"You don't think your business is more important? You don't think your future and your children's future is more important?"

"No, I don't," Ellen said, sure of her ground. "My family is much more important than my business. Much, much more important! And I think *you're* more important. Wilson, I did it for you!" she said, spelling it out. "For us!"

Wilson took a second glass, poured himself a second scotch, sipped at it, and then said, carefully, "I feel suffocated, Ellen. I'm not sure what's going to happen..."

"Happen?" Ellen asked, a stab of fear lacerating her. "What could happen? What do you mean?"

"I mean," Wilson said, finishing the drink in a swallow, "that I don't know what's going to happen with us... in the future..."

They got into bed that night, strangers, careful not to touch. Ellen felt lost... scared and empty.

Two days later they made up in bed, and a week later everything seemed fine again—as if nothing had happened.

Ellen told herself that Wilson had been on edge at Thanksgiving, worried at the presence of his whiny and ultracritical mother and his beefy father, who drank too much. And nervous at having his children meet Ellen and Ellen's children. He had said things he didn't really mean.

During the weeks between Thanksgiving and Christmas, Wilson spent several nights a week in Manhattan, often calling at the last minute to tell Ellen he wouldn't be home for dinner. Things at the office, he said, were especially busy around the holidays. Ellen quashed the small tentacles of suspicion that rose in her and made herself believe him.

But while Wilson was busy, Ellen wasn't. Knowing how busy she usually was, most people did their Christmas planning well in advance of Thanksgiving. And the period before Thanksgiving she had discouraged business. Ellen had time on her hands; she filled it by getting ready for their own Christmas—hers and Wilson's.

She spent hours choosing the perfect presents: a Nehru jacket for Wilson, a Mickey Mantle outfielder's glove for Danny, a Ravi Shankar album and a maxi coat for Brenda. She ordered a huge fir tree, a pine wreath for the front door, and a bayberry wreath for the kitchen door. She bought herself the most expensive dress she had ever owned in her life: a red velvet smock cut like a Victorian girl's with a handmade lace collar.

Christmas, with friends and family, with stacks of presents, carols on the hi-fi, the scent of pine in the room, and a fire in the fireplace, a roast goose with all the trimmings, and a midnight candlelight service, was a dream come true, and the Christmas fight was worse than the Thanksgiving fight.

"I told you these goddamn holidays don't mean as much to me as they do to you!" Wilson said when everyone had gone. He remembered Christmas in Manhattan penthouses, glamorous people, the rich smell of success. "You ought to be building À La Carte, not showing the world what a lady bountiful you are. On *my* money!"

"You won't let me use mine!" Ellen retorted, tormented by Wilson's changes of mind. "You knew all along I was turning down business. By the time you changed your mind at Thanksgiving, it was too late for much Christmas business. You tell me you want a family holiday. You tell me you want us all to be together. You tell me you want me to build up À La Carte, but you won't let me spend the money I earn on anything except clothes and the hairdresser. You want me to be in the city four nights a week, but you want me to be here making dinner for you. You talk about getting married, but you keep postponing the date. Well, I'm confused. What *do* you want, Wilson? A businesswoman? A hostess? A girlfriend? A wife? You'll have to choose. What do you want me to be?"

"Everything," Wilson said, meaning it, not understanding the impossibility his own reactions set up. Domestic women bored him; successful women threatened him. And those were the only two ways he—and Ellen—could imagine a woman to be.

"But I *can't* be everything," Ellen objected. "I'm not Superwoman."

"You used to be," Wilson said. "You were when I met you."

"Things were different then. I was alone. I had the business and the children. That was all. Now I have you, too. I only want to make you happy. I want to do what you want me to do, but I can't pull myself into fifty different pieces. Oh, Wilson, I just want us to love each other . . . I just want us to be happy." Ellen put a hand on his arm.

Wilson looked away from her, over at the windows and the night darkness outside. "Ellen, don't let yourself get too dependent on me."

"What do you mean?" Panic clutched at Ellen, icy fingers chilling her heart.

"I mean I'm not sure if I can make a commitment," Wilson said, evading her eyes, her touch.

"But I do everything for you. I *live* for you!"

"Well, don't!" he said and flung her hand off his arm. "I told you you're suffocating me. I've already been this route. The wife and the kids in the goddamn suburbs—"

"You knew where I lived when you met me!" Ellen said, fixing on something concrete.

"I thought you were different!" Wilson went on, and the expression in his eyes shut her out. "I resent it. I feel trapped, and I can't stand it. You're smothering me to death, Ellen!"

"And you're breaking my heart! You're tearing me apart, Wilson. First you want one thing, then another. I don't think *you* know what you want!" Ellen choked the words out, furious, on the brink of tears, and then, while her defenses were down, the beast jumped out of its cage, the beast that had attacked Phil: "You're having some affair while I'm here devoting myself to you and your career! Admit it!"

Wilson's expression gave Ellen the answer she dreaded. "Yes," he said quietly. "And I don't really know why. I don't love her." There was a moment's silence, and then, "It would be better if I left now."

He went into the bedroom and began to pack.

"Don't! Oh, don't!" Ellen begged, physically trying to restrain him. "Oh, Wilson, I'm sorry I said what I did. I didn't mean it. I'm sorry! Oh, please don't go. Please! Don't leave me. Don't. Please don't leave me . . . I'll do *anything* you want."

The more Ellen begged, the more she pleaded with him, the more grimly he packed. Silently, avoiding her eyes and her touch.

Ellen was crying as he left.

"What am I going to tell the children?" They had planned the whole holiday weekend: a football game and a party afterward, a marshmallow roast and skating at the pond that was frozen over. "What am I going to tell Brenda and Danny?"

Wilson paused at the door. He reached out and touched Ellen's hair. "Tell them I'm sorry," he said and swallowed back his own tears, and he disappeared into the Christmas night, snowflakes gently falling, the whiteness and darkness and candlelight making the night seem an enchanted dream—a dream in which this couldn't be happening, a dream in which he couldn't be leaving, a dream with an unhappy ending—a second dream in which the man she loved went away and Ellen was left alone.

For Johanna, the ending was a happy one. Four years after presenting Max with her ultimatum, she married him the same day his divorce was granted. Four awful years of haggling with lawyers trying to come to a settlement with Esme, who did not want a divorce and didn't care how long it took Max to get one. If ever.

"But I'm worth it," Johanna assured Max as they left for a honeymoon in the south of France.

"You'd better be," Max said.

The divorce had cost him one million dollars.

"And worth every penny," a rejuvenated Max told Lew. "Johanna's the best thing that ever happened to me."

And Lew had to agree. Max had more *joie de vivre* than ever, looked twenty years younger, and, in his invariable mood of self-expression, was making more money than ever. Money and the making of it were to Max as paint and the creation of art were to Picasso. And, at the rate Max was going, it looked as if he'd live as long as Pablo and be as rich.

Lew Swann was very far from stupid, and he realized that to a great extent he had been the architect of his own discontent. Paving the way to his personal hell had been his good intentions.

Lew had passed through adolescence and entered manhood during the unhappy midyears of his parents' marriage. He had seen Max's mindless infidelities erode his mother's self-confidence, her respect for her husband, and, finally, her love for him. Witness to the crumbling of his parents' marriage, Lew had sworn he would be a faithful husband—and he had been. During Reenie's cold spells and her periodic hot spells.

He redoubled his vow of fidelity during the emotional storms of Max's affair with Johanna and divorce from Esme. To finance it, Max had sold a shopping center to raise the cash part of the settlement, giving Esme the house and the cars plus a large life insurance policy and alimony for life.

"What about Decor?" Lew had asked, worried.

"Don't worry about Decor," Max had assured Lew while the terms of the settlement were being worked out. For a man whose main interests in life were sex and money, Max had extremely strong family feeling. He worshiped the memory of his immigrant father, who had started Decor with a high-quality formula for house paints he had brought from the Old Country with money he had carefully saved. "*Nobody* gets Decor. Decor is *ours.*"

"Let me buy you out," Lew offered. The Eagle division had been the success Lew had anticipated. Encouraged, he had begun to think even bigger, had begun talking buy-out and merger with other companies. Just that week he had had a call from a Swiss tycoon named Reinhardt Estes, who owned a prestigious company that made drapery and upholstery fabrics. Estes might be thinking of selling his company. Might Decor be interested in buying Eilberg Fabrics? Lew had asked to see balance sheets. "I don't intend to build Decor and have someone else walk away with the profits."

"No, you can't buy me out. For one thing, I'm a sentimental old bastard. For another, it's worth more now than the last time you asked. You couldn't afford it then, you can't afford it now," Max said. "For Christ's sake, don't worry! Decor is strictly family business. *Swann* family business. You and me. Period! So don't worry. Promise?"

Knowing how ferociously Max felt about family, Lew promised and listened to Max's latest business adventure.

"A beauty parlor, for Christ's sake!" Max said, a little sheepish. "I bought it for Johanna. As a present."

The "beauty parlor" was a chic hairdresser on Fifty-seventh Street between Fifth and Sixth owned by William Ferguson, a former artistic director at Vidal Sassoon. Max had complained about how much time—and how much money—Johanna spent at William's.

"So buy it for me," she had said.

"Why not?" Max had answered when he found out how much money there was in hairdressing. William worked six days a week, was booked eight weeks in advance, and charged fifty dollars a pop. How long, Max asked himself once he got a look at the books, had *this* been going on?

When Lew considered his father's new happiness, he questioned once again his own vow of fidelity. Max was thriving. He was more rambunctious than ever. He was having more fun than ever. While Lew was still the devoted son and devoted husband.

Was he too square? Too much of a straight arrow? Scared to take a risk? And why? What for? For a tepid marriage, with long cold spells and an occasional hot episode?

And Lew would reach for the telephone, ready to take a chance, ready to call Ellen . . .

But then he thought of his mother, of Esme, who was sad and depressed in the aftermath of Max's departure, who sipped sherry and wept during the long afternoons in the big Locust Valley house that was now all hers—and empty. Max said he was convinced Esme would snap out of it, but Lew wasn't so sure.

Lew had offered to send her on a cruise, but she had refused. He had suggested she sell the big house with all its memories and begin a new life somewhere else, but she had turned his suggestion down. Lew had advised her to buy a new wardrobe, but she had said she wasn't interested in clothes. Who would she wear them for?

Lew had given her theater tickets, had taken her to the ballet, had invited her out to Peconic for the weekends, had done everything he could think of to amuse her, distract her, make her feel a little better. But nothing had worked.

Esme, two years after the divorce, still sat in her bedroom sipping sherry and weeping. Lew was afraid she would die, he was afraid she would do away with herself.

When he thought of his mother, he thought of Reenie; when he thought of his mother, he accused his father of selfishness; when he thought of Reenie, he accused himself of selfishness and took his hand away from the phone.

Torn by conflict, Lew looked for magic, dreamed of the impossible.

He wanted to have an affair with Ellen without guilt, without responsibility, without repercussion.

He needed to find the magic that would allow it to happen. He was sure that if only he were patient, if only he were persistent, if only he didn't give up, the magic would be there. Somehow.

18

It was embarrassing to call Al Sheldrock in March. For the past three years—the years with Wilson—Ellen had gone to Wilson's accountant, just as she had gone to Wilson's dentist, lawyer, and internist. But Al was nice about Ellen's defection and didn't, in fact, even mention it. They made an appointment for her to come in in mid-March.

"I've moved," Al told her, giving her his new address. "I'm at Three-o-one Madison now . . . twenty-first floor."

Three-o-one Madison was a Chrysler-Building-vintage office tower with a travertine marble entrance, vaulted ceilings, and glamorous-in-a-subdued-way Art Deco elevators. Ellen couldn't help comparing it to the dun-brick building Cooley & Heiser had occupied, a heavy, clumpy, faceless, squat landlord's money-machine. But the lobby of 301 was no surprise at all compared to the surprise that awaited Ellen when she got to the twenty-first floor.

The walls of Al's reception room and the corridors of the suite of offices were faced with nubby, natural-colored linen, and tawny wall-to-wall carpeting covered the floors. The furniture was classic contemporary, elegant but not intimidating.

Photographs of actors, singers, television personalities—autographed to Al—hung from the linen-covered walls.

Al's own office, the floor-to-ceiling corner windows shielded by vertical blinds that cut the sunlight into ribbons of gold, was comfortable, handsome, reassuring. The big desk, spread with papers, pens, and file baskets, was neither cluttered nor barren and sterile. It was a good-looking, functional working desk with plenty of space for spreading out, organizing, and thinking. Ellen had a sudden, involuntary memory of the drab, cluttered cubicle at Cooley & Heiser.

But the transformation in the office was nothing compared to the transformation in Al himself.

The short-sleeved shirt with the pens clipped to the breast pocket and the rumpled slacks were gone. Instead, he wore a well-cut dark gray flannel suit and a pale blue Egyptian cotton shirt. The unbecoming bookworm glasses had been replaced by good-looking horn-rims, and the chipmunk cheeks were now lean and tanned—Al had lost a good fifteen pounds. But his smile was the same; the intelligence—and the *niceness*—in his warm blue eyes was the same; and so was his remarkably masculine deep voice.

"Success becomes you," Ellen said when she had gotten over her surprise.

"You, too," Al said, thinking how nice it was to see a woman wearing makeup and a soft blouse in a flattering seafoam green that made Ellen's blue-green eyes even more vivid. He even caught the faint scent of perfume—it seemed to him that it was centuries since Gail had worn perfume.

"Not as successful as I was," Ellen said regretfully. "You can see that from the books."

Al nodded. "What happened, Ellen? Last year you made almost twenty-two thousand dollars. This past year you dropped to less than fourteen. Did you have any unusual expenses? Were you ill? Was there a loss of some kind? Something that doesn't show up here?"

"No," Ellen shook her head. "I just didn't work as hard." She was not about to tell him *why* she hadn't worked as hard.

"We'll be able to take advantage of tax averaging," Al said, aware of remaining professional, of keeping his personal curiosity at bay, of not letting himself wonder about what had happened to Ellen. "It's a tax provision for people who have unpredictable earnings," he explained. "People like you."

"Like me? You mean there are others?" Ellen felt relieved as much by the content of what Al was saying as by his matter-of-fact tone.

"Sure," said Al, smiling. "In fact, most of my clients—"

"Are all those celebrities your clients?" Ellen asked, referring to the photographs.

Al nodded. "Actually, accounting is only a small part of my work these days. I act as an agent for a lot of people, negotiating their contracts. And as a financial manager. I handle their money, invest it, pay their bills. Most of my clients are people who are too busy with their careers to take care of their own finances."

"It sounds interesting." Ellen was intrigued; she felt Al's excitement as he spoke. She remembered Phil's excitement whenever he opened a big new account. And Lew's excitement over starting Eagle. And Wilson's excitement the day he'd landed three new clients.

"I just love it!" he said. "I've never been happier!" He meant professionally; personally, his life was going to hell, and he didn't know what to do about it.

"Sometimes I used to feel that way about À La Carte," Ellen said, suddenly remembering. "The time I first earned a hundred dollars, I woke up the kids! And the first party I catered for a hundred. I thought I was Superwoman!"

"You were," Al said. "You did a wonderful job with À La Carte. Very few men could have built a business that successful starting with nothing."

"Really?" Ellen asked. She had never thought of it before. She had thought of À La Carte as something she *had* to do to support herself and the children until she got married again. "Even with a lousy year like last year?"

"Even with a lousy year like last year," Al confirmed. "Businesses have their ups and downs."

"Like the people who run them?" Ellen asked. Al's comments and her own sudden rush of memories made Ellen feel suddenly much better about herself. She began to see her withdrawal from À La Carte as temporary, as reversible.

"Like the people who run them," Al said, and he dropped his professional guard enough to let himself wonder what had been happening in Ellen's life during the years he hadn't seen her. It seemed to him that everyone he knew was going through upheavals of one kind or another. Nineteen sixty-eight had been a year of public upheavals—the assassinations of Martin Luther King and Robert Kennedy; rioting in the cities; President Johnson's decision not to run again; protests against the war in Vietnam. The nation had twisted and turned in spasms of violence. And people's personal lives had not been immune to disruption—every other couple seemed to be getting divorced; every day there were horror stories of people being mugged in broad daylight; young people—people Al had known since they were children—were going to jail for their political beliefs, joining odd religious sects, burning out their brains and their nervous systems with drugs. No one seemed to escape. But he returned to the business at hand. "I'll have the returns prepared and sent to you for signature. You'll have them in a few weeks."

"Thanks, Al," Ellen said, thinking how *nice* Al was. Wishing she'd meet someone like him but knowing that, if she did, she wouldn't be attracted to him. She was attracted only to glamorous men, to exciting men, to men who gave her a hard time.

"Ellen! Ellen Durban!"

Ellen stopped in the elegant lobby and smiled tentatively, trying to remember who this woman was and where she had met her.

"Ellen! You don't recognize me! I'm Gail Sheldrock!"

"Oh! Gail!" Ellen said, and tried to conceal her shock.

She remembered Gail's delicate prettiness, the polished and becoming clothes, the sophisticated New York look Ellen had always admired as she tried to see the old Gail in the new Gail. This Gail wore her hair unset and unstyled in an unflattering half-Afro that almost buried her small features. She wore no makeup whatsoever—not a trace of lipstick, mascara, or blusher—and she wore a baggy T-shirt, braless, with a shapeless pair of workman's denim overalls. Her only jewelry was a Women's Strike for Peace pin.

"I've just come from Al's office," Ellen said, thinking that it was eight years since she'd last seen Gail. "How are you?"

"Wonderful! *Now*," Gail said. "After all these years of diapering, car pooling, and being a support system, I'm beginning to find out who I really am. I've decided to get my CPA and go into practice."

"Al must be thrilled," Ellen said, remembering Al's dreams

of sharing an office with his wife, remembering how afraid Gail had been of failing the exam—so afraid that, in the end, she hadn't even taken it.

"Not with Al! With a woman in my consciousness-raising group. *She's* going back to school and getting her law degree!" Gail glowed with her excitement, and Ellen could see a glimpse of the prettiness she remembered. "I've already begun taking courses at Pace. But, Ellen, I want to tell you how often I've talked about you at my group. About how you started your own business! About how successful you are! Why, you're one of our heroines!"

"Me?" Ellen asked, amazed. "A heroine?"

"Yes!" exclaimed Gail. "Why should we let men define heroines? All they see women as are virgins, sexpots, and hero-worshiping doormats. From now on, women will define their own heroines—intelligent, competent, assertive, successful, complex, fully rounded human beings. *That's* a heroine!"

"And that's how you see me?"

"Not only me," Gail said, "but every woman in my group."

And not only Gail and the women in her group. Women all over the country.

Because the dimly glimpsed image of a new kind of woman that had been just-visible in the early years of the sixties was now a full-fledged portrait. Women were making themselves felt politically. The National Organization for Women was founded in 1966 to achieve "true equality for all women in America..." And the Women's Strike for Peace organized antiwar marches, lobbying campaigns, antiwar vigils, and protests against the bombings of North Vietnam.

Movies like *Funny Girl, The Prime of Miss Jean Brodie*, and *Rachel, Rachel* showed women with more on their minds than only trapping and/or pleasing men. On the book racks, Jackie Susann's immensely popular novels showed that although women wanted love, they also fought and struggled for careers. *Ms.* magazine debuted, and the women's pages of newspapers abandoned their steady diet of recipes, fashion tips, and society notes for issue-oriented articles on abortion, equal pay for equal work, sexual harassment at the office, and psychologically oriented articles on self-assertion and women's fear of success. By the end of the decade, televison would catch up when Mary Tyler Moore played a news producer (instead of a secretary) on a Minneapolis television station.

Women who had been "feminine" and demurely quiet for so long were now speaking up; and if they sometimes went too far, it is well to understand that long-buried anger, finally expressed, is often volcanic.

Ellen was well past her own rage, and in the next few days she thought of Gail's newfound feminism and the energy and determination it gave her. She thought of the excitement the men she knew found in work—and of the excitement she herself had found in it. And she thought of Al's transformation, after moving from Cooley & Heiser's depressing cubicle into those impressive offices, where he did important work for successful clients. He now dressed in an executive style that suited him well, and he projected a self-confidence that obviously came from within.

What had *she* to show for the same amount of time?

She lived in the same house, and although she still loved it, it badly needed painting and a thorough refurbishing. Except for occasional Wilson-inspired indulges—an Italian leather handbag, a designer dress—she still wore the unobtrusive, moderate-priced clothes Phil had always disliked so much, afraid to spend money on herself because she had no confidence that she would continue to earn it. She worried about the bills every single month, the same way she had right after Phil had died. She still went into a depression every time there was an unexpected doctor's bill, an unplanned-for-but-necessary home repair. She had managed to save enough for the children's education, which was in a special account, but she had less than three thousand dollars in her own account and no other savings.

What if she had worked, really worked, for the past eight years? What if she had taken herself, her business, seriously? Had thought of À La Carte as a career instead of a stopgap, something to tide her and the children over until a man came along? What if she had put as much energy into À La Carte as she had into her relationship with Wilson? Maybe she'd be up in the world, too, instead of just lurching along from month to month. Maybe she'd be able to feel secure—at least financially. Because when Wilson had walked out on her, Ellen had felt a double loss. She had lost not only a man she loved, but a business that gave her much more pleasure than she had been aware of. About the man, she could do nothing. About the business, she could.

And now, when Ellen tried to impress on Brenda just how important it was that a woman be able to earn a living, her tone changed: Work was no longer a dire punishment but a challenging opportunity.

That spring and summer, Ellen took every job that came her way; she placed a weekly ad in the *Westchester Record*; she sent another mailing to all her commercial clients and, for the first time, did a mailing to every client for whom she had ever cooked a takeout order or catered a party, no matter how small. By fall, she could no longer park her car in the garage because the garage was full of cases of tinned tomatoes, of imported olive oil, of fifty-pound bags of flour and sugar, of cases of the Swiss chocolate she used for her truffles and mousses, of bags of lemons and oranges and onions, of the two extra secondhand refrigerators she had had to buy for additional storage. Within six months of full-time commitment, À La Carte had grown past the stage of being a cottage industry Ellen could run informally out of her kitchen.

She found herself in precisely the same situation Wilson had been in. To take care of her increased business she needed more space. Much more space. She had two choices: renting or building. Renting would be cheaper in the short run, but Al pointed out that the tax structure favored owning rather than renting.

Equally important to Ellen was that if she added a professional kitchen to the house, she would still be able to spend most of her time there. Next year Danny would go away to college. This year meant a lot to Ellen.

The decision between renting or building turned out to be no decision. A new kitchen was a necessity, and so was borrowing the money to build it.

"Mrs. Durban, it's nice to meet you. Mr. Durban's on his way?" asked the banker, a thin, dry, gray, powerful mouse behind a mahogany desk. His title was vice-president. Since County Mercantile had sixty-seven vice-presidents, the title didn't mean very much, but Ellen didn't know that. *She* was impressed and more than a little scared. *Banks* had taken her father's store away from him; *banks* had ruined his life—and her childhood.

"Mr. Durban is dead," Ellen said, confused.

"Oh, I'm sorry." The banker seemed flustered. "I thought a loan was being discussed . . ." He shuffled some papers.

"Yes," said Ellen. "I want to borrow money to build a professional kitchen. I run a catering service."

"I see," said the banker, who acted as if he didn't see at all. "But who's signing the loan agreement?"

"I am," Ellen said. "Look"—she gestured toward the applications—"I signed the application and filled out the forms. Ellen's À La Carte is *my* business. *I'm* Ellen."

"But we need someone responsible," said the mouse, whose nameplate announced him to be Edwin Garren.

"*I'm* responsible," said Ellen, not understanding why Edwin Garren couldn't seem to understand plain English. "*I* gave you all the facts and figures, the contractor's estimate, my own earnings projections." Ellen was proud of how businesslike and confident she sounded—and felt. Al had told her exactly what to do to apply for a loan, had worked up the figures for her, and, so far, everything had been fine. County Mercantile had provisionally approved her loan application for the twenty thousand dollars she needed to build a kitchen extension on her house. She had come into the bank to sign the final papers.

"Mrs. Durban, we can't give you the loan on your signature alone. You'll need a cosigner. Do you have a partner? Who gave you the money to start your business? Perhaps he'd cosign." Edwin Garren was only trying to be helpful.

"No one gave me money, Mr. Garren. I started À La Carte myself. With my own money," Ellen said, letting the irritation show in her voice.

"Of course." Edwin Garren's expression was dubious. "But we'll still require another signature. It's bank policy. We need someone responsible," he said again, stressing the word "responsible." The mouse was beginning to look like a rat to Ellen.

"And you think I'm not responsible?" Ellen asked. "I started À La Carte from scratch and made it a success. All by myself. And I raised my children. All by myself. I repaid my late husband's debts. All by myself. And you're implying I'm not responsible?"

"I'm sure you've done an admirable job, Mrs. Durban," said Garren. "But the bank isn't interested in how you started your business or in how well you've raised your children. We're interested in making loans and having financially responsible people sign for them." Then his voice turned a notch friendlier. "Believe me, it's nothing personal, Mrs. Durban. No reflection on you or your ability. Perhaps your father would cosign? Or your brother?"

Ellen laughed bitterly. "Mr. Garren, my father is dead. He was a poor man. My brother teaches school and has three children to support. *I'm* the rich one in the family." Ellen gathered up her file folder of papers. No wonder the Gail Sheldrocks of this world were so angry—*and* the Ellen Durbans!

As Ellen walked out of Edwin Garren's office, he was still talking: "Perhaps a former employer. I see you worked in a stationery store . . ."

Ellen stopped in the doorway and turned around. "Mr. Garren, for your information there's a revolution going on. You're not going to be able to treat women the way you've treated me. Not for much longer!"

He looked at her, a blank expression on his mouse face.

There were other banks in the world, but none of them were any more enlightened than County Mercantile. There was, fortunately, one—and only one!—Reinhardt Estes.

19

REINHARDT ESTES WAS A PRUSSIAN PERFECTIONIST. HE WAS the president of a company that imported a variety of fine Swiss products—watches, precision writing instruments, upholstery fabrics. When he had a heart attack at the age of forty-two, his doctor advised him to buy a place in the country where he could relax on weekends.

What Reinhardt bought was a 150-acre gentleman's farm in Dutchess County. It took two years and three interior designers before the seventeenth-century farmhouse was restored to his satisfaction. He converted the barn into a ballet studio for his daughter from his first marriage, built a swimming pool, pool house, tennis court, and stables; and when he had built as much as he could build, he got bored. With nothing left to make perfect, Reinhardt lost interest in his farm.

When he began to talk about selling it, his wife (the third), who had grown to love the farm, told him that he simply ought to find another interest. After dinner one evening at the Pavillion and a discussion with Henri Soulé about the fact that American chickens didn't begin to compare in flavor with the French poultry raised in Bresse, he decided to raise the best poultry in the United States. It took seven years of breeding, experiments, failures, three poultry experts, battalions of advisers from the Cornell School of Agriculture, and dozens of combinations of feed mixtures to produce a superlative chicken.

Chambord and Twenty-One, Soulé and the River Club, the Four Seasons and Lobel's meat market on Madison Avenue at Eighty-second Street, all became customers. Ellen read about Reinhardt's chickens in *Gourmet* magazine and decided she had to have them. She not only disliked Bernie Arkin, but she didn't much like his tasteless, commercially grown chickens either. She drove up to Dutchess County and introduced herself.

"I own a catering service, and I'd like to buy your chickens," she told Reinhardt. They sat in a perfectly restored living room with original wide-plank flooring, leaded-glass windows, rare Queen Anne side chairs, a priceless William and Mary table from Israel Sack, a faded needlepoint rug, and the original fireplace, big enough to roast an ox.

"Mrs. Durban, many people want to buy my chickens. There is, in fact, a waiting list," Reinhardt informed her. He was as perfect as the room. In a blue blazer, a soft yellow shirt, an exquisitely tied ascot, he looked as if he might be having lunch at Balmoral. As he spoke, he removed an imperceptibly less-than-absolutely-perfect petal from a red rose in a Revere silver bowl and crushed it between his fingers. He fixed Ellen with his stainless-steel gray eyes and asked with indifferent, perfect politeness, "What makes you think I would want to sell my chickens to you?"

"Not everyone can go to the Four Seasons, Mr. Estes, but if you sold to me, many more people would eat and enjoy your chickens. Their excellence and their renown would spread outside a very small circle."

"Quite logical," Reinhardt said, "not that I usually expect logic from women. I don't know whether or not I will decide to sell to you. In order to make my decision, there are several requirements: I'll want to taste your cooking. I must know how you intend to present my chickens. I will want personal references—two will do—and financial references. A bank reference and, perhaps, a business reference. Someone with whom you have done business for at least two years. Is that clear? Perfectly clear?"

Ellen nodded, proud of herself for managing to keep a straight face. She *only* wanted to buy chickens, not the Hope diamond.

After Ellen provided the references Reinhardt demanded and

her sample chicken dishes had met with his approval—*poulet au calvados* to show the chicken off against a cream sauce, a *pollo al ajillo* to show it off against a vigorous garlic sauce, and a straightforward chicken-in-the-pot to show it off at its simplest—Reinhardt agreed to sell her his chickens.

There were, of course, conditions.

"The minimum order is two dozen. It doesn't pay me to kill and deliver less. Payment is in cash within ten days. The maximum order is five dozen because that is the maximum we can handle and still maintain high quality. Do you understand the conditions?"

"Perfectly," said Ellen, wondering what she was going to do on the weeks she needed fewer than two dozen and the weeks she needed more than five dozen.

"Good," he said, and then absolutely astounded Ellen by inviting her to dinner. Intrigued and fascinated, she accepted.

Reinhardt took her to the Pavillion, where they were treated like royalty. Even Wilson hadn't been treated with such deference. After dinner, on the way to New Rochelle in Reinhardt's chauffeured Rolls-Royce, Reinhardt took Ellen's hand.

"I've had a lovely evening," he said. "And I'd like to see you again. But before I do I think we should make love. To see if we're compatible."

No wonder he'd been divorced four times. (Wife Number Three had thrown in the towel during the seven-year quest for the Perfect Chicken; Number Four lasted six months and spent four years in analysis recovering.)

"I think it would be better if we kept our relationship a business one." Ellen's response was as formal in tone as Reinhardt's. She wondered if Reinhardt would refuse to sell her his chickens because she had refused to go to bed with him. His proposition made her feel she had to pass yet another of his tests. She was surprised he hadn't asked for references.

"If you really prefer it that way," he said calmly. "You're very attractive, and I would like very much to make love to you. But, if you don't want to . . . Well, I like a woman who knows what she wants."

Which gave Ellen the lead-in she'd been looking for. "What I *do* want is to handle the catering the next time you entertain."

"Everything is up to you," Reinhardt said on the telephone six weeks later after telling her that he was giving a dinner party for twenty—and that he had decided to let her cater it. "Except that the main course must be chicken and the dessert chocolate. Swiss chocolate."

Of course, Ellen thought, plus one other thing: every single detail would have to be nothing less than perfect.

Reinhardt had built his business from nothing. He had started off as an assistant in a jewel box of a shop that sold fine watches on Zurich's fashionable Bahnhofstrasse. Then, in rapid sequence, he worked for Audemars-Piguet, then for the Swiss Watch Council, and then for the Swiss Trade Council, which promoted Swiss-made products all over the world. When he had the opportunity to buy the United States and Canadian distribution rights from his former employers at Audemars-Piguet, he did so.

He relocated in Manhattan, divorced his first wife, a pretty Zurich belle, married his second, a wishy-WASPy Boston deb. He energetically promoted, publicized, and sold the fine-quality Audemars-Piguet watches and added the prestigious Vacheron Constantin Genève line of fine timepieces in due course.

The House of Eilberg, weavers of world-famous decorative and upholstery fabrics, did not really fit into Reinhardt's fine-jewelry empire, but when Frau Eilberg, widow of the founder of the firm, asked Reinhardt to buy the business in 1959, he did so—mostly out of affection for the Eilberg family, whom he'd known since childhood.

Reinhardt lavished the same energetic perfectionism on Eilberg that he devoted to everything he did, and the company and its prestige grew enormously. But, in 1968, Reinhardt was presented with the biggest opportunity of his life. And he needed money—a great deal of money—to take advantage of it.

Carl Storz was Reinhardt's biggest competitor. Storz controlled United States and Canadian distribution for three superb lines of Swiss watches: Girard-Perregaux, Baume & Mercier, and Piaget.

In the autumn of 1968, Carl went to his doctor for a routine checkup. A routine X-ray revealed that Carl—who had never smoked a cigarette in his life—had lung cancer. It was operable, but the operation was major and highly risky.

"If I die," Carl told Reinhardt over *raclette* and pickled onions, "I want my widow to inherit money, not the headaches of running a business. And if I live, I want to enjoy the rest of my life.

"Every year I plant daffodils in November," Carl went on. "Every April it seems I am required to be in Switzerland. I have never once seen my daffodils bloom, and I want to. The point of all this is that I want to sell Carl Storz, Inc., before I go into the hospital. And I want to sell it to you, Reinhardt. You're the only man I know who will give my watches the same love I've given them."

Carl's price for the company was three and a half million dollars—fifty percent in cash, the remaining fifty percent to be paid in twenty years out of profits—not cheap but not outlandish. Carl's price—like Carl, like Reinhardt—was rigidly fair for products of uncompromising quality.

Carl's offer was the chance of a lifetime. If Reinhardt bought Storz, he would have the exclusive right to distribute the most desirable watches in the world throughout the United States and Canada—a rich plum indeed. But Reinhardt needed to raise cash, and the way to raise cash was to sell Eilberg—a company that now more than ever seemed out of place in Reinhardt's kingdom of fine timepieces.

He wanted to find a buyer, the right buyer, the—this being Reinhardt's way of doing things—perfect buyer. The buyer would have to be someone totally honest and honorable, someone who understood quality, someone who knew how to run a top-of-the-line business. After a search that took him through the entire home-furnishings industry, Reinhardt found the perfect buyer. His name was Lewis Swann. The perfect dinner party would set the perfect stage for the perfect deal.

20

"MRS. DURBAN, THE OVEN WON'T LIGHT," ELLEN'S ASSIS-
tant, Gaby, said.

"The pilot must be out," Ellen said, making the final check
of a tray of smoked salmon with dill before she sent her other
assistant, Janice, out to pass it. Ellen herself never left the
kitchen during a party. Like a general, she directed the battle
from behind the lines, and if the guests had included the queen
of England, Ellen would never have known. "Take a match
and light it. But be careful."

"It still won't light," Gaby said a few moments later, the
sulfur from the spent matches a faint odor in Reinhardt's large
kitchen.

"Let me try," Ellen said, taking the matchbook. "While I
do, pass the shrimp."

"Your oven's broken," Ellen told Reinhardt moments later.

"That's not possible." He was annoyed to be called into the
kitchen by Gaby just as he was telling Lew Swann about the
silk damask the White House had just ordered from Eilberg
for the president's oval office. "I do not tolerate undependable
equipment," he added. How dare an oven—a mere oven—
owned by him not work!

151

Ellen handed him a matchbook.

"*You* light it."

Reinhardt snatched the matchbook from her, furious at the interruption, at the oven, at the incompetents who couldn't light it.

The cold hors d'oeuvres would be no problem, Ellen thought as she watched Reinhardt's attempt to impose his will on the pilot. The salmon, the shrimp in their aquavit-flavored sauce, the white mushrooms in a mustard vinaigrette, the caviar mousse.

But what about the hot hors d'oeuvres? The *gougères? The* cumin-flavored mini-meatballs? The Roquefort *mille-feuille*? And what about—her heart fluttered, her mouth went dry— the chicken calvados, all twenty-five pounds of it?

"I hope you have nice neighbors," Ellen told Reinhardt, when, with icy curses, he finally gave up, "whose oven works."

"The Bloombergs," he said. "They own the farm next door."

"Next door" was a ten-minute drive.

It took fifteen minutes to repack the food and load the car. Another ten to drive to the Bloombergs. Another ten to preheat their oven. Twenty more to heat everything. Fifteen more to pack it back up and load the car, ten to drive back to the Estes farm, fifteen to unpack and arrange trays and serving platters.

In total the trip "next door" took one hour and thirty-five minutes. One hour and thirty-five minutes for the guests to have a third and a fourth drink with nothing to eat except the light cold hors d'oeuvres. One hour and thirty-five minutes for appetites to become ravenous.

Ellen worked like a madwoman, rushing, frenzied, anxious, sweating.

Janice served the first tray of hot hors d'oeuvres—the *gougères*—and was back in the kitchen instantly.

"They demolished those *gougères*!" she exclaimed, stunned at the speed with which the tray had been devoured.

Ellen wiped a strand of hair off her forehead and tried not to think about the disaster she was facing. She told Janice and Gaby to serve the dinner while she stayed in the kitchen doing the best she could to keep the seconds hot on the four top burners. She crossed her fingers and hoped that there was enough food to satisfy the alcohol-stimulated appetites of guests who were being served an hour and a half late.

There wasn't.

*   *   *

"Dinner was a disaster. *You* are a disaster." Reinhardt spat the words out like hatchets. "You humiliated me in front of my guests. And you ruined a business deal! You cost me hundreds of thousands of dollars!"

"It's not my fault your oven is broken," Ellen retorted, outraged at his accusation. "I did the best I could—"

"You had one reason for being here tonight," Reinhardt continued, ignoring her words, "and that was to cater a dinner for my guests. A job *you* asked for. I am not, I assure you, going to pay for this disaster. I'm stopping payment on my check."

With that he spun around and left the kitchen. The service door swung back and forth silently, accusingly. Unjustly.

Tears of rage prickled at Ellen's eyes, and she wiped them away with the back of her hand, smearing her mascara. Black smudges ringed her eyes, and she stood in the kitchen contemplating murder. Instead, she filled a bucket with water and detergent, got a mop from the broom closet, and began to clean the floor. She would take out her fury in soap and water and good old elbow grease. She mopped, attacking the floor as if it were Reinhardt, and was not even aware of the swinging door opening.

"*I* liked the dinner."

The voice was an hallucination. A steel-and-velvet hallucination. Ellen thought she was hearing things. She thought she was seeing things . . . a mirage in Reinhardt Estes's kitchen.

"In fact, I *loved* the dinner. Best goddamn dinner I ever had!"

"Lew Swann! What are you doing here?" Ellen stopped in mid-swipe, suddenly aware of the mascara smeared all over her face. She probably looked like a raccoon!

"Getting buttered up for the kill," Lew said in the voice that always sent shivers through Ellen. He was fresh and clean and handsome as a movie star in his dinner jacket, a whole generation of dream lovers come to golden life in one man. "Reinhardt needs to raise cash. He wants me to buy one of his companies."

"And the dinner party was part of his sales strategy?" Ellen asked, beginning to understand Reinhardt's rage. He had not, of course, confided in her the purpose of the dinner. Clients virtually never did unless it was something like a bridesmaid's dinner or an engagement party.

"Yep," said Lew. Ellen was aware of her sweaty forehead, shiny nose, smeared mascara, the lipstick that had worn off hours before, all mercilessly highlighted by the harsh overhead fluorescent kitchen lighting. "He wants to sell me a company called Eilberg Fabrics. He's decided that I'm an acceptable buyer. He gave the dinner party to show me what an honor he was granting me. And to get the price up. Way up," Lew explained. "He was telling me that Lady Bird Johnson had just ordered some Eilberg damask for the oval office drapes. It was nine-thirty, and no one had eaten yet. I told him I hoped he ran Eilberg a little better than he ran his dinner parties."

Ellen rolled her eyes to the skies imagining Reinhardt's reaction to that one. "No wonder he was so furious!" she said, and turned back to the kitchen floor.

"At the time I didn't know who was doing the cooking," Lew said. "I'm sorry if I screwed you up. I was just looking for an advantage."

"I guess you got it," Ellen said, mopping away.

"For Christ's sake, will you put that mop down!" Lew took it out of Ellen's hands before she could speak. "The broken oven wasn't your fault. If he's going to stop payment on the check, you don't owe him one more thing. Let him clean his own goddamn kitchen."

"But I've never left a client's kitchen in less than perfect condition," Ellen said stubbornly. "I have a *very* strict rule about it."

"You made the rule, you break it," Lew said, and took her hands in his, not allowing her to touch the mop or the scouring pad or the mountain of pots and pans in the sink.

"But I don't want him to be able to say I walked out leaving the job half-done. I don't want to give him fuel for his fire," Ellen said persistently, half-aware through her numb fatigue that she *was* being perverse.

"Don't worry about Reinhardt," Lew said, and he knew what he was talking about. With a father like Max, Lew knew plenty about dealing with impossible men—when to resist, when to rebel, when to con, when to say one thing and do another. After Max, Reinhardt was amateur night. "He's pissed off right now, but his bark is much worse than his bite. He'll get over it."

"But he'll tell everyone he knows not to hire me," Ellen protested.

"Fuck him. He's not God. Although sometimes he gets confused and thinks he is. Come on. Wash your hands and face and put some lipstick on. I'm taking you out for a drink. You deserve one."

"Champagne?" Ellen asked as the waiter uncorked the Moët. They sat at a corner table in the paneled bar of the nearby 1770 Inn. A fire sputtered on the hearth, flurries of snow winked past the window, dim lights burned on the red tablecloths, a couple in the opposite corner sat with hands entwined, heads close together, smiling and whispering and occasionally kissing.

"Definitely!" said Lew.

"What's the occasion?"

"Magic" was the word that went through Lew's mind.

"The occasion," he said, "is my forthcoming purchase of Eilberg Fabrics."

"But Reinhardt thinks the deal's off," Ellen protested, as the waiter poured the champagne. "He told me I cost him thousands of dollars. *Hundreds* of thousands of dollars."

"He's right!" Lew exulted. "He thinks the deal's off because that's what I want him to think. Look at it this way, Ellen. Maybe that dinner party *cost* Reinhardt a few hundred thousand. On the other hand, it *saved* me a few hundred thousand."

Through the haze of her exhaustion and preoccupation with her own nasty encounter with Reinhardt, Ellen began to get the message.

"I fully intend to buy Eilberg Fabrics," Lew went on. "I wasn't sure before tonight. I was afraid it was too big a step, too expensive. But not now. Now I can buy it at Lew Swann's price . . . *not* Reinhardt Estes's price. Thanks to *you!*"

The I've-got-him-just-where-I-want-him smile on Lew's face was answered with the it-serves-the-bastard-right smile on Ellen's face.

"And when I buy it," Lew concluded, "guess who's going to cater the party making the official announcement?"

Lew and Ellen picked up their glasses, toasted Victory, laughed, and they both felt as if it had been two and a half hours since they'd last seen each other . . . not two and a half years.

*   *   *

The Eilberg party with its Swiss *fondue* and *raclette* and chocolate-dipped—Swiss-chocolate dipped!—stemmed strawberries was a great success.

"Even Reinhardt said so!" Lew told Ellen the next day with a grin.

And, when Eagle Paints introduced a line of coordinated Williamsburg-derived wallpapers at a press party, Ellen created an array of eastern seaboard specialties: mini-crabcakes, poached oysters, Vermont cheddar puffs, Down East fried clams, blueberry muffins, cornbread sticks, and Pennsylvania sausages with a mustard-horseradish sauce.

"How the hell do you do it in that kitchen of yours?" Lew asked when the party was over.

"With difficulty," Ellen answered. "The fact is that I need a real kitchen with professional equipment."

"So why don't you build one?"

"With what? It'll cost twenty thousand dollars," Ellen said. "I haven't got it, and the banks don't seem to want to lend to women."

"Twenty thousand?" asked Lew.

Ellen nodded and showed him the contractor's estimates, which were in her briefcase.

"You'll need more than twenty," Lew said, skimming the figures.

"More?" Ellen asked. She had, God knows, felt timid enough about asking to borrow twenty. Money was, by far, the most difficult part of running a business for her. Thinking in sums of over a few hundred dollars still intimidated her, and twenty thousand dollars was a frightening amount of money to her in 1968, when a quart of milk cost 30 cents and a pound of steak $1.25.

"You'll need twenty for the construction, plus you ought to allow another ten percent for overruns," he advised. "*And* once you have a bigger kitchen, you'll be able to take on more work. That means you'll need more staff, more phone lines, more everything."

"Maybe that's why the banks turned me down," Ellen said, realizing she hadn't totally thought through her plans for expansion.

"Bullshit! But what would you think of selling À La Carte to Decor? You'd run it exactly the way you've been running it. The advantage to you would be access to Decor's capital.

The advantage to Decor would be a share of À La Carte's profits."

"But why would you take a chance on me when none of the banks would?" Ellen was tempted; she was also afraid. It would be a big commitment. Suppose she let Lew down?

"You've already repaid one loan to me, so I know you're good for it," Lew said. "And you've done a hell of a job running À La Carte out of your kitchen. Imagine what you could do with a professional kitchen and a professional staff!"

Ellen nodded. "I *have* gotten very ambitious," she admitted. "I want À La Carte to be the best caterer in the area. The best and most successful."

"Terrific!" said Lew. "That gives me even more reason to want to add À La Carte to Decor."

"Can I have a week to think it over?"

"Okay," Lew said. "One week."

He really liked this new Ellen. He remembered when she had been so tentative, so self-effacing, that he often felt like shaking her. It was a crummy thing to think—even to himself—but having to run her own business, because of the way Phil had left her, had done her a world of good.

Ellen tried one more bank, was turned down, and decided to do what she really wanted to do anyway: she accepted Lew's offer, but on her terms.

She took Al's advice and incorporated À La Carte. Two hundred shares were issued. Ellen kept one hundred shares; the other one hundred were the property of Decor.

"I guess you own half of me now," Ellen said when they signed the papers in Lew's unpretentious office, the one she remembered so vividly from the day she had cleaned out Phil's desk.

"Decor owns half of À La Carte," Lew corrected. "I don't own you."

Their eyes met for an intense moment, then each looked away.

As Lew walked her to the elevators, he gave her—at her request—a tour of Max's office. An eighteenth-century mahogany partners' desk was centered in the large square room, surrounded by a set of six museum-quality Chippendale chairs on an antique navy-and-cream silk Chinese rug. Heavy silk drapes—the fabric hand-loomed in Switzerland by Eilberg—

framed the three north windows and the three west windows. The other two walls of the room were wood-paneled; and the paneling, Lew demonstrated, concealed built-in cabinetry, storage drawers, and an elaborate wet bar. One of the panels was a door leading to a knock-your-eyes-out marble bath and twenty-first-century gym.

"Doesn't your father ever use his office?" Ellen asked, thinking what a shame it was for such a glamorous room to sit empty.

Lew reddened slightly. "It's supposed to be my office now."

"Yours!"

"It was Johanna's idea. She got Dad to agree to give me the office, since he's never here anymore. And she decorated it. She told me she was doing it for my father, but when the work was finished, she asked me how I liked it. When I said I did—who wouldn't?—she said, 'Surprise! It's yours. A present from your father and me!'"

"Then why don't you use it?"

"It embarrasses me," Lew said flatly in a very Lew-like way.

"But aren't Johanna's feelings hurt?"

Lew looked at Ellen and remembered the time Johanna had walked in on them.

"Johanna, you may have noticed," he said, "is about as sensitive as a Titan missile. She wanted me to like her. She wanted me to be on her side when my parents divorced. The office was a bribe."

"I wish she'd bribe *me*," Ellen said, impressed at the beautiful work Johanna had done.

"No, you don't," said Lew. "Believe me."

21

ELLEN'S NEW KITCHEN WAS, AS SHE HAD PLANNED IT TO BE,
a large, old-fashioned country kitchen—with every modern
convenience.

There was a ten-burner Garland stove with a salamander,
three large stainless-steel sinks, and plenty of butcher-block
counter space. A marble counter was especially for pastry making. S-hooks on cast-iron bars lined one entire wall from floor
to ceiling and held an array of saucepans, whisks, *sauté* pans,
roasters, beaters, colanders, strainers, pastry rings, and copper
au gratins—all out in the open, immediately and instantly at
hand.

There was a professional mixer with a pastry hook, a com-
mercial-sized, continuous-feed Robot Coupe, slotted wooden
racks for Ellen's collection of carbon steel knives, and a pair
of Zero King stainless-steel, restaurant-sized refrigerators big
enough to walk into. "My Rolls-Royce plus chauffeur," Ellen
called them.

A large, antique pine harvest table found in a shop in Litch-
field stood at the window, surrounded by twelve comfortable
captain's chairs.

"It's a dream come true," Caroline said the first time she saw it.

"*My* dream," Ellen said. "I wouldn't have it without Lew Swann."

Caroline looked at Ellen carefully and then, considering her words, cautiously asked, "Is there anything between you and Lew Swann? Besides business?"

"No," said Ellen truthfully. "No, there isn't. I'm very happy now, Caroline. Happier than I've ever been."

And that *was* the truth, a truth that no longer surprised Ellen. And she found it hard to believe that she had once thought marriage was the *only* definition of happiness for a woman. Freedom, she had discovered, was another.

She had gotten over Wilson, sad that the affair was over, poignantly aware now of her own contributions to its failure. She was not yet ready to fall in love again, but she also was not ready to dismiss love entirely from her life. In the meantime, she reveled in the first stage of real freedom in her adult life.

Brenda was away at college on partial scholarship, winning straight A's and holding down a part-time job as hostess in the dining room of Providence's best country inn.

Danny, who handled the books for À La Carte as he had since Ellen had gone into business, was a senior in high school, looking forward to going away to college—to the University of Pennsylvania, where Ellen and Phil had gone.

Free of an absorbing relationship with a man, free of the demands of young children, Ellen was no longer a woman divided. She was no longer torn between her guilt toward her children and the need to support them, no longer divided between her wish to love and serve a man and the rediscovered, long-suppressed image of herself as Ellen the Conqueror. Ellen was free to devote herself to her business, and À La Carte was quickly becoming what Ellen had dreamed of: the best and most successful caterer in the area.

"My friends were so impressed. They all *raved* about the red caviar mousse!" the mother of the bride told Ellen on the phone the day after a wedding for two hundred and fifty. Four of the guests at that wedding called Ellen when *their* daughters got married.

"Simply exquisite! From the poached striped bass with *sauce verte* right through to the *crème brûlée*!" read a thank-you note from the wife of a New Haven insurance tycoon whose birthday party Ellen had catered in their lavish house on Long Island Sound. "Please save the second Friday in June. That's *my* birthday, and I want you to do it all over again!"

Ten guests at that party—all of them rich bankers, insurance executives, lawyers, and doctors—called À La Carte when *they* next entertained.

"I'd like a poached salmon with dill sauce. Can you make that?"

And: "My husband is on a salt-free diet. Can you plan a menu around that?"

And: "When my husband and I were in Paris, we had the most divine leg of lamb with an herb-garlic breadcrumb crust. Do you know how to make it?"

Ellen could—and did. And soon À La Carte became *the* caterer to call in Westchester.

By the summer of 1969 she had hired a full-time chef, Clarence Sailes, a graduate of the "other" CIA—the Culinary Institute of America—and a talented young cook from Seattle, Washington. She had a freelance staff of thirty-five waiters, waitresses, bartenders, and car parkers on call; and her clients— private and commercial—now spread all over Westchester, into southern and western Connecticut, into northern New Jersey, and into Nassau County. But the surest sign of success was the visit from Countess Tamara:

"*Dollink*! I don't appreciate the way you undersell me," she said, lighting her thin, black, gold-tipped cigarette.

"Tamara, I have no idea what you charge," Ellen replied. "I arrive at my prices based on cost plus labor plus profit."

"*Dollink*," Tamara said conspiratorially, "why don't we agree on a scale of prices together? That way we can *both* make more money."

Ellen turned her down. "Price fixing, my dear Tamara, is against the law."

Tamara looked at her as if she'd just landed from Mars.

Then she left. Down but not out.

Success, Ellen found out, was fun and exciting. And so was her relationship with Lew Swann. As Ellen expanded À La Carte, Lew expanded Decor, and they became, over the months and years, cohorts, collaborators, counselors, and compadres.

A client with Spanish grandparents wanted Ellen to cater a

summer fiesta for one hundred and fifty friends. Ellen let her imagination go when she planned the menu.

"Grilled *chorizos*, imported Seville olives, toasted almonds, gazpacho, saffron-flavored mussels, paella, roasted peppers, flan, and Sangria," she told Lew, who got hungry just listening. "But I have an idea I want to try out on you. I always wanted to coordinate the serving platters, dishes, and glassware with food. This might be the perfect opportunity. What do you think?"

"Terrific!" he said. "Why don't you call the Spanish Trade Council and see what you can find here in the city?"

The Spanish Trade Council sent Ellen to Casa Moneo on West Twenty-third Street for pottery pitchers with designs of roosters made in Granada, to an importer in the Giftwares Building on East Twenty-second Street for raffia trays made in Seville, to Bloomingdale's sixth floor for handsome twig baskets used in the harvesting of olives in southern Spain, and to an importer of wine who helped her purchase sherry in wooden casks directly from Jerez.

The fiesta, needless to say, thrilled Ellen's clients and led to all kinds of other work—and to all other kinds of ideas.

Ellen began to concentrate as much on *how* food was served as how it tasted. She used mirrored serving trays to present hors d'oeuvres, and moss-lined and ivy-planted trays with concealed metal inserts for roasts. She made woven baskets of grapefruit peel to serve fruit, and decorated glamorous desserts with fresh tender pink rosebuds. She served crudités in Shaker baskets, poached fish on one-of-a-kind platters found in antique shops, and her homemade chocolate truffles on "spaghetti" nests made of white chocolate. She became as well known for the beauty of her food as for its taste—and every single idea was one she had first tried out on Lew.

And it was a two-way deal.

"I have a chance to buy Conso," Lew told her. Conso was an old-line manufacturer of office furniture.

"I hear a 'but,'" Ellen said. "What's the problem?"

"It's a solid company," Lew said, and thought a moment, trying to put his finger on what bothered him about Conso. "Solid but not sexy," he said, realizing as he spoke that he had just put his finger on Conso's biggest plus and biggest minus.

"Why can't you retain what's solid about it and do something to jazz it up at the same time?" Ellen asked.

And Lew did just that. He hired William Machado, one of the country's best designers of furniture and architectural interiors, to design a line of posturally correct office furniture. The new Conso line was accepted almost immediately and knocked-off even faster than immediately—and Decor had another winner on its hands.

Then there was the problem of indoor plumbing.

Chaise Percée was a company that made bathroom fixtures: black onyx sinks, gilt-swan water faucets, marble bathtubs with gold-leaf designs, bidets with decorated porcelain that would have been at home in any grandee's palace, pink marble vanities, and marbled dressing tables.

"It's for sale," Lew told Ellen. "A fantastic company with a fantastic balance sheet, but I'm afraid Max will have a heart attack when I tell him that Decor's getting into the plumbing business."

"Chaise Percée isn't exactly plumbing," Ellen said. "It's more like Tiffany's. Tell your father you're buying the Tiffany's of toilets, and he won't object."

"Now why didn't *I* think of that?" Lew asked and made his decision.

The business conversations Lew had with Ellen he would have had in the past with Max. Max would have brought up a dozen objections, come up with ten immensely complicated ways of handling the financing, suggested another eight companies that Lew ought to look into before buying Conso or Chaise Percée, told Lew about a half-dozen buy-outs that had flopped and about another half-dozen that could have been concluded for less if only the buyer had been more patient. By the end of the conversation, Max would have introduced so many possibilities, so many considerations, so many alternatives that Lew would have been overwhelmed and decided to hell with it. Why not just stick with Decor, which was, after all, a pretty good business just the way it was?

But Ellen's reactions were simple and to the point; and, with her as a sounding board, Lew began to feel like Lew Swann, not like Max Swann's son. And Lew's long-time dream of building a small and successful family company into a big and successful family company was no longer just a dream. It was becoming a reality.

And as Decor grew, so did À La Carte.

Every time a new company was added to Decor, every time

a new line of furniture, paint, wall covering, or upholstery fabric was introduced at a press and to-the-trade party, À La Carte did the catering.

And, as for Ellen, the work she did for Lew opened other doors. André Taylor, a famous society decorator renowned for his gorgeous sense of color and exquisite use of glazed chintz and lacquer, turned out to be a plump, sweet, nervous wreck from Scranton, where Ellen had grown up. As chairman of the Winter Antiques Show, André invited her to put in a bid for catering the opening-night cocktail party for a thousand. The entertainment editor of *House Beautiful* asked Ellen to contribute ideas for a feature on summer graduation parties, and the director of Lord & Taylor's decorating staff took Ellen's name and number, mentioning the upcoming cocktail party preview of that season's model rooms.

Success, Ellen found out, was fun and exciting. And sexy.

Lew and Ellen lit up when they were around each other; they could not keep their hands off each other; they finished each other's sentences and laughed at each other's jokes. People noticed—not just Caroline.

But also Max: "I hope you're not resisting," he told Lew.

And Johanna: "Lew's crazy about you," she told Ellen. "You can get him if you want."

And Brenda: "Lew's a dreamboat," she told Ellen. "But he's *married*!"

And Danny: "Are you and Lew in love?"

22

Love. What about love?

Ellen remembered young love, idealistic love, the dependent love she had shared with Phil with great affection. But she knew that she would never have another marriage like the marriage she had shared with Phil, that she would no longer *want* a marriage like that marriage. A marriage which, when she thought about it realistically, had been beginning to show the strains of too much domesticity, too much rigid separation between the roles of husband and wife. But after Phil died, Ellen had, for a long time, idealized her husband and her marriage. And love.

Then she met Wilson. And she had, for a time, shared love with Wilson, a different kind of love from the love she had shared with Phil. Love on a new horizon, a love between a man and a woman who had grown past the intense, self-absorbing romanticism and illusion of their twenties. A man and a woman who wanted and needed love *and* the outside world, and tried to find a way to have them both. In the end, though, it hadn't worked. Wilson had wanted an independent woman who was dependent on him—and then resented her when she was. And Ellen, for her part, had tried to please Wilson, had tried to be and do what he wanted, making the same mistakes she had made with Phil: in the process of trying to please, she had abandoned the very essence of herself, the essence that had first attracted them both.

But, even so, for almost a year after Wilson left, Ellen desperately wanted him back, had telephoned him not once but twice and, humiliatingly, begged him to come back. But he hadn't, and Ellen finally accepted the fact that he wouldn't.

With Wilson gone, Ellen's life was that of a secular nun. Living in a couples-only suburb in the era before singles bars (which Ellen would not have gone to anyway), Ellen found it hard—virtually impossible—to meet eligible men, and the ones she did meet never seemed to fit.

There were men who expected her—because she ran her own business—to run them as well. Men who wanted her—despite the fact that she ran her own business—to forget her competence and become a shrinking violet hanging on their every word and every whim. Men who, with a thousand dreams, wanted to take over À La Carte and turn Ellen's suburban success into another McDonald's or Pizza Hut.

There were men who bluntly told her that she was over the hill; they were interested only in girls in their very early twenties. There were men clearly interested only in sex and nothing more, men who were looking for a mommy, and, once in a while, men who wanted someone to support them.

Now and then there would be a man who seemed to really like Ellen, to be genuinely attracted to her, who kissed her good-night and said he'd call the next day or next week, who was simply never heard from again, as if he'd dropped off the edge of the earth. And there were, of course, the utter misfits that well-meaning friends dragged out of the corners of their lives for her, the ones who couldn't hold a job, the alcoholics, the neuters, the ineffectuals, the losers.

And Ellen wondered what would have happened if Phil had lived. Would she have started À La Carte? No. Absolutely not. Would she and Phil even have stayed married? Ellen didn't know. She *did* know, as she looked around her, that what she saw was disheartening.

Of the ten couples that had been at the Saturday night party the day before Phil's accident, four were divorced, one had moved away because the husband's job involved a transfer, and another was seeing a marriage counselor in an effort to stay out of the divorce courts. Sam Whittier had moved way up in the corporation he worked for, and Alice, who had helped engineer his success, felt left out of his increasingly busy life and wafted through her days on a combination of Valium and Dubonnet. And, although the Mattisons weren't divorced, Carol Mattison's husband had left her to live in a free-love commune in western Massachusetts, and Carol was living with a police sergeant whose own wife and five children lived in nearby Pelham.

Only two of the couples at that Saturday night party were still married, and both wives had, at different times, expressed to Ellen their envy of À La Carte and of the fact that her life was so much more interesting than their own. When Ellen told them that she had worried every single day of her life because she had had to leave Brenda and Danny alone so much when they were younger, they seemed relieved, as if guilt were the one flaw in Ellen's paradise—one they could identify with, one they could imagine, one that made their envy bearable.

And while Ellen told herself that she envied no one, she did envy people who were in love.

Ellen once thought she knew exactly what love was all about. Now she no longer knew. None of her old definitions applied anymore, and no new ones had taken their place.

Ellen wondered if she'd ever fall in love again.

And she wondered what it would be like.

Cooperation and collaboration, fun and excitement, electricity and comradeship, and that special, tingly, us-against-the-world feeling . . . could that be love?

In the beginning, Lew didn't think about love. He thought about magic.

First, there was the magic of compliments from Max.

"You've done one hell of a job at Decor," he told Lew. "Every move has been the right move."

And, because Max was so happy—happy with Johanna, happy with his construction and real estate businesses that were pouring out profits in a golden stream—there was no edge of competitiveness to mar his pride in his son. Lew, Max told himself, was doing exactly what he would have done with Decor if he had had the time. And, of course. Max was honest enough to admit to himself that he wasn't feeling competitive with Lew because Decor was still peanuts compared to the empire Max was building. Kid stuff, but impressive kid stuff.

Then, there was the magic of loving attention from Reenie, who responded to a Lew who radiated a new masculinity, a new confidence, a new magnetism—a husband who seemed suddenly as exciting as a lover. "Every year you get handsomer," she said. "Lew, let's go away for the weekend. Just us . . . alone . . ."

And there was the magic of the proof that every decision he'd made had been the *right* decision. Eilberg Fabrics had been chosen to create the upholstery and other interior fabrics for the Concorde. The Honors Award of the American Institute of Architects was awarded to William Machado for the new line of Conso office furniture. And every division of Decor showed a profit—including À La Carte.

"We made a twelve percent return on our investment in À La Carte," Lew told Ellen in the fall of 1969, the year (appropriately) that Dick bought Liz a sixty-nine-carat diamond ring. "And that's *after* the repayment of the loan. You ought to be very proud of yourself. I am."

He seemed to her in that moment—his eyes intelligent and perceptive, his mouth firm with character yet gently curved with sensuality—as tawny and noble as a lion. Every time Ellen saw him, she reacted with a physical thrill that was brandnew in its intensity.

"I wouldn't have done it nearly as well without you," Ellen said. Lew had been right: the new kitchen had cost more than twenty thousand dollars. And the costs of additional staff and cooking equipment and the unique trays and serving pieces were more than she could have afforded without him, and she never would have taken the risk to expand without the support of his crackling energy and imagination.

"I wish we—" Lew began suddenly, and just as suddenly stopped. He smiled at her, aware of her vulnerability, of the niceness her success had never changed, of the electricity he always felt between them, of the way her presence in his life had freed him to do all the things he had long dreamed of doing. And he was conscious of her silky, coppery hair, her generous smiling mouth, her lovely blue-green cat-shaped eyes, and for a moment he was almost dizzy with the sheer physical pleasure of her.

"We what?" Ellen asked, softly, wanting him to go on, not

wanting him to stop, no longer wanting to resist, no longer feeling that "no" was the only answer.

"—were alone . . ." Lew said. "Somewhere."

Somewhere was a yellow-and-cream suite in the Carlyle, *somewhere* didn't matter.

"I've never done anything like this," Ellen said, suddenly shy and awkward when the door closed behind them and they were alone.

"I haven't either," Lew said, and for a long, exquisite moment they gazed deeply into each other's eyes. And then he moved toward her. "I want to be in you . . ."

"I want you to be," Ellen said simply. and opened her arms to him.

In that autumn of 1969, a part of Ellen that had been a secret— even from herself—flowered and blossomed. Not only was Ellen the Conqueror free to work, to achieve, to succeed, but another Ellen, a sexual, sensual, sensuous Ellen emerged. An Ellen that, until now, had been hidden.

Sex with Phil had been wonderful sex but domestic sex, sex in a permitted context, framed by home and marriage and children. And sex with Wilson, at first adventurous, had also become domestic sex, allowed sex. But sex with Lew was stolen sex, illicit sex, wild, abandoned, profound, private sex, unfettered and undampened by the restraints of dailiness and routine. Until Lew, Ellen had not known that sex did not have to be tamed. She had not known or even guessed that to openly ask for pleasure and to unashamedly give it was to be, finally, womanly, and to know, without question, that she was beautiful.

Until Lew, Ellen had not known that every part of her body could respond to her lover's touch, that her skin could be so acutely sensitive, her mouth so hot and sweet, her ears and toes and thighs and the insides of her arms, sites of extraordinarily intense pleasure. Until Lew, Ellen had not known her legs could open so wide or that her breasts were capable of such sensation. Until Lew, Ellen had not known that a fully eroticized life was life fully lived and fully experienced.

And she never thought about tomorrow, never thought about commitment, never thought about how to please or *if* she pleased because her very existence pleased.

So it was for Lew, too.

Intoxicated by stolen hours and evenings, by a time-out-of-time weekend in a borrowed house high on the dunes of Montauk, excited by secret rendezvous and surprise phone calls, rewarded with fulfillment of every kind, and reeling with sensual pleasure, Lew and Ellen, like everyone else embarking on an adulterous affair, thought they were different. In the beginning, they, like everyone else, thought they could handle it.

September turned rapturously into October and October into November . . .

23

LOVE AND WORK. LOVE IN ONE COMPARTMENT; WORK IN AN-
other. Sex without commitment; open marriages without guilt;
relationships with no strings. That was what men wanted; that
was what Wilson wanted; that was what, in the autumn of
1969, Ellen told herself she wanted.

That wasn't what Lew Swann wanted.

From the very beginning he wanted to marry Ellen. He
wanted to marry her because he wanted to be happy the way
Max was happy. He wanted to marry her because he wanted
to be with her all the time—he wanted their hours to be un-
scarred by guilt, unlimited by the clock. He wanted to marry
her because cheating—in business, on a woman, in life—made
him sick to his soul.

The first time he proposed to her was on Thanksgiving Day.
The Swanns, as always, gathered at one of the children's homes.
This year it was Lew and Reenie's turn. His sister was there
with her second husband; his brother, about to be divorced,
was there with his girlfriend-of-the-week; his mother was there,
alone; and his father wasn't there at all. The very first year of
Esme and Max's divorce, Esme made it clear that she would
not go anywhere Max went.

The whole day Lew, surrounded by family and the remnants of families, kept asking himself why he was there. Why wasn't he with the person he most loved? Why wasn't he with Ellen?

Excusing himself to get the newspapers, to pick up heavy cream Reenie needed for the pie, to take his nieces to the duck pond, he telephoned Ellen three times.

"Lew Swann called," Brenda said when Ellen got home after eleven. À La Carte had catered a dozen Thanksgiving dinners; and, although she now had staff she relied on and trusted, Ellen made a point of personally dropping in on every client, making sure the food was perfect, the service attentive, the clients happy. "Three times."

"Thank you" was all Ellen said, and Brenda thought her mother was awfully cool. "What's going on between you two?" Brenda asked.

"Nothing," Ellen said, and Brenda wasn't sure if her mother was lying or not—not that her mother's private life was any of her business.

The next morning, before seven, Lew called again.

"I want to divorce Reenie," he said. "I want to marry you. Marry me, Ellen."

"Lew, let me think," Ellen said, not really telling the truth. She wanted everything to stay the way it was. She wanted more of the success she was having with À La Carte. She wanted more of the pleasure she was sharing with Lew. She didn't want to get married and have to begin making choices all over again.

Later, she realized that she had lied twice. To her daughter and to her lover. Ellen hated the feeling, and she hoped it would go away.

"I want us to be best friends," Johanna told Ellen in early December. They were at one of the booths facing the bar in the Russian Tea Room, and Johanna leaned forward and said, "I've never seen Lew so happy. You're the best thing that's ever happened to him. And just remember, Ellen, I'm on your side. Don't forget"—with a smile—"I've been there."

Ellen, embarrassed and uncomfortable at the presumed intimacy with its undertones of sexual conspiracy, let the comment slide by, which did not faze Johanna—not in the least. And she proceeded to give Ellen a little advice.

"Believe me," she said, the voice of experience, "they never

leave their wives unless you give them an ultimatum. How do
you think I got Max to divorce Esme? He kept saying he'd tell
Esme about us, kept saying he'd ask for a divorce, kept hem-
ming and hawing around. I was patient. I was understanding.
I was sympathetic. Finally, I realized I could go to my grave
being patient and understanding, so I put it to him in words of
one syllable: no ring, no more blow jobs."

Ellen cringed. "Really, Johanna, I don't want to listen to
this."

"But I can help you," Johanna insisted. "You could get Lew
to leave Reenie in a second. He's ripe for the right woman.
Has been for years and years. Be smart, Ellen. All you have
to do is apply a little pressure," she said running her fingers
through her hair. Sheer Amber Blonde. "And that's where I
come in. I can help you finish Lew's marriage once and for
all, and then the coast will be clear for you. Just remember,
Ellen, I'm on your side."

If Lew and Ellen married, Johanna and Max wouldn't be
so isolated anymore. There'd be a second branch of the Swann
family, and Johanna and Max would be at its head.

"Johanna, I don't want you on my side," Ellen said bluntly,
repelled at Johanna's wicked carelessness about other people's
lives and, for the first time, seeing her relationship with Lew
through a different set of eyes. Seeing *herself* through a different set of eyes and not liking what she saw. "And, anyway,
what makes you think there's anything between Lew Swann
and me other than business?" she asked, her third lie.

Johanna didn't answer. She didn't have to. The look of utter
disbelief on her face said it all.

Johanna, who behaved like an angry person, was, in fact, a
hurt and wounded and disappointed person. She had thought
she would, at last, have everything she craved when she married
Max—love and happiness and acceptance. She thought that
being loved by others would finally make her able to love
herself. It hadn't worked out that way at all.

Max's family excluded her. And so did her own family.

Johanna's mother, extremely capable, extremely competitive, disdained other women and forced Johanna out of the
family business. Johanna's father and brothers, their egos already dented by Johanna's brilliant mother, were happy not to
have to confront the driving presence of another energetic and

ambitious woman, and thus allied themselves in shutting Johanna out.

From the very beginning, the Swanns had made it clear that Johanna was an intruder and that she wasn't welcome. Esme, who would never forgive Max for leaving her, did not blame Max for the divorce; instead she blamed Johanna, seeing her as an enticer, a devil luring Max with irresistible sexual temptation. Esme, feeling powerless, found a certain power in powerlessness. She found that victims can get sympathy, support, and attention, and Esme rallied the Swanns around her. Esme hated Johanna; she infected the Swanns with her hatred. Johanna wasn't allowed at Swann family gatherings; Johanna's invitations were rejected; Johanna's gifts went unacknowledged; Johanna's attempts at rapprochement were ignored. The more Johanna wanted to be wanted, the more Max's family drew together and excluded her.

Johanna, in turn, began to divide the world into two camps: winners and losers. Esme and her allies were losers; she and Max were winners. Lew, who had begun to emerge from his father's shadow, was a winner; and so was Ellen. If Lew and Ellen married, there would be more Swann winners, more people on Johanna's side. She told Max as much.

"Stay the hell out of Lew's marriage," he warned. "Whatever Lew and Reenie and Ellen do is up to them. Don't meddle."

But Johanna couldn't resist. And Ellen's rejection of her offer of help surprised her. But it didn't stop her.

Johanna and Max, unwilling to bear their banishment passively, spent Thanksgiving in Bermuda; they would go to Saint Maarten for Christmas and New Year's. Winners had a good time; losers stayed at home.

But Max, who adored the role of paterfamilias, was cruelly wounded by Esme's ultimatum forbidding him—with or without Johanna—to appear at family gatherings. Unable to blame himself, unwilling to blame Esme toward whom he felt guilty, he blamed Johanna for his exclusion. The marriage that was supposed to make them both happy made them less happy than ever.

Everyone uses money—to one extent or another—to express emotion. Johanna and Max used it more than most, and Max began to express his resentment toward Johanna with a stinginess that was totally out of character.

Johanna, who found herself with less love than she wanted, now found herself with less money.

She wanted to move William from Fifty-seventh Street to the General Motors Plaza, and Max refused to finance the move, giving Johanna the excuse that the overhead would be more than William's business could afford. He'd even had the nerve, as Johanna saw it, to send in his own accountants to go over William's books! The General Motors Plaza was one of the most prestigious locations in the city; and Johanna, who wanted to show her family what she could do without them, wanted William to be there. And she meant to get what she wanted. After all, she was one of the winners.

Ellen's unanticipated rejection of her offer to help prod Lew into a divorce caused Johanna to change her plans about what to do with the letters she had found in an envelope of Phil Durban's while redecorating Max's old office at Decor. Instead of showing them to Lew, she'd show them to Max... Max, who had told her in violently obscene terms "not to meddle, there've been enough divorces in the family," would go crazy... and she'd burn them right in front of him as soon as he gave her the money she needed to lease the space in the plaza of the General Motors building.

"Ellen," Lew said the week before Christmas, "you've never said that you love me. Do you?"

Ellen wanted to say it; she wanted to feel it. She was touched by his need. She felt pressured, too, and she felt guilty. She felt the way she now knew Wilson must have felt. She didn't want to hurt Lew with the truth, but she didn't want to tell another lie. She remembered too clearly how it had felt and how much she had hated the feeling.

"Everything but," she had finally said, searching every corner of herself for the words. "I like you. I'd do anything for you. I admire you. I trust you. I sometimes adore you. I believe in you. Not a day goes by that I don't think about you and hardly a night that I don't dream of you. I care for you more than I care for anyone except my children. I would go to the ends of the earth for you. But, no, I don't love you."

The expression on his face tore at her, and Ellen's image of herself as a nice person lay shredded and in ruins.

But how could she love him? How could she allow herself

to love him? He was married. And no matter what was said about open marriages, it still made a difference.

To Lew. And to Ellen. No matter what she told herself.

"It's none of my business," Max told Ellen the day before he and Johanna left for Saint Maarten for Christmas, "but did Lew propose to you?"

Ellen nodded.

"And what did you say?"

"That I wanted to think it over," Ellen said, "but it was a lie. I don't want to marry Lew. I don't want to marry anyone."

"You're sure of that?" Max asked. "Absolutely sure?"

"Absolutely," said Ellen. "Why do you ask? Has Lew said something?"

"No," said Max. "Lew hasn't said anything. Johanna has. She'd like you and Lew to get married. She'd see it as a victory for herself."

"Johanna!" Ellen was astonished and annoyed. What business of Johanna's was her and Lew's private life? "I told her what I told you. I'm not interested in breaking up Lew's marriage."

"She doesn't believe you."

"I know," said Ellen. "Do you?"

Max looked at her for a moment and then nodded. "I've got a thousand percent accurate bullshit detector," he said. "I believe you."

"So?" Ellen asked, relieved to have the air cleared. "Now what?"

"Now nothing," Max said. "I just wanted to know from you how you felt."

"Now you know," Ellen said. "I hope you don't think I—" She stopped, not even knowing what word to use.

"Me?" Max looked shocked. "I'm the last person in the world to make moral judgments."

Ellen smiled in spite of herself. Why couldn't more people be as frank as Max. Why couldn't she?

"Max?"

"Yes?"

"Tell Johanna to stay out of my life. And Lew's."

"Don't worry," growled Max with the same steely expression Patton must have had every time he thought of Rommel. "That's exactly what I plan to do."

He went home, wrote the check Johanna demanded, told her—in impressively obscene terms—to butt out, and watched while she burned the letters.

The Swanns celebrated Christmas at Esme's house. Except that it wasn't a celebration—only an empty charade of a celebration. At ten o'clock at night Lew got into his car and drove to New Rochelle.

Ellen and Brenda and Danny were at the kitchen table sharing what had become a family tradition: pizza for Christmas. After cooking and serving turkeys and geese and hams all day long, pizza, right out of the cardboard box, half with "everything" for Brenda and Danny, half with extra cheese for Ellen, was the Durbans' treat. A jug of Mountain Red sat on the table, a fire danced in the fireplace, and Christmas carols played on the stereo. Ellen, in jeans and a sweatshirt, her hair pulled off her face, looked all of fifteen. They looked so happy, like a family who loved each other and enjoyed each other. Lew so much wanted to feel the way they felt . . . so much wanted to belong.

"Lew!" Ellen exclaimed, amazed to see him at the door, ashamed to have her children know.

"I had to see you," he said. He looked worn: there were dark smudges under his eyes; even his normally gold-struck hair seemed dull, tarnished. "My mother wept all through dinner. Max called from Saint Maarten, more than just a little drunk. And Reenie and I had a terrible fight. She accused me of having an affair—"

"Oh, my God! Did Johanna . . . ?" Ellen asked, appalled, glancing at Brenda and Danny. Her eyes asked them to leave her and Lew alone. Quietly, they left.

"Johanna?" Lew looked surprised, shook his head. "Johanna doesn't know anything. Anyway, Reenie is on my mother's side. She won't speak to Johanna."

"Well, what did you say?" Ellen asked, feeling sick. "You didn't admit . . . anything, did you?"

"No," Lew said, and he sat down, almost sagging. "That much brains I've got. But she's suspicious. I don't spend as much time at home as before . . . that weekend in Montauk . . . I guess I mention your name quite a bit. I can't live like this. I don't want to live like this. Ellen, please marry me." He held his arms out to her, wanting her to come to him.

"Oh, Lew," she said gently. She took his outstretched hands into hers. "You make me feel like a life raft."

"Is that all? Like a life raft?" he asked. He seemed physically collapsed from within. Punctured. Then deflated.

"Is that *all*?" Ellen repeated. "It's too much, Lew. I can do many things for you. And you for me. But I can't save you from your own life. *You* have to do that." She was sad but not tearful; she was being, finally, honest.

"I hadn't realized," he said quietly. "Not until now . . ."

He had handed her the burden of his empty marriage and the self that wanted to escape from his father's shadow. He had wanted her to help bring him to life, and to a great extent she had. But now he began to realize how high the price must have been for her, how much of herself she had poured into him.

"Do you hate me?" he asked.

"No," she said softly. "How could I?"

He smiled gently and kissed the hands that were still in his.

"I wonder what's going to happen," he said. "To me. To you. To us."

"Why does anything have to happen?" Ellen asked. "Why can't everything stay just the way it is?"

Although Ellen offered to let Lew stay over, he refused. He got home at almost five that morning. Reenie never asked him where he had been, and he never told her.

Lew telephoned Ellen at a little past midnight on New Year's Eve. He wasn't surprised that there was no answer, and he wasn't surprised at how forlorn he felt.

Ellen was in Bedford Hills catering a large, elegantly festive party. When the clock struck twelve, she thought of Lew, missing him, glad she had À La Carte, happy that she didn't have to choose between them.

The unhappy end of her affair with Wilson had taught her that demands and expectations strangle love. She wouldn't make the same mistake with Lew.

But the next morning she had her terrible fight with Brenda, when Brenda announced that she intended to marry Jeff immediately after graduation. But after she calmed down, she had to ask herself if Brenda might not be right.

What if she weren't liberated, just scared? Too scared to do more than just share a man with another woman.

* * *

Danny, who had often played the part of peacemaker between Ellen and Brenda while he was growing up, did it again. For almost six weeks after their New Year's Day battle, Brenda and Ellen weren't on speaking terms. Danny finally got fed up with their childishness, and two weeks before Valentine's Day he telephoned Brenda.

"Clarence has the flu, and Mom has ten Valentine's Day parties," he told her. "Could you come home and help out?"

"Of course," said Brenda without hesitating.

No matter how much they fought with each other, when anyone or anything threatened one of them, they all drew together, wagons in a circle, tighter than ever. When the chips were down, no matter what their own battles were, the Durbans had each other, much more so than most families. And many times Ellen wondered whether they would have been *that* close if Phil had lived. Somehow, she didn't think so.

"I'm sorry about what I said on New Year's," Brenda said as they worked together in the kitchen making *coeur à la crème* with strawberries. "I guess I have a big mouth."

"That you do," Ellen agreed. "So did I at your age."

"That still doesn't make it right," Brenda said. And then she added soberly, "I never knew all that about Dad. That he left us penniless and in debt. Why didn't you ever tell me?"

"It was hard enough for you to lose your father. I didn't want you to lose your illusions, too," Ellen said. "Maybe I was wrong not to tell you. Maybe I should have been more realistic. It was a hard decision to make. At the time, *all* decisions were hard to make. I prayed and prayed . . . trying to do and say the right things . . . trying to make it more bearable for you and Danny."

There were tears in Ellen's eyes, tears in Brenda's eyes, and for a long moment mother and daughter embraced: Ellen, almost forty, still head-turningly attractive, exuding vitality, midway between the good girl she'd once been and the heroine she had yet to become; Brenda, a more conventionally pretty version of her mother, her *self* not yet formed, a young woman touched by death but so far untouched by life.

"You're still the best *sous-chef* anyone ever had," Ellen said, thanking Brenda for her help over the weekend. "I couldn't have done it without you."

"You know you can count on me," Brenda said as she left. "Whenever. Wherever."

On the day before Brenda's graduation from Brown, Ellen did something she'd been thinking about for a long time. She went to her safe deposit box and took out twenty-five shares of stock in À La Carte. Maybe what she had in mind was bribery; maybe it was just good business. In any event, she realized with a combination of wistfulness and pride, Phil would most definitely have approved.

At the same time Ellen visited her safe deposit box, Johanna visited hers, not to take something out but to put something in—the envelope with the Xerox copies of the letters Reenie Swann had written Phil Durban during the torrid love affair they were having when Phil died.

II

A WOMAN'S WORLD

1

ALL THE GOOD THINGS THAT HAD HAPPENED TO BRENDA WERE reflected on her face as she left the stage with the Class of 1970.

After four years of straight A's in high school followed by four years of equal achievement in college, she had gotten fabulous job offers from top pharmaceutical companies. She had a loving relationship with Jeff Musser, the young ophthalmologist she had met while working at a summer job in Providence, the man she was about to marry. Unlike women of her mother's generation who had to choose between marriage and a career, Brenda, like the rest of the women of *her* generation, took it for granted she would have it all.

Radiant, excited, smiling, Brenda stood at the side of the stage, anxiously scanning the audience for her mother, spotted her, and waved. In a tailored gabardine dress-for-success suit and handsomely coordinated burgundy silk blouse, Ellen looked like the woman every girl in Brenda's class wanted to be. Accepting kisses and hugs of congratulations, Brenda made her way through the crowd toward her mother.

"Congratulations!" Ellen said, hugging Brenda and kissing

her. "The Calcott Science Prize, too! Aren't you wonderful! Just wonderful!"

Brenda blushed with pleasure and smiled with pride, her face marked with blurry, sunny lipstick kisses.

"Not *that* wonderful," Brenda demurred.

"Don't be modest! You did the work!" Ellen said. She took the envelope holding the shares of stock out of her bag and held them out toward Brenda. "I have something for you, Brenda. A present . . ."

Brenda tore open the envelope, and for just a split second Ellen remembered her opening Phil's chemistry set with the same impatient glee. Brenda looked at the stock, knew what it was and what it signified, and tears glazed her eyes.

"Oh, Mom! I don't know what to say!" The stock represented almost a lifetime of work and struggle. "I don't know how to thank you enough . . . or tell you what it means to me."

"You just did," Ellen said, her mouth smiling, her eyes misty. "I'll give Danny twenty-five shares, too, when *he* graduates. One day I'd like the two of you to take over À La Carte."

A little later, on the way to a festive and celebratory lunch with Danny, Jeff, and Brenda's best friend, Toni Reese, and her parents, Ellen asked Brenda which of the three job offers she had chosen.

"*Four* job offers," Brenda said, her eyes alight. The fourth offer had just come in that week.

"Four!"

"Four," Brenda confirmed. All spring long, corporate recruiters had been swarming over the campus trying to scoop up the best students. Brenda with her straight A's and chemistry major had been a prime target. Straight A's, a science major— and female! Brenda was a corporate dream girl in an era of equal opportunity employment. "And the worst one pays thirteen thousand five hundred dollars."

"The *worst* one!" Ellen could barely conceive of it. Thirteen thousand five hundred dollars was more than Ellen's father had ever made in a year in his life. It was almost as much as Brenda's father had earned the last year of his life, and it had taken Ellen almost ten years even to get close. It was certainly far more than Ellen could offer to pay her to start at À La Carte, and Ellen knew it was one of the reasons Brenda wanted to work in the outside world—at least to begin her career. And it was more than Jeff would be earning.

"*And*," Brenda continued, unable to suppress her pride in the latest success in her young lifetime of success, "you'd better believe I'm not going to take the worst offer. I'm going to take the *best* one—assistant research scientist. It pays fifteen thousand a year. MedLabs is the name of the company, and their headquarters are in Boston. Jeff and I used our graduation presents from you and his parents to make the down payment on a garden apartment in Newton. A condo."

Jeff was a gentle and altruistic young man, a product of the sixties, who had done one of the few things a doctor could do and not expect to get rich: he had gone into public health. He had a job with a clinic in Roxbury. His salary, set by the federal government, was eleven thousand dollars a year.

"You're going to be earning more than Jeff," Ellen said, keeping her voice carefully neutral. She had doubts about young men who were going to save the world, particularly when their wives were going to pay most of the bills. "Isn't that going to be a problem?"

"No," said Brenda with all the certainty of her twenty years. "Not at all. A lot of the girls in my class earn as much as—or more than—the guys."

Ellen raised her eyebrows and said nothing.

Phil had expected her to quit college and her part-time job when they got married, and Ellen had done so without a second thought. She tried to imagine how Phil would have reacted if she had earned as much as he did, never mind more. She tried but failed.

"Thirty before thirty!"

That was their slogan.

Thirty thousand dollars a year before they reached thirty, Brenda and Toni promised each other, practically licking their chops. Since Brenda's first job out of Brown at MedLabs, Inc., paid fifteen thousand a year and Toni's first job at Edder and Stern as a market analyst also paid fifteen, the only real issue seemed to be: Who would get there first? About *that* they had a bet: loser owed the winner lunch at the Four Seasons.

"Start saving your money!" Toni teased.

"Hell, no!" said Brenda. "I'm already trying to decide what to order."

And so, two of the first liberated generation of women that seemed to have it all, Brenda with her B.S. and straight A's and Toni with her brand-new M.B.A., went out into the world dressed and prepared for success: Brenda to Boston, Toni to New York.

Brenda and Jeff got married the week after they graduated from Brown. Ellen gave them a reception—with, at their special request, all-organic foods—and they spent a weekend honeymoon in the Green Mountains of Vermont. They decided—mutually, the way they planned to decide *everything*—that Brenda would not give up her maiden name. The mailbox in the garden apartment, equidistant from MedLab's sleek headquarters in suburban Lowell and the Roxbury public health clinic where Jeff worked, read "Durban-Musser."

Toni and *her* boyfriend, Tucker Berns, a lawyer, lived in a small, killingly expensive walkup in the limbo between SoHo and Greenwich Village. Toni's parents were uptight (as Toni put it) because she and Tuck weren't married.

"Do you believe they actually bribed us this weekend?" Toni told Brenda. "They said they'd buy us a co-op if we got married!"

"*My* mother bribed me *not* to get married," Brenda said. "Just this winter she offered to send me to grad school if I didn't."

Brenda and Toni laughed. Parents!

Brenda had been one of the most sought-after, fought-over women graduates of 1970. With her four plummy job offers, her biggest problem had been which to choose.

She had chosen MedLabs, Inc., because MedLabs was a fast-track company with a small but impressive product list—some prescription, some proprietary drugs.

And because MedLabs was in the forefront of developing a non-habit-forming diet drug with no significant side effects, and Brenda's honors project senior year had been on the obesity-causing ob-ob chromosome.

And because the recruiter who had taken her to lunch stressed that at MedLabs there was no limit on how far a woman could rise; he pointed proudly to the fact that there was a woman on the board of directors.

And because MedLabs' headquarters were near Boston, where Jeff was already working.

And because MedLabs was a big, publicly held corporation.

It offered safety, security, stability, and a chance at a fabulous career.

And, finally, because the one thing Brenda had promised herself was that she would never do what her mother did: run her own business—too many headaches, too many hassles.

Brenda's boss, Heinrich Leben, had a little chat with her the first day of work.

"You'll do well here, Brenda," Heinrich told her. "Just don't be too impatient."

A Berlin-born research chemist, Heinrich Leben had had to okay Brenda's hiring. He had been impressed by the Calcott Science Prize she'd won senior year, by her unbroken record of straight A's, and by the fact that he was under a lot of pressure from management to hire women. He was a small, wiry man—a tennis player—who smoked a pipe because you didn't inhale pipe smoke and because he liked the feeling of something in his mouth.

Brenda smiled. "Patience isn't one of my virtues," she said, knowing that she wore her ambition like a beacon. "You'll get the dividends of my impatience, though. I'll work twice as hard as anyone else."

"One day you'll undoubtedly be my boss," Heinrich said, pulling on his pipe. "I've no doubt about it."

Brenda did not hear the condescension in his voice: his accent covered it; the fact that he never put all his cards on the table covered it; the fact that Brenda hadn't had a father to tell her businesses weren't like school and that bosses weren't like teachers caused her to miss it.

MedLabs' approach to obesity control was based not on limiting the intake of calories by suppressing the appetite but in nullifying the disposition of calories once they had been ingested. Brenda was assigned to work on the development of a drug that would coat the small intestine, thus effectively decreasing the absorption of calories. Most of the caloric load would simply be excreted.

To Brenda, work at MedLabs was just like Chem 35 back at Brown except that she was being paid a terrific salary and worked in an ultramodern lab with the resources of a multi-million-dollar company behind her. With dreams of making the breakthrough discovery that would put MedLabs' obesity-control drug on the market first to urge her on, Brenda could not wait to get up in the morning and go to work.

"Thirty before thirty?" she asked Jeff one morning. "Whoever's first on the market with a safe, effective obesity-control drug is going to make billions. Literally. MedLabs will give me anything I want. Anything!"

And she rushed off to work, fired with ambition.

Ellen, too, was fired with ambition.

She sent off her bid for the Winter Antiques Show opening-night party and plunged into the busy summer season. She took everything that came her way: picnics and pool parties; engagement parties and weddings; birthday parties, bar mitzvahs, and christenings. Her commercial catering business, which she had never dropped, continued to grow. She catered press parties, sales meetings, brunches and cocktail parties, marketing conferences, think-tank sessions, and executive lunches. Back in Reinhardt Estes's good graces, she catered all the events for the Swiss Trade Council, of which Reinhardt was president, and those for his own highly successful watch and fine-jewelry importing companies.

"I function in two modes," Ellen told Caroline. "On weekends I work like a slave. Weekdays, I take it easy and only work like a dog."

"I'm all for success," Caroline said. "But I wonder if you really ought to work *so* hard. I remember when Tommy was working *he* always made time for his squash, and twice a week, religiously, he swam in the Yale Club pool. Why don't you take an afternoon off now and then? Have a massage . . . go to an exercise class."

"Exercise class!" Ellen laughed. "I get plenty of exercise lifting five-quart cast-iron casseroles twelve hours a day."

"Well, I still think you should spend a little time on yourself," Caroline insisted in a gentle way. "I never heard of any man who worked as hard as you do."

"I have time to make up, Caroline," Ellen said. "I spent a lot of years not really concentrating . . . and I can do it now that both children are away from home."

Danny, away at the University of Pennsylvania, was majoring in finance and minoring in marketing.

"I'm going to be a tycoon," Danny said. "A millionaire." He was, at seventeen, handsome the way Phil had been hand-

some: with a strong beak of a nose and gold-flecked olive eyes.
Women found him irresistible; men saw in him the friend—
or the son—they most idealized. "Unless you make it before
I do!"

"I doubt it!" Ellen smiled. "My ambitions are much more
realistic. I want to be a good caterer. A very good caterer.
Maybe the best in the county."

And by working at it, Ellen was. In fiscal 1970, À La Carte's
profits were at their highest ever: Ellen cleared almost thirty
thousand dollars that year.

"Excellent investment," Lew said in a rare self-congratu-
latory mood. "À La Carte is on its way to becoming a valuable
property. Your stock is getting more valuable all the time," he
told Ellen.

Max had also become a fan. "You wouldn't have to bug
me for money all the time," he told Johanna, "if you ran your
businesses half as well as Ellen does."

Johanna did not appreciate the comparison.

To his parents' generation Jeff looked like another hippy-dippy.
He was tall and very thin, had a sandy beard, a gentle mouth,
and, behind wire-rim granny glasses, intelligent and compassionate eyes. People of an older generation tended to think that
people like Jeff lay around smoking grass and listening to rock,
but their perceptions were stereotyped. They were way off-
base, because Jeff was a worker.

He worked just as hard as Brenda. He was fueled by an
equally compelling—although far different—motivation: the
need to do something good. He had started out in med school
planning to do what every other med student he knew planned:
to graduate, work for a few years for a senior man, and then
set up his own practice.

The Democratic National Convention of 1968 changed all
that for Jeff. He had worked as a volunteer treating the eye
injuries of demonstrators who had been Maced by Mayor Daly's
cops, and that experience had awakened in Jeff a dormant, but
powerful, sense of the injustice in the world. It made him an
idealist; it made him a feminist; it changed his plans for the
future. He decided to work in public health and devote his
time, his energy, and his education to making the world a better
place.

Working with the poor and disadvantaged—prescribing

glasses, running glaucoma tests, excising cysts, treating wounds, applying eye patches—Jeff saw for himself how powerless his clients felt in the maze of welfare red tape, SSI payments, and confusingly defined Medicaid and Medicare benefits. The poor, in Jeff's experiences, were *not* ripping off the system. On the contrary. They were mostly scared, they were timid, and their predicament made Jeff feel more and more compassionate, more and more on their side. He worked longer hours than he had to, patiently filling out miles of bureaucratic forms; and after work, on his own time, he visited patients in the hospital.

Brenda and Jeff got home late, exhausted and exhilarated. Brenda, a wonderful cook, never cooked. She never had the time.

"Dinner's a multiple choice," she told Ellen, who sent weekly care packages. "McDonald's, Kentucky Fried, or Chinese—and pizza when we're in a hurry."

But Brenda and Jeff didn't care about the food, and they didn't care about the fatigue because they were happy—happier than they had ever been, with unlimited futures and new excitement every day to spur them on. After working eight months, Brenda was already setting up her own experiments and had been assigned a lab assistant of her own. She was rewarded with a ten percent raise and used it to buy a present for Jeff: the MacIntosh amplifier and preamplifier he had been lusting for.

And just before her first year at MedLabs was up, Heinrich Leben called her into his office to tell her that she could do MedLabs—and herself—a lot of good by speaking at college campuses evenings and weekends.

"We want young people—especially young women—to think of MedLabs as a good place to work," he said. "And you'd be a perfect example for them to see."

And Brenda began going to nearby colleges—to B.U., to Amherst, to Vassar, which was now co-ed, to the University of Vermont, Smith, M.I.T., and Bowdoin—spreading the word about MedLabs and taking the names of particularly outstanding students.

Brenda made no effort to hide her prejudice—in favor of women. When MedLabs began recruiting from the new year's crop of graduated, Brenda wanted to make sure that there would be outstanding women to follow in her path. She could help them and make things easier for them.

"God, I admire you," Jeff told her. "Most people talk. You *do*."

"I grew up with a good example," Brenda said. "I always saw my mother in perpetual action."

Brenda's words surprised Jeff slightly. He was well aware of the resentment and disdain Brenda sometimes showed toward her mother and had often heard her vow *never* to trade personal happiness for a career—a trade-off Brenda considered completely unnecessary. After all, she and Jeff both managed busy careers *and* a happy marriage. An unusually happy marriage.

With speaking engagements a few nights a week and most Saturday afternoons and with Jeff "on" alternating weekends and Monday and Thursday nights, Brenda and Jeff joked that they barely saw each other and that their busy lives were the best thing in the world for romance. There was no time for dull domesticity to put their relationship into a rut.

Jeff still bought Brenda daisies, and Brenda still liked to nibble Jeff's toes. They couldn't have been happier . . . except for one thing.

Brenda hated to bring that one thing up. It was so beneath her, and so beneath Jeff, that it embarrassed her to have to mention it. The problem was housework.

Brenda hadn't particularly minded when she had had evenings and weekends free. But now that she was traveling around to nearby campuses—trips that often took her away overnight—she just didn't have the time to do all the housework herself.

She didn't want to be a drag, she told Jeff. She was hardly a cleanliness freak—in the past, she had done only enough cleaning to keep typhoid at bay. Nevertheless, there was a certain bare minimum—like cleaning the bathroom and the kitchen and doing the laundry—that absolutely had to be done.

"I hate to mention it," Brenda said, feeling like one of those simpleminded housewives in television commercials obsessed with clean floors and sparkling bathtubs, "but this place is a sty. Jeff, I don't have the time to do it alone, and I really resent being stuck with the shit work."

"I don't blame you," Jeff said immediately. "I wish you had said something sooner. We'll divide the work, that's all. It's a question of fairness."

They agreed on an informal division of labor. Brenda would drop off the laundry at the laundromat, and Jeff, who got home earlier than she did, would pick it up. Ditto the dry cleaning. Cleanup, dusting, and scrubbing would be alternated: one week Brenda would do the bathroom and kitchen, while Jeff would clean and vacuum the rest of the small apartment. On the next week, they would swap duties.

"I feel much better," Brenda said after they had posted a work schedule in the kitchen. "I don't feel so much like a martyr."

"I feel better, too," Jeff said. "It just bothers me that I was so oblivious that I didn't say something first."

"Anyway, from now on things will be different."

"You bet," said Jeff fervently.

That night, when they made love, Brenda enjoyed it more than she had in a long time. It surprised her to realize how much her resentment over such a trivial matter as housework had caused her to hold back during their lovemaking.

That night, they talked, as they did from time to time, about having a family.

"Definitely," said Jeff. "I definitely want children."

"So do I," said Brenda. "But later . . . I have my thirty before thirty to think about first."

2

"WE'RE SENDING YOU AND ED SLOWACKI TO REPRESENT
MedLabs at the biochemists' conference at the University of
Illinois at Urbana," Heinrich Leben told Brenda early in 1972.
She now had a better title: associate chemist. And a bigger
salary: she was earning eighteen thousand dollars a year. "I
can tell management you've agreed to go, can't I?"

"Of course," Brenda said in a consciously dry, businesslike
way. Normally, she would have answered a question like Heinrich's with a flip-but-true: wild horses couldn't keep me away.
But she had learned that humor did not go over with Heinrich,
and so she disciplined herself: "It's an honor."

Ed Slowacki had graduated from college—Cornell, Heinrich's alma mater—the same year Brenda had. Also a biochemist, Ed had B's with a few C's to Brenda's all A's. He had
gone to work at MedLabs the same week Brenda had at a salary
of two thousand dollars more a year—which Brenda did not
know. He was one of those all-blond people—he even had
blond eyelashes—and, although assigned to a section that was
doing research on an arthritis drug, he seemed to Brenda to
spend more of his time indulging in office politics and going
to Cornell functions than he did running his lab section.

Brenda took the trip to Urbana as a sign that she and Ed were being groomed for bigger and better things at MedLabs. Ed seemed to take it as a brief, paid break from the daily routine. On the flight to Urbana, Brenda read the latest copy of the *Journal of Biochemistry*, while Ed drank white wine and chatted up the stewardess.

For three days biochemists read papers, discussed new experimental models, talked over promising new research leads, and, most of all, swapped the latest hot gossip: who had gotten grants and who hadn't, who was up for tenure and who had landed a juicy consultantship, who was going to head up a brand-new lab in Houston, and who was on his way out at USC. But while everyone concentrated on personalities, Brenda kept her mind on insulin receptors.

She was already familiar with the experiments on the role of insulin receptors in obesity being done at UCLA by James Reinking. She had read his paper ten months ago in the *Bio-Chemical Review*, and when she saw that he was scheduled to bring his fellow scientists up-to-date on lab data covered since the publication of the paper at Urbana, Brenda signed up.

When Professor Reinking—who was built like a linebacker and wore glasses with lenses as thick as Coke bottle bottoms—had finished, Brenda introduced herself and told him about what she was doing and the problems she was having doing it.

"Our research has been focusing on interfering with absorption in the intestinal tract," she told him. "But we're stuck. We can't seem to get rid of the side effects—nausea and excessive bloating. I've been at MedLabs for two years, and in two years we haven't gotten any closer to a solution. I wonder if taking an approach concentrating on the insulin receptors might not be more useful."

"I don't know," said Professor Reinking, being scientifically correct but still, at the same time, lighting up. "But would you like the raw lab data? I'd be happy to share it with you."

"That would be wonderful," Brenda said, herself lighting up.

"I'll get you Xerox copies."

That night, while Ed Slowacki went out and got drunk with some chemists from Ryder & Evans, a MedLabs competitor, Brenda, acutely conscious of being the only woman except for secretaries at the conference, went to her room and carefully went over Professor Reinking's data.

The day after she got back from Urbana, her proposal was on Heinrich Leben's desk. Using Dr. Reinking's *Bio-Chemical Review* article and his updated raw lab data for documentation, Brenda suggested that MedLabs add parallel experiments pursuing the provocative insulin-receptor leads to their obesity-control research program.

Brenda ended her proposal by asking for a go-ahead to submit a budget. Buoyantly, she waited for the answer and spent the Saturday morning before she left to give a talk at the University of Syracuse indulging in her favorite occupation—shopping at Jordan Marsh.

"I can't understand it," Brenda told Jeff. "Two weeks have gone by, and he hasn't said a word. Do you think I ought to say something to him?"

Brenda was mystified. The kind of aggressive, innovative work she'd put into her proposal to set up experiments pursuing the leads opened up by James Reinking's work on insulin receptors had earned her straight A's, the Calcott Science Prize, the praise of her teachers—and, ultimately, the MedLabs job. Now it seemed to earn silence. Brenda was hurt and confused.

"I just can't understand it," she kept telling Jeff. "Maybe I ought to say something."

"Why not?" Jeff answered logically. "Everything you told me about your idea makes it sound like a good one."

When Brenda went into Heinrich Leben's office and asked if he'd had a chance to read her proposal yet, he said that he hadn't had the time.

And it bothered Brenda that he didn't even bother to say that he'd *make* the time, that he'd get to it.

"Do you believe it?" Brenda complained in outrage to Toni when Toni and Tuck came up to Boston for the weekend. "They paid to send me to Urbana, and now they don't even want to hear what I learned there. We seem to be at a dead end with the anti-absorption approach; the insulin-receptor angle is at least a way off dead center. You'd think they'd already have me setting up a program!"

"*You'd* think and *I'd* think," said Toni. "It's not how *they* think!"

They were that other sex. Men. The adversary. The members of the closed circle Brenda and Toni wanted to enter—either by invitation or by frontal assault. Men had the money, the power, the fun. Brenda and Toni wanted in, too.

And Toni was becoming an expert on *them*. Her job was making her one. Toni's job was to analyze companies whose stock Edder and Stern traded for its clients. She traveled around the country interviewing management, touring plants, analyzing figures. The results of her work went into the reports sent to Edder and Stern's brokers, who used it as a basis for their buy-and-sell recommendations.

"You've got to be one of the boys," Toni told Brenda. "I bet if one of Heinrich's boys wrote the report things would be set up already."

A brief flash of Ed Slowacki with his blond eyelashes and indifferent B's and C's went through Brenda's mind, but she canceled it immediately.

"Maybe there are male chauvinists in the businesses you deal with," Brenda said, unwilling to believe Toni, "but we're *scientists*. Scientists go by lab results, by objective data. Sex has nothing to do with it. Nothing! In fact, Heinrich always assigns me the priority experiments because he knows I'll get things done right, on schedule, and within budget."

"Don't fool yourself, Brenda," Toni said. "You're just Heinrich's good little girl. He's using you."

"Toni, you sound bitter," Brenda said.

"Maybe," Toni agreed, her brown eyes serious under her dark, glossy bangs. "I call it realistic."

Toni was the only woman—except for the toiletries specialist, Rheta Ash, who had worked for Revlon and Rubinstein, who spoke in an obscenity-studded, whisky-soaked voice and kept everyone cowed because she supposedly "knew where all the bodies were buried"—in research at Edder and Stern.

"They call me 'the girl,'" Toni told Brenda that same weekend. They'd both been working for just over two years. "Do you know what happens to me every single time I go out to update a company report or research a new company? The first moment I walk in and announce myself, the looks on their faces tell me one thing: they're insulted because they got a woman. To them that means one thing: that Edder and Stern isn't taking them—and their stock—seriously; that they got the second team.

"So the first thing I have to do is come on very strong, very knowledgeable, very authoritative. Sometimes that gets them through the first disappointment. Mostly, it doesn't. They call New York. They ask why they're getting 'the girl.' While I'm standing there! Then one of the partners has to talk to them and calm them down. And do you know the second thing they do?" Toni went on.

Brenda, fascinated and appalled, shook her head. She stayed in the lab; her work life was involved mostly with other biochemists and Heinrich Leben. She realized that, compared to Toni, she had very little exposure to the business world in general. "No," said Brenda. "What happens?"

"They make a pass," Toni said flatly.

"Come on!" said Brenda. "Not in this day and age!"

"Oh, yes! In this day and age. They act like I—my body—comes along with the deal. The subtle ones say something like: 'You're not going to spend tonight in that Sheraton all alone, are you? I've got an apartment, a friend's apartment, whatever...' The unsubtle ones say something like: 'You liberated women put out. Why don't you put out for me?'"

Brenda shook her head in disbelief, although now that she thought about it she realized that the male lab assistant inevitably brushed her breasts when he was taking out and replacing test tubes.

"What do you tell them? How do you handle it?" Brenda asked. She herself "handled" the assistant by pretending she didn't notice.

"Not too well," Toni admitted. "If I say I'm not available, they want to know about my love life. If I refuse and say I don't do that, they tell me I'm a ball-breaker. If I tell them to get lost, they accuse me of being hostile." Toni shrugged. "It's a tough situation because I feel defensive. I shouldn't, I know. But I do."

Then Toni went on, "And you'd be surprised at the number of guys who've said they've gone to bed with me. Untrue, of course. But that doesn't stop them from saying it. And then the next guy says, 'You put out for Joe Blow. What's wrong with me?'"

"It makes MedLabs sound like paradise," said Brenda, who vowed she would *never* let herself get as tough and bitter as Toni seemed to be getting. Toni had begun to wear ultratailored suits that seemed more like armor than clothes, and she had, for the first time since Brenda had known her, gained weight. Brenda wondered if she'd done it to make herself less attractive. But, while she promised herself she wouldn't let herself get as hard as Toni, she also decided she was not going to sit around passively until Heinrich got around to reading her report. She would give him another week. If he still hadn't read it by then, she'd *do* something...

Brenda resubmitted her proposal a week later. She attached a reminder note for Heinrich and through the interoffice mail sent a copy to Heinrich's boss, Sam Vincent, head of all research at MedLabs.

Two days later the copy was back on Brenda's desk with a penciled "good idea—sv" and a request that she work up a rough estimate of the costs for her proposal. Within the week, Brenda had the estimate on Heinrich's desk, carbon to Sam Vincent, whom she now saw as her protector.

When Heinrich called her into his office to discuss her proposal, Sam Vincent, tall, suave, leonine, a soft roll of fat just blurring the waistband of his trousers, was also there. But although Sam Vincent did the smiling, Heinrich did the talking.

"The insulin-receptor approach seems... promising," Heinrich said, drawing deliberately on his pipe. "And the estimate seems in line."

Brenda had trouble restraining her smile. She forced herself to look serious, scientific.

"We'll have to find a place for it in the budget, but I think we can stretch it," Heinrich said. "You'll set it up... be in charge. It's your baby."

"Thank you," said Brenda, feeling the way she used to feel in college when a teacher singled her out for praise. "I'm glad you agree with me. We seem to be stuck on the other approach."

"Good girl!" Sam Vincent said, speaking for the first time. His tone was hearty, approving, and, nodding at Heinrich, he left the office. It was the first time an executive on as high a level as Sam Vincent had seemed to notice she was alive, and only later would Brenda remember the 'girl.'

"Don't ever go over my head again, Brenda," Heinrich said when they were alone. He spoke in a mean, low voice, turning several degrees colder, from slush to ice, as he continued, "Never, ever, do it again. Don't ever *think* about doing it." He put his pipe down and looked squarely at Brenda, compelling her eyes to hold his. "Because if you do, I'll fire you so fast you won't know what hit you."

"But why?" Brenda asked, startled. "You didn't have time to read the memo, and the work could be important to MedLabs. I thought it would save time if I went to Mr. Vincent."

"Well, I don't appreciate it. I run this department. And I happen to run it very well." Heinrich's tone was bleak and wintry, February following fast on the heels of January.

"I'm sorry," said Brenda, who wasn't. She had been working for MedLabs, trying to get them off dead center in their research, trying to point them into a promising direction. She realized that Toni's observations about the delicacy of the male ego were on target, more than she had originally wanted to admit. Still, if Heinrich wanted an apology, she'd give him one. The point was that the insulin-receptor program could get under way.

"What section of the lab should I set up for the new project?" Brenda asked, thrilled at the thought of being project director. Lab space was always at a premium at MedLabs, now more than ever.

"I don't know," said Heinrich blandly, sucking on his pipe. "I haven't given it any thought. It's *your* project. You clear the space."

Brenda went home that evening feeling let down and anxious. "I don't understand it," she told Jeff. "I won! I got my way. I got what I wanted! We're going to go ahead with my idea! I won—but I feel like I lost. Something happened today, but I don't understand what..."

Jeff was preoccupied with his own problems at the clinic— the supervisor wanted him to process patients more quickly ("process" was the supervisor's bureaucratic verb). More patients meant a bigger slice of the federal funds that supported the clinic—and, consequently, a bigger slice of state funds, since Massachusetts had to match federal funding. Jeff, who was used to medical problems and bureaucratic problems, did not know what to tell Brenda. But he tried.

"It's probably nothing," he said, holding her, comforting her. "Just office bullshit."

Brenda wanted to believe him

3

Eight weeks later Heinrich Leben made a big move up: he left MedLabs and went to Ryder & Evans as director of research—the same job as Sam Vincent's but at a much bigger company. Ed Slowacki went with him—as executive assistant and heir apparent.

"But Ed Slowacki is barely competent!" Brenda complained to Toni, torn between hurt, confusion, and anger. "He never even filed one completion report at MedLabs. Just a few interim sheets! He even had a chance to work on the insulin-receptor project. He turned it down. Ed Slowacki wouldn't know a new approach if it bit him!"

Toni shrugged, a bland what-do-you-expect look on her face.

"It's not fair!" Brenda continued. "*He* moves up while I stay behind. I thought I'd at least get a promotion, but so far not even that! I'm still hoping, though . . ." Brenda concluded, trying to make herself feel a little better.

"You're worried about the wrong thing," Toni cautioned.

Brenda looked at her. "What do you mean? The wrong thing? What's the right thing?"

An unreadable expression flickered across Toni's face; then she took a deep breath.

"You may as well hear it from me."

"Hear what?" There was a sinking feeling in the pit of Brenda's stomach.

"You've been set up," Toni said. "Ryder and Evans is one of the companies we follow closely. It's on our 'buy' list. They've just written off the project you're starting up."

"The insulin receptors?" Brenda thought she'd throw up.

Toni nodded. "They spent almost a year on it. Reinking was a consultant. But they got nowhere, and the FDA put the kiss of death on that approach. There's no way the FDA would have gone along with altering such a basic cellular structure at this point. No one knows enough yet about how it works."

"And Heinrich knew?"

Toni nodded again. "Probably. He must have been talking with Ryder and Evans for quite a while before agreeing to head up his research. And they must have told him what lines they'd been working along."

"Reinking had research and nowhere to take it. *He* was gunning for another consultantship. Ed Slowacki must have known. *He* got drunk with the Ryder and Evans guys at Urbana. Heinrich finally went along with it because it would put MedLabs on the wrong tangent. *He'd* have time to look good at Ryder and Evans..." As Brenda quickly worked it through, she recognized every exquisite nuance of the double cross that she'd not only walked into but actually set up for herself. "And *I'm* left holding the bag. *I'm* going to take the blame."

"Not if you move fast enough," Toni advised.

"What do I do?"

"Get out. Find a new job. Stick someone else with the insulin receptors. After all, officially, Heinrich gave you the go-ahead. Let it ride on *his* record."

"But that's not nice!" Brenda was appalled at Toni's suggestion.

"He'd do it to you," Toni said matter-of-factly. "In fact, he already has."

Brenda thought for a moment. How had Toni gotten so tough? Or was she just savvy? Was she playing the hard ball the men were always talking about at the office?

"You're right," said Brenda. "You're absolutely right!"

That afternoon she wrote a résumé. With her academic record, three years' experience at MedLabs, extensive speaking experience on campuses, and the Decade of Women on her side, she knew she'd look good to would-be employers.

"But what if I have to move to Cincinnati?" Brenda asked Jeff from the depths of a late-night anxiety attack. Her résumés had gone to pharmaceutical and chemical companies all over the country.

"We'll figure it out when—and if—that happens."

"Do you love me?" Brenda asked, asking a question she asked at least once a day.

"Yes," Jeff said. He had always thought that Brenda's need to be reassured was connected with her father's death. "I love you. Very much."

"We'll survive my career, won't we?" Brenda had always wanted a career *and* a marriage. Every magazine, every newspaper's women's page, every role model from architect-wife-mother to journalist-wife-mother had told her that career plus marriage was not only possible but desirable and, after all, not very hard if you were simply organized enough. This was the first real conflict Brenda had faced between marriage and career, the first inkling that what the magazines and newspapers and role models contended wasn't exactly the lead-pipe cinch they'd promised. "Won't we?"

"Of course we will," said Jeff, holding her.

Brenda's career meant almost as much to Jeff as it did to Brenda. All his life he had known he wanted to marry someone who worked.

Jeff's mother had been a dental hygienist before she had married Jeff's father, a dentist. The marriage had been neither outstandingly happy nor unhappy. It had idled in neutral for all the years Jeff could remember, and for all the years Jeff could remember his mother's one regret was that she had given up her job when her children had come along. She called that decision the one great mistake of her life.

"I should have hired someone to take care of you," she used to tell Jeff and his sister, "and kept my job. Even if it took all my salary."

She had urged Jeff's sister to have a career of her own, and she urged Jeff to be sure to marry someone who had a career.

"A working wife is a happy wife," she used to say, knowing

that her own boredom and resentment was largely due to the fact that leaving her job had created a gaping hole in her life, a tremendous emptiness. "I used to be a somebody with an appointment book and a phone that rang" was the way she put it. "Now I'm 'just a housewife.'"

Nellie Musser's words had had their impact. Jeff's sister was a dentist like their father, and Jeff had always taken it for granted that he would marry someone who worked. He had believed his mother when she said a bored wife was an unhappy wife—after all, wasn't she a prime example?

Jeff had thought, simply, that a working wife would be a more interesting and stimulating partner. He had never given a thought to the economic implications.

"I'm setting up an office in Newton," Wayne Elbaum told Jeff over coffee. Wayne had been a Brown classmate of Jeff's, an ear-nose-and-throat man who'd been associated with a top ENT man at Boston General and now wanted to strike out on his own. "I'm looking for people to share space," Wayne went on. "I've got a bank lined up for the financing, so all you have to do is hand in your resignation and move to Newton. You're good, Jeff, and I'd like to cut you in. What do you say?"

Wayne at twenty-eight looked thirty-five. A good, well-exercised, well-nourished, well-intentioned thirty-five. He was a man who clearly knew where he was going and how he was going to get there, and he had enough confidence for a whole hockey team.

"What I'm offering, Jeff," Wayne said, "is practically a license to coin money. The bank loan will be paid off in five years, easy, and after that it's all cream. What do you say?"

Wayne dangled visions of a Mercedes and winter vacations and an expensive house in an exclusive suburb. And Jeff wasn't even tempted.

"I know, Wayne," Jeff said. "And I appreciate the offer. I really do. But I'm happy at the clinic."

"There's no money in it, man!" Wayne exclaimed, appalled at Jeff's recklessness.

"But there are other rewards," Jeff said.

"You always were the class altruist," Wayne said, shrugging.

But the rewards Jeff spoke of weren't entirely altruistic. Jeff's work at the Roxbury clinic made him feel good. He felt important when a new pair of glasses helped a ghetto kid raise his grades, when a cataract operation saved the sight of an old woman who subsisted on welfare, when properly fitted contact lenses helped a talented schoolyard athlete land a professional contract.

"I want to continue at the clinic," Jeff told Brenda that night. "Do you think I was wrong to turn down Wayne's offer? I would have made a lot of money."

"I'm proud of you for turning it down," said Brenda, who knew how much of himself Jeff put into his work, who shared his aversion to the doctors Jeff had gone to school with who talked obsessively about their Advent large screen TV's, their real estate deals, and the latest wrinkle in tax shelters. "I'm glad you're not like the rest of them. I couldn't stand it if you were."

In the first three years of their marriage, Jeff had turned down four offers to go into private practice—and always with Brenda's complete agreement. What he wanted, she wanted; what she wanted, he wanted. They shared ideals, and the only thing they fought about was housework because no matter how many fights or discussions they had or how many times a work sheet was posted in the kitchen, sooner or later Brenda ended up doing most of it.

"For a feminist," she told Jeff during one of their rare calm discussions of the housework problem, "you sure can't seem to remember which end of a mop is up."

It was such a sensitive subject that Jeff didn't even smile.

Brenda had sent out a dozen résumés. She got, almost instantly, ten responses. Eight companies were interested and asked her to name a time for an interview; two wrote to say that although they had nothing at the moment, her résumé would be kept on file; two were never heard from.

A month after she'd found she'd been set up at MedLabs, Brenda had six firm job offers, more than she'd had when she'd graduated from Brown.

"Everyone who knows you knows you're sensational! But *this*!" Ellen was proud and happy and was never shy about letting Brenda know how she felt. And, not wanting to divert attention from Brenda's triumph, did not mention that not only had she—finally!—won the Winter Antiques Show opening-night party but had just been chosen to cater a country-and-western reception for five hundred people for a Houston-based petroleum company that was opening new offices on the sixtieth floor of the World Trade Center. The year was 1975, inflation was beginning to be a factor, and companies were spending like there was no tomorrow. What else did you do with dollars that were getting cheaper day by day?

Toni tried—but not very hard—not to be an I-told-you-so: "See! I told you so! The mark of a winner is turning a defeat into a triumph! And you did it! You beat them at their own game!" The "they," as always, was the adversary—men.

And Jeff was supportive, loving, always interested in Brenda's happiness: "Just make sure you pick the job that will make you happiest." Exactly what her father would have said, thought Brenda, and, confidently, made her decision.

She accepted the offer from All Chem, a multinational company headquartered in Pittsburgh, at a salary of twenty-one thousand dollars. She warned Toni that she'd better start saving up for champagne at the Four Seasons. Toni was earning "only" 18K—which was how they referred to it at Edder and Stern.

She told Jeff she thought a "weekend marriage" would be sexy. She'd read articles in a new lifestyle magazine that spelled out—in text and lavish color spreads—just how sexy a marriage could be if the partners didn't live together seven days a week! She told Ellen she was looking forward to a ride on the All Chem executive jet. The one thing she didn't tell anyone was that she was now earning considerably more than Jeff.

Jeff, of course, knew, but he and Brenda didn't think it would be a problem. Neither of them was particularly materialistic. Besides, Brenda spent more than she made.

"MasterCharge's best customer," she bragged to Jeff, not realizing that she sounded exactly like her father. But after a week of hard work (and most of the housework, too!), Brenda felt like treating herself—to an expensive silk blouse, a pair of unnecessary but irresistible shoes, and a frilly, lacy teddy. After all, what was she working so hard *for*?

"No more Ms. Nice Guy," Brenda warned Toni before she moved to Pittsburgh. Her experience at MedLabs had been a sobering lesson.

"You're learning," said Toni. "Just remember to smile all the time. It keeps them off balance."

Brenda and Toni, girl infiltrators, broke up.

At All Chem, Brenda went to as many departmental meetings as possible. She made a point of having lunch with one or another of her coworkers almost every day. She went to as many weekend conferences and think-tank sessions as she could humanly fit in. She spent what she called quality time in the lab, delegating the routine work whenever possible while devoting most of her in-office time to keeping a high profile.

At first, despite Toni's cheerleading, it all felt wrong to Brenda. "I feel like I'm cheating the company by not writing up the lab data myself," she told her.

"Don't you have an assistant for that?" Toni asked.

Brenda nodded.

"Then let the assistant do it. That's what he's being paid for. You're being paid to be an executive. You have to show you can function like one."

"Okay," Brenda said tentatively. "I just hope to hell you know what you're talking about."

She found out that Toni was right when All Chem decided to send a team to Germany to liaise (their word) with an All Chem unit that was developing a contact lens that could be worn permanently—an extended-wear lens not yet cleared even for testing in the U.S.

"You're a first-class administrator, Brenda. People like you, and obviously you're a first-class chemist," Brenda's boss told her.

Sid Erlau had been head of research for All Chem for four years; he was the youngest man in the industry to hold the job and, perhaps because of his age, did not seem unduly agitated by the fact that Brenda was a woman. Also perhaps because Sid Erlau—short, bespectacled, and running to pudge—had a fabulously beautiful wife who towered over him and seemed to literally worship the ground he walked on. Whatever the reason, Sid Erlau was, at least on the surface, a very different cup of tea from Heinrich Leben.

"I'm sending a six-man team to the Munich branch," Sid told Brenda, talking in his captain-of-the-hill manner. Including Brenda in the "six-man" team was Sid's idea of a high compliment, and Brenda had long since given up correcting his grammar. "One day the FDA is going to give us clearance for the extended-wear lens, and we want to be ready to pounce. I'm putting you in charge of the team, Brenda. I know you'll make me proud of you."

Brenda *was* a good administrator—a talent she had learned

not in school and not at MedLabs but in her mother's kitchen. She had watched her mother direct Janice and Gaby and Clarence, seeing to it that assignments didn't overlap, that recipe steps dovetailed, that the right orders got to the right people at the right time. Administration was not something Brenda had learned; it was something she had *breathed*.

She spent a month in Munich, surprised to find her college German actually serviceable. She saw to it that an extensive and detailed memorandum of progress-to-date on the extended-wear lens was made and that copies of raw lab data were sent back to Pittsburgh. She personally drafted a confidential memo to Sid Erlau outlining the pluses and minuses of the to-date discoveries, suggesting ways procedures could be adapted to eventual U.S. testing requirements.

Although the work itself was interesting, although Brenda particularly liked the fact that, for once, she was doing something she could talk to Jeff about, the most important part of the trip was the way it made her feel.

From the moment she stepped into the first-class section of the Lufthansa flight and the steward offered her champagne and smoked salmon to the moment she left Munich in an All Chem limousine, her luggage prechecked through from Pittsburgh via the All Chem Public Relations Department, she felt special. She was important to All Chem, and they treated her as if she were important. A secretary and a research assistant were assigned to her during her stay in Munich; All Chem supplied her with theater and concert tickets; the All Chem car waited for her outside the Bayerischer Hof Hotel, where she stayed in a luxurious All Chem suite.

Her month in Munich was the first taste of luxury Brenda had ever had; and, although she was a member of a generation that had prided itself on being nonmaterialistic, she enjoyed every moment of the luxury, the pampering, the attention, the professional respect with which the All Chem executives treated her. Perhaps because she was an American and the Germans expected almost *anything* from the Americans, the fact that Brenda was a woman—and an attractive one—was for the first time in her career a real plus. She stood out in every meeting, every seminar, every lab tour. She had visibility, and she had clout—visibility because she was the only woman in a male-only atmosphere, clout because she had been vetted by the all-powerful home office.

Brenda returned home, flushed with success, her ambition for the first time rewarded with something beyond a good salary and a pat on the head. She was professionally respected; the sky was the limit.

And she got home just in time for a happy event: Tuck and Toni's wedding.

"I guess we've finally gone Establishment," Tuck said after the reception, which Ellen catered. Brenda had spent the weekend helping her mother with the cooking—the first cooking she had done in a long time—and she remembered how much she liked doing it. Cooking was one of the pleasures Brenda had given up for her career; at the time it hardly seemed much of a sacrifice.

"You *are* the Establishment," Brenda teased. "You're a lawyer and Toni's on Wall Street. What could be more Establishment than that?"

"I could be president!" Toni suggested, and everyone broke up. They were sitting on the floor of the West Sixty-eighth Street co-op Toni's parents had contributed as a wedding gift. "The first female president!" Everyone giggled, helped along by the grass they were smoking, a habit left over from college.

"To tell you the truth, it was getting embarrassing at Coles, Watkins and Forrest," Tuck said seriously. Coles, Watkins and Forrest was Tuck's law firm, and Tuck knew if he didn't make partner within the next three years, he'd either have to move and try again at another law firm or resign himself to being a drone. He wasn't about to do either. "You'd be surprised how much the partners care about whether or not you're married. They keep saying things about it, teasing and not-so-teasing. Like: When are you going to make it legal, Tuck, you and Toni? So Toni and I decided that if I want to make partner—which I do, naturally—it would make sense to get married."

"Same thing at Edder and Stern," Toni said. "They like me. They're used to me. But they're an uptight, half-WASP, half-Jewish firm. Hints have been dropped about my making partner. A woman along with the WASPs and Jews! Too bad I'm not black, too! Anyway, I'll look good on their prospectus. And a husband on the fast track doesn't hurt." She looked affectionately at Tuck, who returned the look. "God knows, the next thing we'll have babies and anniversaries—"

"I thought you two didn't want children," Brenda said.

"We don't," Toni said at the same instant Tuck asked, "Why not?"

Toni and Tuck looked at each other for a second, puzzled and surprised.

Then Toni blushed. "Maybe," she said. "I could always change my mind."

"Really?" Tuck said, and he looked very happy.

For sentimental reasons Toni and Tuck wanted to spend their wedding night in the small apartment on Thompson Street that they'd shared for the past five years. They offered the co-op to Jeff and Brenda for the night, an offer they accepted.

The apartment, still smelling of the brand-new paint job, was completely unfurnished except for a bed, a card table, and four folding chairs—a state of affairs Toni's mother was determined to remedy as soon as possible.

"Reminds me of Pittsburgh," Brenda said as they got ready for bed. She was thinking of the studio she'd rented when she'd first gone to work for All Chem almost a year before and which was almost as empty as the day she'd moved in. She had a bed, a dinette set that had been abandoned by the previous tenants, and a rag rug from her old room in New Rochelle. She simply had never had the time to furnish it. Another sacrifice she considered meaningless that she had made for her career.

"Brenda, does it bother you that I'm not on the fast track?" Jeff asked as they got into bed.

"Bother me? I've never even thought about it. It's never crossed my mind." That was the truth, but even as she spoke, Brenda suddenly wondered whether a successful husband might make a difference to the honchos at All Chem.

"I didn't think so," Jeff said. "But still I'm relieved to hear it from you." He paused for a moment. "Brenda? What would you think of having a baby?" he asked suddenly, taking Brenda completely by surprise.

"Well," she temporized, "I think it would be—"

"What?" Jeff prompted. "Would be what?"

"I think it would be nice."

"I hear a 'but' in your voice."

"I think it would be nice," Brenda repeated, "but later. I feel that big things are ahead for me at All Chem. Sid Erlau keeps hinting. Now just wouldn't be a good time to get pregnant."

"But you still want children?" Jeff asked.

"Oh, yes," said Brenda. "But later . . ."

The subject of children was more or less dropped, and life went on as it had ever since Brenda had gone to work for All Chem. She spent weeks in Pittsburgh, weekends at "home" in Boston, except for those weekends she attended out-of-town symposia or Jeff went to public health conferences.

Those weekends, Brenda left her barren apartment and went to New Rochelle where, with pleasure, she helped her mother. À La Carte had grown to the point where Ellen had hired a second full-time chef to help Clarence.

"You're turning into a real tycoon," Brenda told her mother. "Staff and all."

"Business *has* been good," Ellen said. "And we may be expanding. Tamara wants to retire. She asked me if I'd be interested in buying her out."

"And?"

"Lew and I are thinking about it. Tamara, being Tamara, wants a fortune."

"I'll bet!" Brenda said, and she wondered about Lew and her mother. She wondered how long her mother would be contented with a shared man, thinking that she had been alone for a long time. Too long. "And how *is* Lew?"

"Fine," said Ellen. "Whatever you think, Brenda, he means a great deal to me. I don't think I would have made À La Carte *quite* the success it's becoming without Lew to inspire me, without Lew as a sounding board."

And although Ellen didn't say anything to Brenda, her relationship with Lew was changing. Subtly, but unmistakably. It was becoming comfortable; it was becoming a retreat; it was becoming, for Lew *and* for her, almost a second marriage.

What she wasn't ready to admit yet—even to herself—was that a relationship that didn't grow and change was a relationship that, slowly, ran out of life.

Jeff had always been faithful to Brenda, and Brenda had always been faithful to Jeff. Although men made passes at Brenda—exactly as they made passes at Toni—Brenda had learned, just as Toni had learned, how to turn them down without hurting feelings or egos. She had gotten to the point—just as Toni had gotten to the same point—where she didn't even take it personally, and, if the man were attractive, she sometimes thought it flattering.

But, absorbed as she was in her career, sex was not a major concern to Brenda. She had grown up liberated by Helen Gurley Brown, by Masters and Johnson, by *Playboy* and *Penthouse*, by frontal nudity, by the Beatles and the Love Generation. Brenda, like most of her generation, took sex for granted. And, like many of her peers, she wondered what the big deal was about sex. Why her mother and her mother's generation had made such a big deal of it. Whatever the thrill was supposed to be, Brenda had thought it was just the propaganda of another generation.

Until she met—or more accurately remet—Sandor Tobias.

4

For a long time, Jeff had been everything to Brenda. The first time she had met him he had saved the job she needed to help pay her way through college.

It was the summer of 1969, the summer between Brenda's junior and senior years, the summer after Wilson had left—the second important man who had deserted her in her short lifetime. She had finally worked up the courage to tell her mother that she didn't want to come home to New Rochelle that summer, that she didn't want to work for À La Carte that summer the way she had every other summer.

"I want to be on my own," she had told Ellen. "I want to see if I can make it in the outside world."

"I understand," Ellen said, proud to see Brenda growing up, understanding her wish to be independent; sad, suddenly, that the years had gone so quickly, that her little girl was now a young woman. She had wished Brenda good luck, then added, "But I'll miss you. You're the best *sous-chef* anyone ever had!"

Brenda had applied for and gotten a job as a lab technician at the Rynde Eye and Ear Clinic in Providence running basic biological tests. The work demanded precision, although it was, basically, quite mechanical. The salary was excellent, and Eye and Ear was a nice place to work.

The atmosphere was not like an ordinary hospital because the patients were rarely really sick. Their conditions were most usually those that could be cured with either surgical or non-surgical treatment. The pediatric floors had the air of a perpetual birthday party with ice cream and balloons because kids who came in with crossed eyes left without them, and kids who came in with hearing losses left with corrected hearing. The same upbeat mood pervaded the adult floors, where cataract surgery was extremely effective, and patients who were admitted in a semi-blind condition usually left able to see, while patients who came in for eye nips and face-lifts left feeling and looking years younger.

Unlike general hospitals, Eye and Ear did not get the drunks and drug addicts, the Saturday night stabbings and shootings, and the wandering confused, washed-up-in-the-back-tides-of-a-big-city. The atmosphere at Eye and Ear was, in general, pleasant, efficient, and positive. Except for very rare occasions, the only clashes were clashes of personality, and it was when she was embroiled in one of these that Brenda first met Jeff.

Ralph Kierman, whose father was chairman of Rynde Eye and Ear, was a very, very young surgeon. And he had a surgeon's temperament. Everything had to be done sooner than immediately, and it was in that mood that Ralph barged into the ground-floor lab over the Fourth of July weekend.

"Goddammit!" he said, his usual form of address to his inferiors (that is, anyone who wasn't richer, better socially connected, or more aggressive than he). "Where are the Hurst results?"

"They aren't ready yet," said Brenda. Hurst was Celinda Hurst, whose photograph in a lavish apricot chiffon dress by Oscar de la Renta and an even more lavish necklace of marquise blue-white diamonds by Harry Winston had once been on the cover of *Town & Country* magazine. Brenda was about to add that the cultures needed another fourteen hours in solution to get a result, but she barely had a chance to open her mouth.

"Then why the hell not? Does this place run on nigger time or white man's time?" Ralph Kierman glowered so close to Brenda that she could see the hairs between his eyebrows.

Jim Hart, another technician, shook his head silently. Jim

was black. He was also used to Ralph Kierman and referred to him as "the black man's burden."

"Dr. Kierman, we received the culture Friday at four P.M. It was in solution by five P.M.," Brenda said, reading from the neat notes she had taped to the side of the petri dish. She was about to say that it was not physically possible to get a reliable result before forty-eight hours. The bacteria needed that much time to grow. Again, Ralph Kierman cut her off.

"I don't know why I can't get results when I need them," he said, his voice low the way it always was when he was really angry (as opposed to his more usual high-pitched wail).

"You can't because no one can—" Brenda began.

"Listen! I'm not 'no one.' I'm a god here!" Ralph Kierman said, seemingly unaware that anyone might care to take exception to that last statement. "Miss Durban," he said, reading the name plaque pinned to her lab coat, "maybe you'd like to find a job somewhere else. Somewhere leisurely. You can be replaced, you know. Easily!" Ralph Kierman had a reputation for firing people the way Howard Hughes supposedly used Kleenex.

"Hey, Ralph, lay off!" cut in a male voice belonging to a doctor Brenda had seen around Rynde. He was tall and slender and had a sandy-colored beard and warm brown eyes. Ralph Kierman spun around, still angry.

"I'm sick and tired of this incompetence," he said, still in that ominously low tone.

"Come on, Ralph! Those tests have to run forty-eight hours. Even you learned that in med school. I mean, I sat in some of the same classes you did. They didn't suspend the laws of nature. Even for you!"

"I want that result," Ralph persisted but, nevertheless, blushing slightly, an abashed grin lurking at the corners of his mouth. "I'm going to Celinda Hurst's fireworks party tonight, and I want to be able to tell her what's going on with that eye of hers."

"You'll be able to tell her. Tomorrow," Jeff said.

"Shit!" muttered Ralph Kierman and stalked out of the lab.

"What was all that about?" he asked Brenda when Ralph had gone, the rubber-faced doors to the med lab swinging to and fro in silent testament to Ralph's fury and frustration.

"He was going to fire me!" Brenda said in disbelief. "Can you believe that?"

"Sure," said Jeff. "He thinks he owns Rynde and all the people in it."

"You handled him very well," Brenda said. "Thank you."

"I went to med school a few years behind him," Jeff said. "Ralph's saving grace is that along with his horrible temper he has a vestigial sense of humor. It's the only way to get to him."

"I appreciate it," said Brenda, thanking Jeff again. He left off a batch of cultures for her to test.

"I'll see you in forty-eight hours," he said and left with a wink.

And that was the beginning. In no time, Jeff got into the habit of coming down for coffee breaks and, soon after, of walking Brenda home to the apartment she shared with Toni, who was working that summer in a brokerage office tallying trades.

On the way back to the apartment, Brenda and Jeff shopped for dinner, and then they'd cook together. Fast, simple, cheap things like chicken and pasta, hamburger, and a hundred different kinds of egg dishes. Toni said the best thing that had ever happened to her was walking into the apartment to find a good dinner well under way, and Jeff said that the best thing that had ever happened to him was walking into the lab and finding Brenda.

"I *know* he likes me," Brenda said. But she was confused. "He's so nice. He's so attentive. But I can't understand it. He hasn't even tried to kiss me." She wondered whether he might be homosexual. She had, after all, come of age during a period of aggressive sexual liberation. Boys and girls went to bed with each other matter-of-factly, seeming to consider sexual intercourse as casual as a handshake, only a little friendlier, of course.

"He's shy," said Toni. "And sensitive. That's all. Just be patient."

At the beginning of August, on a Sunday, Brenda and Jeff packed a picnic and drove out toward the beaches near Newport. As they got out of Jeff's beat-up VW, their hands accidentally touched. The next thing Brenda knew, they were holding hands, and it was as if they had been born holding hands. When, later that day, Jeff kissed her, it was as if they had always kissed, and when, that night, they made love, the experience was so sweet and so filled with tenderness that sex, which had always been a disappointment to Brenda, seemed as natural and as good as breathing.

Other women went for men with bedroom eyes, for men who were maddeningly unavailable, for men who exuded power and authority. Not Brenda. Brenda went for feelings, and when she fell in love with Jeff, she fell in love with the way he made her feel.

Brenda was nine when her father died, and she had many memories of him. She remembered how he took her to the factory where Decor paints were manufactured, where the chemists let her mix a sample batch of colors that she used to paint each of the rooms in her dollhouse. She remembered that her father had told her all about the exotic animals and primitive tribes in the *National Geographic* and that he had explained the intriguing diagrams in *Scientific American*. She remembered that he had taken her to the ice shows at Madison Square Garden, to the Automat where he let her put the nickel into the slot and open the little door, and she remembered that, as a very special treat, he let her use his good German camera, the one with all the knobs and dials. She remembered how she had sat on his lap and "driven" the car, and how he had always asked her advice about what to buy her mother for Christmas or her birthday.

But although Brenda remembered things she had done with her father and things he had said, the memory that was most vivid was the memory of how her father had made her *feel*: as if the world had a center, as if there were permanence, as if, even if she did something wrong, even if he were mad at her, he would always love her. When he died, those feelings of security left Brenda. And those feelings were the feelings Brenda had always associated with love.

And so, unlike her women friends who sought romance or excitement or abandon in their love lives, Brenda sought a center, and in Jeff she found it. Seven years after they'd met, Brenda and Jeff were just as affectionate as they had been seven weeks after they'd first fallen in love. Brenda's friends yearned to know what her secret was.

The secret, Brenda told them, was never, never to take anyone you loved for granted. To do that was hard for a lot of people but not for Brenda.

She remembered what it was like to have her father and

mother fight, to have her father leave to buy the newspaper, never to return again. Every time she and Jeff said good-bye, every time she went to Pittsburgh for the week, every time Jeff left to go to the clinic, there was always that split second when Brenda feared she would never see him again. A moment when her heart clutched and she swallowed hard.

There was always a moment when a spat over housework, over who had left the gas tank almost empty, over who had overdrawn the checking account, threatened to grow into a major battle. It was at that moment that Brenda always drew back. She had never won a fight with Jeff—she had never wanted to.

The secret of guarding love, of keeping it new, Brenda knew, was having your father die. It was a terrible secret, and Brenda shared it with only a few friends; and she knew, even as she told them, that although they understood with their heads, they didn't understand with their hearts.

Brenda had not fallen in love with Jeff in a romantic, heart-stopping, earth-shattering instant, because the qualities that Brenda had fallen in love with were invisible and therefore did not reveal themselves all at once in a life-changing *coup de foudre*. Instead, over a period of time. Brenda came to realize that she could always count on Jeff, that Jeff meant what he said, that Jeff would do what he said he would do, that when Jeff said he would call, he would call, and that when he said he would pick her up at eight, he would be at the door at eight.

Jeff never disappointed her, never let her down, and even when she and Jeff fought—which they generally did the week just before Brenda got her period—she knew, even as they hurled angry words, that she loved him and he loved her. No spat could change that.

Jeff was the best thing that had ever happened to Brenda in her whole life, just as her father's death had been the worst. Brenda knew it, appreciated it, treasured it, did not take it for granted, and was not about to throw it away, which is why Sandy Tobias threw her for such a loop.

Brenda had never been unfaithful to Jeff; she had rarely been attracted, however fleetingly, to another man; she had never even had the fantasy of having two men in love with her at the same time, much less thought about the possibility of loving two men at the same time.

Because, for a while, Brenda loved them both.

5

SANDY TOBIAS, WIRY, TOPAZ-EYED, INTENSE, AN ANGULAR Roy Scheider look-alike, had been a post-doc at Brown when Brenda had been a freshman. He had taught a section of Chem 101 and, noticing Brenda's talent (and green eyes), had taken a special interest in her, encouraging her, prodding her, and bugging her whenever she got lazy. In short, Brenda used to tell him, he took up exactly where her mother had left off.

"I'd like to meet your mother," Sandy used to counter, only half-teasing, Brenda thought. "She sounds like my kind of woman."

Sandy, a brilliantly talented scientist (his mind worked in rigorously disciplined ways *and* was capable of inspired intuitive leaps), was also considered a wildman. Not only did he teach the freshman chemistry courses, he was analyzing DNA/RNA polymerase for his own Ph.D. in biophysics. On top of it all, he ran a very successful campus business, Sticks, which bought dorm furniture from seniors and resold it to entering students.

"You have the brain of a genius and the soul of a peddler," one of his professors told him. It was not a compliment.

"Good combo!" Sandy flipped, further irritating his teacher.

Sticks's warehouse was a basement room off campus. Students in need of sofas, rugs, chairs, desks, lamps, and so forth could buy them from Sandy. Brenda, in fact, had bought her bed, a typing table, and a chair from Sandy's basement and paid for them in installments—four monthly payments at an interest rate of eight percent.

When Brenda was a sophomore, Sandy had gotten his Ph.D., sold Sticks to a junior, an economics major, and the next Brenda had seen or heard of Sandy was at an All Chem-sponsored seminar in New York City. Sandy, who was working for Omega Chemical, one of the world's largest chemical companies, was director of research.

"I hate every minute of it," he told Brenda at the Saturday afternoon cocktail party. "I'm not a company man. Before that, I was at Princeton. I hated that, too. I'm not an academic." A large part of Sandy's undeniable charm was that he said exactly what he thought.

"There's always the furniture business," Brenda suggested.

"There's always the recombinant DNA business," Sandy corrected.

"So that when you come up with a bacteria that lives on air, doesn't pollute, and manufactures pure energy, you'll be rich, right?"

"Someone's going to," Sandy said calmly. "It might as well be me."

Brenda enjoyed Sandy, who had always been a live wire, but she didn't give him another thought until she got back from a second trip to Munich and wrote a paper on German developments in post-polymer lenses, which the *Bio-Chemical Review* published. She got a congratulatory note from Sandy with a P.S. He was going to be in Pittsburgh on business. Did she want to have dinner with him?

"Why am I in Pittsburgh?" Sandy said, repeating Brenda's question. "I'm in Pittsburgh because there's plenty of money in Pittsburgh."

They were having French food in an expensive restaurant that made Brenda remember just how wonderful chicken with leeks could be in the hands of a talented cook like her mother, like herself.

"I'm raising money," Sandy went on. "I've got an investment bank behind me—behind my company, that is. BioTech.

All the money boys are hot, hot, hot for DNA, and I'm their brightest star."

"You always used to say you never knew how to choose between money and science," Brenda recalled. She wore an aqua angora sweater that intensified the color of her eyes. It was the first time in a long time that she'd dressed for a dinner that wasn't strictly a business dinner. She'd almost forgotten what a social dinner was like.

"Yeah," said Sandy, remembering that he used to feel cursed because his greatest talent lay in the sciences, an utterly non-commercial talent in the do-your-own-thing sixties. That had been the era when rock was *the* commercial talent, and Sandy had all the musical sense of a famished camel. "Now I won't have to. I'll be able to have them both: science and dough-re-mi."

"I'm sort of jealous," Brenda said.

"Only sort of?" Sandy looked at her over the candles. His eyes, she noticed, were topazes, shot with golden flecks.

"I can control it," Brenda laughed.

"Why bother?" Sandy was serious.

Brenda had no answer.

She had been telling Sandy how much red tape was involved in her work, how much government controls and company play-it-safe policies slowed the work down. She complained about all the time she had to spend keeping the peace between the lab chemists, who were interested in the thorough process of research for its own sake, and the demands of management, who pushed for results that would show up on the bottom line.

As she spoke to Sandy, Brenda began to realize that she never spoke to anyone about her work; no one she knew really understood all its facets. Toni understood—and could advise on—the political, in-fighting aspects of it; Jeff understood some of the biochemical aspects of it; but neither of them understood both sides of it—the conflict between research and results, the difference between doing a good job and having a good career. It was a relief to have someone to talk to who understood both sides, and it also made Brenda realize that she sounded rather bitter, the way she had accused Toni of sounding.

"You wouldn't have to deal with the interoffice shit if you ran your own show," Sandy said. "It's one of the reasons I'm starting BioTech—besides the money, of course."

"Sandy, I think you're the only materialistic scientist I've ever met," Brenda said. Most of the scientists she knew thought it disreputable to be interested in money, clothes, or possessions—disreputable and faintly embarrassing.

"Then you're hanging around the wrong scientists."

"Seriously," Brenda chided.

"Seriously," Sandy corrected. "Every biochemist I know is falling all over himself/herself trying to get into the DNA gold mine."

"Then I'm just in the wrong field," Brenda said. "You know, even though the company that comes up with a safe anti-obesity drug, a permanent contact lens, a non-habit-forming sleeping pill is going to make *billions*, everything seems to move at a stately pace. And I mean *stately*."

"You ought to be in business for yourself," Sandy said over ponies of Courvoisier.

"Never!" exclaimed Brenda. "My mother runs her own business. I know what it's like. Thanks but no thanks! I'll put up with the problems at All Chem. They're an improvement over sleepless nights."

"Suit yourself," Sandy shrugged. "But if that's your decision, I won't listen to you complain."

"You mean if I go into business for myself, you'll listen to me complain?"

"Brat!" Sandy said and threw a crumpled napkin across the table at her.

They talked animatedly until midnight, then lingered over the Courvoisier and small talk until one. Brenda couldn't believe the time when she looked at her watch.

"My God! I've got an eight-thirty meeting tomorrow morning!"

"Company girl!" Sandy teased, but he paid the check and dropped Brenda off in front of her apartment building.

"Tomorrow?" he asked as she got out of his rented car. "Same time, same place?"

"Sure," Brenda said. "Same time. Not the same place. I'll cook. You might as well know what chicken and leeks *really* tastes like."

There wasn't a thing wrong with it, Brenda told herself. For one thing, she was in love with Jeff. For another, Sandy wasn't her type. Not at all. He was too slick in his well-cut suits and dashing Porsche Carrera yellow-tinted glasses. He didn't even look like a scientist, most of whom affected the Albert Einstein look: baggy, saggy, and draggy, with—if possible—holes in the sleeves. They thought it made them look "serious."

Except that the third straight evening in a row that she had dinner with Sandy, Brenda couldn't sleep. She tossed and turned and finally admitted to herself somewhere close to four o'clock in the morning that she was attracted to him. And that he was attracted to her. She was glad she wouldn't see him again. Thank God, he was leaving Pittsburgh first thing the next morning.

"I can't stop thinking about you," Sandy told Brenda via telephone two days later. He was calling from Cleveland. "There's a lot of money in Cleveland," he said. "The trouble is that you're not here."

"Don't say that!" Brenda told him sharply, and he obeyed. But four days later he was waiting outside the All Chem building at six-forty-five when Brenda left the office.

"What we had was special," he told her. "Feelings like those don't come along every day in the week. I know I'm taking a risk. You can tell me to get lost. But I'm not about to disappear. I'm not about to let it drop between us."

He held the car door open for her, and, as if drawn by a magnet, Brenda got in.

"I shouldn't do this," she said.

"'Shouldn't,'" Sandy said, steering the car away from the curb and into the mainstream of traffic, "is a word you 'shouldn't' use."

They went back to Sandy's hotel, and the moment he closed the door behind them Brenda found herself in his arms, her mouth clinging to his, answering his passion with her own. She cast herself away, losing herself in him, finding herself in him. They made love, and they talked all night long, too excited to sleep, too excited to stop.

"I didn't know it could be like this," Brenda said, knowing as she spoke that her words were a cliché but knowing no others with which to express her feelings.

"I did," Sandy said. "I knew it could be like this—with you. That's why I came back. That's why I'm not going to walk away."

"But what about . . ." Brenda let the question trail off. Sandy knew, of course, about Jeff. "What's going to happen?"

"I don't know," Sandy said. "You're the one who's going to decide. You're going to have to choose between us, and I'm going to do everything I can to make sure you choose me."

Brenda went home to Boston that weekend and clung to Jeff as if to dear life.

"You really must have missed me this week," he said, touched by her affection.

At first being in love with two men was enormously exciting, and Brenda was on a never-ending high. She saw Sandy whenever he could get to Pittsburgh and she went home to Jeff on weekends. She seemed to need hardly any sleep, and work and work problems seemed to resolve themselves effortlessly. Without even trying, she lost the five pounds that made the difference between a nice body and a spectacular body. Her mind seemed razor-sharp, and her emotions seemed as lucid and clear as a mountain lake.

Sandy challenged her; he wanted her to extend herself, to be better. Jeff comforted her; he wanted her to be happy, to do whatever felt most comfortable for her. Sandy saw her enormous ability, and he encouraged her ambition; he wanted her to take risks even if they made her uncomfortable. Jeff saw her warmth, her need to give love and to receive love; he wanted her to stay as she was, the way he had first loved her. Jeff thought she was perfect the way she was; Sandy kept telling her she was wonderful but that she could be even better.

It never occurred to Brenda to ask herself why she couldn't have both and be both: loving and stretched; happy and at risk. Instead, she procrastinated for almost three months, putting off the decision Sandy demanded, not telling Jeff about Sandy.

"I want to take you to Bermuda for a week," Sandy said. "I want an answer, Brenda: yes or no."

She kept asking for time.

"You seem different," Jeff said. "Wired. Can't you sit down? You're making me nervous."

Brenda drifted along in her paradise, and then her need for less sleep than usual turned into the first insomnia she'd ever had. She lay awake at night, unable to sleep, tossing and turning, bits and pieces of conversation with Jeff and Sandy replayed endlessly on a stop-start cassette over which she had no control.

And her magic weight loss disappeared, replaced by a raging, insatiable hunger. Giving up on sleep, Brenda got out of bed in the middle of the night and went to the kitchen, where she made herself big bowls of oatmeal drowned with butter and heavy cream and brown sugar, which she then devoured with a soup spoon. She regained the five pounds she had lost and added five more. She felt stuffed and starved at the same time. She was so hungry. She felt uncomfortably full. She couldn't stop eating. She ate candy bars at the office and ice cream cones on the way home from work. She couldn't stop trying to fill herself.

One morning Sandy reached over in bed. Brenda thought he was going to make love to her. Instead he squeezed the soft flesh of her hip.

"*Zaftig*," he said and got up. It wasn't a compliment.

"Is everything all right?" Jeff asked that next weekend.

"Sure," said Brenda casually. "What makes you ask?"

"You've gained weight," Jeff said. "I've never known you to gain weight."

"I haven't been able to stop eating lately," Brenda admitted, aware of the irony that she had spent much of her professional life trying to develop a safe, effective diet drug. If only there were one now! All the ones on the market had some form of amphetamine. If Brenda took them, they made her feel that she would—literally—jump out of her skin. "I'm hungry all the time. No matter how much I eat."

"Maybe you ought to have a physical checkup," Jeff suggested.

"Maybe," Brenda agreed. "But I'll give it a while. Let's see what happens."

Brenda's emotional temperature was feverish, agitated, and mercurial. She felt high as a kite one moment, flattered by the love of two desirable men; despondent the next, a cheater who would end up being the one who got cheated. The longer she put off making a choice, the less able she was to make one.

"It's the fourth time I've asked you about Bermuda," Sandy said. "I love you and you say you love me. But I'm possessive, Brenda. And I'm getting impatient. You've got to choose: Jeff or me. Who's it going to be, Brenda? I'm not going to hang around forever."

"Let's go," Brenda said, almost holding her breath. It was like diving off a high board. "I want to go."

She told Jeff that All Chem was having a conference in Sarasota. That weekend, on a white coral beach, Sandy asked Brenda to get a divorce and marry him.

"Please say yes," he said and held her in the sunlight.

The next weekend, Jeff reminded Brenda that they hadn't spoken about having children since Toni and Tuck's wedding.

"I know," Brenda said. "But—"

"We can't keep postponing it," Jeff said. "You're twenty-seven. Time is going by."

Like an out-of-balance gyro, Brenda spun between Sandy and Jeff. With Sandy, love was sparks and flares; with Jeff, love was tranquility and affection. Now Brenda began to ask herself why she couldn't have both. But she had no answer, could make no choice, either.

It all came to a head one Thursday evening when Jeff surprised her by flying into Pittsburgh for the weekend.

"You must be Jeff," Sandy said, suavely, opening the door to Brenda's apartment. "I'm Sandy. Sandy Tobias..."

Jeff looked from Sandy to Brenda—to the stricken expression on her face—and he instantly understood the weight gain, insomnia, and even the unusually passionate times in bed.

"Brenda," he said. "Oh, Brenda..."

Tears blinded his eyes, and Brenda's choice was made. She didn't even have to think. She acted from a much deeper well than choice or passion or even love. She acted from her deepest need—the need for a center, the need for someone who wouldn't abandon her.

"Oh, Jeff, I didn't mean..." She went to him and put her arms around him. "Oh, Jeff, I never meant to hurt you. Never..."

She held him tight, feeling more sharply than she had ever felt that she would lose her love and that, this time, it would be her own fault. It was one thing for her dad to die in an accident; it was another to drive her love away.

Sandy saw every bit of it on her face. He left, and when he said goodbye and closed the door, Brenda didn't hear the door closing. What she heard was the sound of the crumbling

of half of herself, the half that wanted to be challenged, dared,
the half that knew she could soar. She shut out the sound and
buried herself in Jeff's arms, calming herself with safety and
comfort and love.

Choices. Choices delineate the contours of a life. And so often
we make them not understanding their consequences. Not out
of an inability or an unwillingness to understand but because
the intensity of our needs and the blind dictates of emotion
preordain our choices. Which, from that point of view, of
course, are not choices at all but biographical imperatives.

For Brenda, the choice to marry Jeff had not been the most
important choice of her life so far, nor had the choice of a
career. The choice between Sandy and Jeff was, so far and by
far, the most significant choice she had yet made. This choice—
between the personalities of two men—cast into bold relief
the two—until now and beyond now—irreconcilable needs
she most deeply required be met.

The need for safety versus the need for new horizons. The
choice between a good man who would always be there for
her and an exciting man who would inspire her to explore all
she was capable of doing and being.

And what Brenda did not know—and, understandably, could
not know in the intensity of the moment—was that there had
once been a man who had been both for her. A man who had
excited her and stretched her, yet who had been safe and always
there for her. That man had been her father.

"Lucky seven!" Danny exclaimed, making the champagne toast
at the small party Ellen gave for Jeff and Brenda in June of
1977 to mark their seventh anniversary.

"Lucky me!" Jeff replied. "I have Brenda," he said, and
looked at her with an expression that combined the ardor of a
suitor with the possessiveness of a husband.

"And lucky me," Brenda said with an expression of grati-
tude. "Jeff's put up with me for seven years."

Ellen intercepted the look that passed between them and
wondered how their marriage was. *Really* was. Other people's
marriages, she thought, were among the profoundest mysteries
of all.

"Well, you aren't the only lucky ones," Danny said a little
later. "I'm not doing so badly myself. Sophie just gave me a

promotion. From assistant buyer to buyer." Sophie De Witt, Danny's boss, had founded the KitchenWorks Catalog, a mail order Dean and De Luca, a Horchow's devoted exclusively to fine kitchen equipment and gourmet food items.

"That's not luck," Brenda told her brother, giving him a big hug and kiss. "That's talent!"

"She's right!" Toni said. "Danny's talented . . . and Sophie's smart. She promoted you because you earned it!"

No one mentioned the fiasco of Danny's first job out of college with Sherri Phrainer. Especially not Danny.

But Brenda's anniversary and Danny's promotion weren't all that were celebrated that day. When the second round of congratulations died down, Ellen had news of her own.

"I had a call from Countess Tamara," she said.

"For chicken kiev or beef stroganoff?" Danny teased.

"Wise guy!" Ellen teased back. "For a big deal," she explained. "Tamara wants to retire. Again. She wants to sell out. Again. To À La Carte. Again. The last time she told me that our offer was an insult!"

"Tamara's done well, hasn't she?" Brenda asked.

"That's an understatement," Ellen replied. "In addition to the Scarsdale branch, she now has branches in Greenwich, Westport, and Rye."

"What are you going to do?" asked Toni.

"I'm going to talk it over with Lew and Al. Again. If it makes sense. I'd like to make an offer."

Everyone wished Ellen good luck. Especially Toni and Brenda, who were thrilled to see another woman getting up in the world because, as they passed through their twenties, the man's world in which Ellen had grown up seemed about to become ancient history, a subject fit only for the excavation of archaeologists. The seventies promised to witness the birth of a woman's world.

In the mid-years of the nineteen seventies, worlds that had been closed to women began to open up to them—not always willingly, not always gracefully but, it seemed at the time, inevitably. Worlds that had been exclusively men's worlds were now women's worlds, too: the worlds of finance, diplomacy, religion, employment, sports, medicine, law, labor, and politics.

In 1973, plans to organize the First Women's Bank were

announced; two all-women law firms were organized; a Boeing 737 flew from Denver to St. Louis with a female flight officer—Emily Howell—a first; requirements for women in both the State Department and the army were eased; and the first female chaplain in the U.S. Armed Forces was sworn in. The Waldorf-Astoria employed its first woman chef in forty-two years, and Sarah Lawrence College was the first to offer a graduate program in women's studies. The Senate unanimously passed a bill prohibiting lenders from discriminating on the basis of sex or marital status in all credit transactions, a law that came a little too late for Ellen and a little too soon for Edwin Garren.

And, not to forget sports: Billie Jean King blasted Bobby Riggs off the court at the Astrodome. In straight sets!

In 1974, Little League Baseball allowed girls to play, President Ford urged ratification of the Equal Rights Amendment (no doubt with a little encouragement from Betty), and a Gallup Poll showed that support for the Equal Rights Amendment was 58 percent in favor and only 24 percent opposed. The number of women in medical school had doubled since the beginning of the decade, organized labor had registered a marked increase in women members, and three out of five corporation presidents said they planned to increase the number of female executives over the next five years. And, in 1974, three thousand women ran for local, state, and federal office, triple the number of candidates in 1972.

The year 1975 was designated International Women's Year. In 1976 Barbara Walters became the first woman to co-anchor a network news program. And in 1977 Jill Volner became general counsel to the Department of the Army, Rose Bird became the new Chief Justice of the California Supreme Court, Ella Grasso was in place as governor of Connecticut, and Patricia Harris became the first black woman to reach cabinet rank.

Brenda, with her tailored suits and polished briefcase and discreet makeup, seemed the very picture of a post-liberated young woman on her way up, the woman other women yearned to be, a woman who defined the aspirations of the newly emerging woman's world. She had it all—brains and beauty, career and husband—and she made it look easy.

"Because," she said, "my mother was my role model. Women like her paved the way."

And Ellen, now in her mid-forties, was at last in charge of
her business, in charge of herself, in charge of her life. There
were many who thought she had never looked better, had never
been more attractive, had never seemed so sensational.

6

ED SALOMAY WANTED A SPOT ON ENTERTAINING AT HOME. HE
wanted a woman, a cook, a good personality, but not a glamour
puss. He wanted a woman other women could relate to. Ed
Salomay was the producer of AM/USA. AM/USA was Number
One in the ratings, and what Ed Salomay wanted, Ed Salomay
got.

He wanted Paula Wolfert, but Paula was on the Coast teach-
ing. He wanted Barbara Kafka, but Barbara was in Houston
setting up the menu for a new restaurant. He wanted Eileen
Weinberg of Word of Mouth, and *she* was in town. She was
free, she agreed to appear. She would demonstrate how a working woman could entertain a group of friends after a hard day
at the office.

Eileen, good humored, relaxed, down-to-earth, a superb
cook of pungently flavored food straightforwardly presented,
would be perfect! Everything was arranged. Except that, the
night before the AM/USA limousine was to pick Eileen up for
the six A.M. makeup call, Eileen fell, most unglamorously,
while taking out the garbage. At midnight she called Ed Salomay from the Lenox Hill Hospital emergency room to tell

him she'd have to cancel. Her partner, Christi, who could have substituted, was vacationing in St. Bart's.

"Now what?" Ed asked Wilson Hoback at one A.M. Wilson was, by now, a godfather in the food establishment mafia. "The time is blocked out. I've got to find someone. You know everyone. Who do you know who can bail me out?"

At two A.M. Ellen said yes.

At three A.M. she wondered what on earth she'd gotten herself into.

At four A.M. she decided she'd dreamed it.

At five the phone rang. The woman on the other end—whose name Ellen never quite got—asked a number of questions: What was the name of Ellen's business? How long had she had it? How had she come to start it? What was the best party she'd catered? The worst? What was she planning to demonstrate on the show? The conversation was enormously pleasant—like a phone chat with a very close friend—and when it was over Ellen went into the kitchen.

At six A.M. she got into the AM/USA limo with hampers packed with food and table accessories. By ten past seven, made up, she was in the Green Room. Between seven-ten and eight-twenty-five, she went to the bathroom a dozen times. She was not the only one. The bathroom was two inches from the Green Room, and Ellen decided that whoever had designed the backstage area knew what he/she was doing.

And at eight-thirty A.M. a very pretty young woman led her over the thick ropes of cables snaking along the floor to a set made up like a kitchen/dining room. "You're on next," the young woman said. "You'll be terrific!" And she disappeared, leaving Ellen alone on the dimly lit set. The cameras, the activity, the action, were focused on the main set, where the host—whose voice was thick with a cold—did a lead-in to the national news. Ellen watched, so nervous that when she tried to press the button for the oven light to check on her moussaka, she missed the first two times.

Then the lights were on her.

Through the quaky spasms of nerves that made her palms wet and her throat dry, Ellen heard the introduction and realized with distant amazement that they were talking about her!

"The working woman's dinner party!" said the host in his nasal, raspy voice. "A dinner party you can give, without help, after a long day at the office. And it won't bust your budget!

Ellen Durban, owner of the À La Carte catering service, will show you how!"

Then, turning to Ellen whom he had never seen before in his life, he said, as if he'd known her forever, "Well, Ellen, what's for starters?"

"String beans vinaigrette," Ellen said, her own voice quavery and notes too high with nervousness. "Before you go to work in the morning you can blanche the beans, rinse them in cold running water to cool them, drain and dry them on paper towels, and refrigerate them in a covered dish. When you get home, the sauce can be made in moments just before serving."

And Ellen demonstrated how to prepare the garlic vinaigrette, mixing the mustard and vinegar and whisking in the oil to make a creamy emulsion. As she added the chopped garlic, her hands trembled, and she was sure the whole world was commenting on her nervousness as she tossed the bright green beans with the sauce.

"And that moussaka smells sensational!" said the host. "*Even* with a cold!"

"The moussaka, a combination of ground lamb and eggplant, topped with yogurt, eggs, and cheese, can be assembled the night before the party and baked an hour before dinner is served," Ellen said as she slid the gorgeously browned moussaka out of the studio oven. By now concentrating on what she was saying and doing, Ellen was barely aware of the big camera as it dollied in for a closeup of the moussaka. "Serve it with some hot pita bread—which can be warmed in the same oven as the moussaka—and a cucumber-and-scallion salad, and you'll have an easy-to-make, economical, delicious dinner for eight."

Ellen took the baking dish with the moussaka into the dining room part of the set. She had already set the table with inexpensive blue-and-white pottery dishes, bright blue napkins, and a bunch of blue-and-white cornflowers.

"There are some very good—and inexpensive—Greek wines," Ellen said as she served a portion of the moussaka. "A Rodytis rosé is a wine everyone loves. And for the adventurous, try a retsina."

"Ellen's dinner," the announcer said, "will serve eight people for about twenty-five dollars. And in these double-digit inflation days, that's good!"

As Ellen worked with food and moved around the set, she forgot her nervousness and the bright lights and the unfamiliar feeling of the television makeup. And when the host, sampling the moussaka and declaring it wonderful, asked her for her theories about what makes parties good—and bad—she answered as if she had known *him* forever.

"One thing and one thing only: people," Ellen said, showing the layers of eggplant, seasoned lamb, and brown, bubbling topping to the camera that had wheeled in for another closeup. "You can have the best food, the most beautiful flowers, the most expensive wines, but the fact is that people make the party. Boring people make boring parties. Interesting people make interesting parties."

"You're right about that! I've been to both kinds—lethally boring champagne and caviar parties and sensational parties where we ate spaghetti on the floor," said the host. "And there's something else I want to ask. I'm the world's most nervous host—at home, not on a set," he added and smiled into the camera, a sexy, boy-next-door smile. "I *always* think there's going to be a disaster. What do you do? Not, I'm sure, that you've *had* a disaster."

"Have I ever!" said Ellen and smiled for the first time, a genuine, amused smile at the thought of Reinhardt Estes. "It was the first really important party I ever catered. I was young and inexperienced and even more nervous than I am now. The oven had broken, and there was no way I could cook the dinner. I panicked. By the time I got the dinner together—and it wasn't very good, either—the cocktail hour had gone on for over an hour and a half, the guests were half-drunk and famished, and I ran out of food!

"Running out of food is the caterer's all-time number one nightmare. What I should have done was heat up small batches of the main-course chicken, cut it into pieces, and served it as hot hors d'oeuvres on toast while I found the nearest restaurant where I could send someone to buy food. I could then have doctored it the best I could and served it with aplomb. People wouldn't have had so much time to drink, they wouldn't have been famished, and *I* wouldn't have run out of food! The trouble was that I was desperate to impress . . . and trying to impress is practically a guarantee of a party disaster."

"Sensational working woman's dinner! Sensational moussaka. Sensational salad. The crew is going to love this!" the host said and then led in to the teasers and commercial break. The lights went down on the set, the host thanked Ellen and moved away briskly to the next interview. Ellen stood alone in the again-dim set, unsure of what to do.

"I hope my wife paid attention," one of the cameramen said. "She's the most nervous hostess in the world. In fact, we almost never have anyone to the house she's so nervous."

"Do you think people could see how nervous I was?" Ellen asked anxiously.

"Only in the beginning," said the cameraman. "You calmed down."

"Being nervous is a plus," said the young woman who had led Ellen onto the set. "When people see that you're nervous, they're on your side. They know *they'd* be nervous, too. And I loved what you said about trying to impress."

She led Ellen back off the set, warning her to watch out for the thick coils of cable. Two minutes later one of the stagehands returned Ellen's pottery, napkins, and glassware to her, all carefully packed; and a few minutes later she was back on the street, her hampers on the sidewalk next to her, frantically trying to flag a taxi, competing with the rest of the rush-hour travelers.

She no longer had a long limousine waiting, no longer was the center of attention, professionally made up, spotlighted by the glare of bright lights, her opinions flatteringly courted. She now was just another New Yorker trying like hell to get a cab.

When Ellen got home, the phone was ringing off the hook. Brenda called from Phoenix, where she was visiting an All Chem branch, and Danny called from Chicago, where he was attending a small appliances regional trade show. Caroline, who had skipped her exercise class to watch AM/USA, called, and so did people Ellen hadn't heard from since high school. Her dentist's receptionist called, as did at least twenty-five clients, Jak Busch, Jimmy Mattison, Toni Reese's mother, and Danny's boss Sophie De Witt. Countess Tamara called from a diet week at La Costa.

That afternoon flowers came from Wilson and a magnum of champagne from Lew. Ellen had the feeling that the whole world watched AM/USA.

Maybe not the whole world but a good portion of it. Including Johanna Swann, who looked at Ellen, then looked at herself, and didn't like what she saw.

Johanna had always thought of herself as a man's woman—

and now, for the first time she could remember, she was without a man. And it was hard to tell whether Max had said, "Get out!" before Johanna had said, "I'm leaving!" Or vice versa.

The story of Max and Johanna's love affair and subsequent marriage was a story of making up and breaking up. They both loved to fight—in public, in private, in the office, and at the apartment that, early in their affair, Max had rented for Johanna in Gramercy Park—and then make up in bed.

The worse the fight, the better the sex.

Everything would have been perfect—except that Max and Johanna decided to get married. A fatal—and classic—mistake.

The sexy, passionate, jealous lover cheating on a wife he felt guilty toward turned into another tired businessman-husband who wanted only a hot meal and a few hours in front of the TV night after night. Johanna began to get the feeling she was disappearing into the wallpaper.

She quickly found two ways to get Max's attention: one was by spending ferocious amounts of money; the other was by sleeping with other men.

The fireworks of fighting, making up, and breaking up quickly became routine. Not a week went by when they didn't talk about or actually threaten divorce; not a week went by without Max buying Johanna a lavish present; not a week went by without broken dishes and passionate sex. The last fight, at first, didn't seem much different from the rest of the fights.

Johanna had followed an afternoon at Bendel's fur department with a *cinq à sept* quickie. Max got home to an empty apartment. He was tired; he was hungry; he wanted dinner. Johanna wafted in smelling of sex and Bal à Versailles.

The usual accusations were countered by the usual counter-accusations; the usual threats were countered with the usual counter-threats; the usual curses and name calling hurled around the room. Broken dishes and sex would be next, except that Max departed from the script.

"I'm bored with fighting, Johanna," he said suddenly, almost visibly deflating. "I'm sick of it, and I'm sick of you."

"And I'm sick of you and your indifference. I wanted a lover and I got a husband. Why don't you go back to Esme? She'll put up with your crap and see to it that you get your precious hot dinner every night."

"Maybe I will," said Max. The memory of his tranquil marriage had a suddenly magnetic nostalgic allure.

"You wouldn't!" Johanna flared. "You wouldn't dare!"

"Oh, yes, I would," Max said. "Right now it sounds like a very good idea." He got up to put on his coat. Johanna beat him to the foyer closet and pulled the coat out of his hands. She raced out to the incinerator and dumped the coat into it, Max following close on her heels.

"Get out of here, you bitch!" he screamed and slammed the door to the apartment shut, locking Johanna out.

"I'm leaving!" she screamed and punched the elevator button. It was early December, cold, Johanna had no coat, and she didn't care.

The smell of burning fabric permeated the building. The neighbors, long used to the screams and curses coming from 9-D, just turned up their television sets a little louder and got out the Airwick.

Johanna bought herself a three-room co-op on Park and Eighty-third and had the bills for its purchase and decoration sent to Max, who screamed and yelled and swore he'd never pay them. He and Johanna made up in their usual way at the new apartment.

"I've got a lawyer," Johanna told him when they were sharing a post-O cigarette. "I want a divorce."

"Me, too," said Max, stroking her hair. "Maybe we'll get along a little better."

"What did my husband say when you turned down his offer?" Johanna asked her lawyer, Mel Factir, the week before she saw Ellen on AM/USA. Max had offered a lump-sum settlement of three hundred thousand dollars.

"He raised it to half a million," Mel reported.

"That's ridiculous!" Johanna said. "His first wife got a million."

"I don't think he's going to go much higher," Mel said.

"Do you think I should accept it?" Johanna asked. Money had always been a sore point with her. Although her mother had started the family box-and-carton business, when she died she left it to her husband and Johanna's brothers, excluding Johanna, a final rejection Johanna had never really been able to forgive. Her mother, an excellent businesswoman, had no confidence in women—a paradox that cost Johanna her share of an inheritance *and* an eternal, almost-but-not-quite-hidden doubt about whether or not her mother might have been right. Johanna was possessed with the deep, angry feeling that *someone somewhere* owed her something, that she had been cheated, and that it was up to the world to make it up to her. Right now the world was Max Swann.

"That's a decision you'll have to make yourself," Mel advised.

"Let me think it over," Johanna said.

When she saw Ellen on AM/USA, Johanna's old angers and resentments stirred. Ellen was successful, À La Carte was successful. Ellen looked better than Johanna had ever seen her look (probably due to the studio makeup man, Johanna quickly told herself), and now she was a celebrity.

Ellen had everything, and she, Johanna—who was at least as pretty, at least as smart, at least as ambitious—had nothing.

No husband.

No money.

No lovers.

No status.

The men who had swarmed around her when she had been Mrs. Maximilian Swann had disappeared like cockroaches diving for a dark hole the moment word of her separation and impending divorce began to get around.

There was no reason Ellen Durban should have everything and she, Johanna, should have nothing. The moment Ellen's face faded from the Sony, Johanna telephoned Mel Factir.

"I've made up my mind," Johanna said. "Tell Max I'll accept his offer."

But there was a silent "but." Johanna would accept the cash offer, *but* she also wanted a share of Max's businesses, too: the shopping malls in four states; the chain of real estate brokerages; condominiums in New York, Fort Lauderdale, and Phoenix. They generated plenty of money, and there was no reason Johanna shouldn't have her share.

Johanna planned her strategy like Cleopatra snaring Caesar, like Liz trapping Dick: she would get Max to a meeting, pick a fight, make up over champagne and sex, and then, when Max remembered how much he still loved her, she'd spring her additional demand.

By the time Johanna left her apartment for her session with Patrick at Pilates—she was scheduled after Jill Clayburgh and before Candy Bergen—she felt pretty good about herself. After all, she was looking a million dollars straight in the eye.

And what did Ellen Durban have? A crappy four-minute one-shot on AM/USA that left her hands smelling of garlic.

The reaction Ellen got to her appearance, while gratifying, didn't mean anything. The reaction the show got meant plenty.

People wrote to the network and telephoned. They wanted menu ideas and table-setting ideas; they wanted advice on how to cope with drunks, bores, prima donnas, burnt roasts, underdone potatoes, unexpected guests, unanswered RSVPs, and other party dilemmas.

People liked Ellen, and they responded to her. Her admission of panic and failure turned out to be a stroke of genius—people could see themselves in Ellen and realized that if she could cope, they could cope.

The mail was forwarded to Ellen, and she answered it all. A month after her first appearance, Ed Salomay called to invite her back on the show.

7

By the spring of 1978, it was difficult—if not impossible—to wallpaper a dining room, paint an entrance hall, recover a sofa, tile a kitchen, mirror a bathroom, or install new carpeting without Lewis Swann. No sumptuous four-color spread appeared in *Architectural Digest* without a fabric, a wall covering, or flooring manufactured by Decor or a Decor subsidiary. Hardly an issue of *House & Garden* or *House Beautiful* appeared without featuring a new tile, a new line of paints or lacquers, a new color choice in blinds manufactured by Decor or one of its subsidiaries.

The home-furnishings empire of Decor now covered the entire spectrum of home furnishings, ranging all the way up and down the price and quality scales from class to mass. Over the years, Lew had created a major-league home-furnishings conglomerate by buying companies and changing their management, if necessary. He then hired big-name designers to redesign and upgrade the line, and followed this up with aggressive promotion and advertising campaigns to promote the restructured subsidiaries.

In the early sixties, Decor had been a little family company worth maybe a quarter of a million dollars on a good day to

239

the right buyer. It was now, to Max's eagle eye, a little seven-million-dollar company—using a conservative accountant—and definitely not for sale on any day to any buyer. Although to Max Decor was still kid stuff, he was impressed by the success Lew had made of Decor. And, in his opinion, there was one reason for that success, and that reason was Ellen Durban.

"He never had the balls to think big until you came along," Max told Ellen in his inimitable way.

"Has it ever occurred to you," Ellen replied, "that I came along at about the same moment you moved on to bigger and better things and left Lew alone?"

"Never thought of it," Max agreed and laughed. "You're probably right..." he admitted and then added, "You're terrific, Ellen. You're the best thing that ever happened to Lew."

"You're only saying that because À La Carte is making money for Decor, too." Teasing Max Swann had become one of the pleasures of Ellen's life.

"Probably," Max said. "Nothing turns me on like the bottom line."

Ellen raised her eyebrows, thinking that there were most certainly "other things" that turned Max on. But *that* wasn't a conversation she wanted to get into with him, and she kept her mouth shut.

And the fact was that as Decor had grown, so had À La Carte. If Ellen had been the positive influence on Lew, helping him to "think big," then Lew had been the positive influence on Ellen, helping her to expand À La Carte. The negotiations with Countess Tamara had just been concluded, adding Tamara's five branches to À La Carte. (Tamara was retiring to Palm Springs with her sixth husband.) And, in a surprising development, Lew and Ellen had just been offered the opportunity to buy out KitchenWorks, an offer they were seriously considering.

The business Ellen had started in desperation in her own kitchen was now worth three quarters of a million dollars, which was staggering to her, impressive to Lew and Al, but peanuts to Max.

On the same morning that Ellen appeared for the second time on AM/USA, Lew and Max had breakfast together in the co-op Max had once shared with Johanna. The *Times* was spread over the table, turned to the financial pages; the television set was on, the volume turned off. Max was breakfasting on a redolent and raunchy goat cheese on onion rye(!) while Lew confined himself to an English muffin and tea.

"Johanna and I are meeting at the lawyer's today," Max said. "She's finally accepted my offer. Five hundred thou, no alimony, no bullshit, no nothing. I told her, invest it at seventeen percent, and you've got eighty grand a year. Even *you* can live on that."

"Good," said Lew. "It's about time you two came to an agreement and moved on to other things." Max and Johanna had been torturing each other over money for almost three years. Enough was enough.

"I suppose you're right," Max said reluctantly. "The problem is we really like to fight."

"You don't have to stay married for that," Lew observed tartly. "Ellen..." he said as he turned up the sound.

"A caterer... a mother... a hostess... a working woman," went the introduction. "You've met her before on AM/USA ... Ellen Durban..."

"I used to think it was too bad things didn't work out for you two," Max said, slathering a last piece of onion rye with chèvre, "but maybe you're better off staying with one wife."

"I think so," Lew said. His marriage was better than ever. And it was better than ever because his affair with Ellen made him realize that he had put all of his energy into his business and damn little into his marriage. "Reenie and I have been doing a little work on our marriage, and it's paid off. We've rarely been happier."

Max looked at Lew and thought that of the two of them, it was Lew who had the real balls.

"Ed Salomay asked me if I had an agent! Can you believe it?" Ellen chortled one morning a few hours after her fourth AM/USA appearance. "Well, I didn't miss a beat! Al Sheldrock, I told him. Al, you *will* be my agent, won't you?" Ellen leaned forward, putting her elbows on Al's desk, grinning a smile a mile wide, waiting for his answer, pretty sure of what it would be. "Well?"

Ellen had not entered Al's office so much as she had floated in, almost touching the ceiling. She was, she didn't have to tell Al, as high as a kite. That morning, after her spot was

over, Ed Salomay had approached her about doing a regular
weekly segment on entertaining at home.

"I'll not only be your agent, Ellen, but I'd be grossly insulted
if you hadn't asked me," Al said. He, too, leaned forward in
his chair, resting his forearms on the desk top. Ellen approved
of the dark worsted suit, the good-looking navy-and-white tie
with the discreet crimson stripe, the handsome Tiffany corded
cuff links. Al had good taste. And Al was a brick, always
there, always reliable, someone Ellen had leaned on, over and
over, through the years. He was, Ellen had told him many
times, the best thing she had inherited from Phil.

"AM/USA!" Ellen gloated. "Can you *believe* it? Can you?"
A television star! At forty-seven! A smashing, energetic, pulled-
together forty-seven!

Ellen had never felt better in her entire life, and she wondered, sometimes, why women ever worried for an *instant*
about turning forty. They ought to get down on their knees.
The anxieties of the twenties. Gone. The overload of the thirties. Forgotten. The forties were, as the kids used to say, where
it was at.

Ellen's excitement communicated itself to Al, not only in
her words and her glow but in the airwaves that passed between
them. Ellen was, as the French say, a woman of a certain age.
And she dazzled Al. A dozen times he had wanted to invite
her to dinner, and a dozen times he had hesitated. He had
hesitated because of the way she treated him—with a certain
casual sisterliness, a definite sexlessness. He sensed that although Ellen liked him very much, she did not consider him
sexually attractive, and that knowledge had always stopped Al
short. But even as he admired her and even as he wondered
what there was about him that turned her off, he was thinking
about how to get the best deal for her.

"AM/USA," he said thoughtfully. "I love it! They've been
beating Wake Up, America by two ratings points. That's a
bundle of viewers. That's a few million in revenues. And, as
fate would have it, I'm having lunch today with Hank Roman."

"Who's Hank Roman?"

"Producer of Wake Up, America."

"But I've been appearing on AM/USA . . ." Ellen said, confused.

"Ellen, do me a favor," Al asked, settling back, already
mapping out his plan of manipulation and escalation. "Go home

to your kitchen. Lose yourself in *vol-au-vent aux fruits de mer*. Abandon yourself to *bar rayé poché au fenouil*. You want me to be your agent, you let me handle things. Is that a deal?"

"It's a deal," Ellen said, her eyes shooting sparks. She smiled. It was the two of them against the mighty millions of the network, its phalanxes of vice-presidents and battalions of lawyers. She loved it! "By the way, Al," she asked suddenly, "where did you learn such perfect French?"

"The Bronx."

He paused, savoring Ellen's double-take. But before she could put it into words, Al explained:

"The family next door was from Aix-en-Provence. I had a crush on their daughter. She spoke French to me while we necked in the back seat of her father's Oldsmobile."

Ellen giggled and blushed and left Al's office trailing waves of excitement and allure.

And, oh, yes! She was sexy, too.

On her way from Al's office to Grand Central, Ellen passed the Waldorf-Astoria. She did not know, had no way of knowing, that as she passed, Max Swann in Suite 1207 was on the phone to Room Service ordering Dom Perignon and caviar while Johanna was in the marble-and-mirror bathroom changing into something more comfortable. And, even if she had known, she wouldn't have cared. After all, what did Max and Johanna's private life have to do with her?

Mel Factir's office had been the scene of a screaming argument. Face to face with Max and his insulting, cheap-o offer, Johanna's careful plans were forgotten.

"Five hundred thou! Period! That's the deal, Johanna. Take it or leave it!" Max was beet red; a vein throbbed in his temple.

"Five hundred thou *plus* a percentage of the businesses: the condos, the shopping malls, the brokerages. I helped you get them," Johanna said in a voice like nails. "I *earned* a share."

"You were a secretary," Max shouted.

"An assistant," Johanna snarled.

"An assistant!" Max sneered. "Like hell!"

"I took care of the day-to-day nitty-gritty and left you free to wheel and deal," Johanna persisted.

"You gave me blow jobs so I could relax and get some sleep at night," Max corrected, trying to put things in their proper perspective. "Five hundred thou—and that's it! World's most expensive blow jobs!"

Mel sat there, a bland, noncommittal expression on his bland, noncommittal lawyer's face. Even when, faster than the speed of light, the screaming suddenly stopped.

"Gee, your hair looks terrific," Max said, reaching out to touch Johanna's cloud of hair (Gold Desert Sand), a split second after he had vowed that she'd never get a red penny out of him.

"Thanks, Max," Johanna smiled. "I got rid of William. I'm going to someone new now. Hiroko. He's at Suga. He's thinking of setting up his own shop."

"Not on my money!" Max warned, wondering what this Hiroko was doing for Johanna besides her hair. This business about heterosexual hairdressers! Max fondly remembered the good old days when hairdressers were a bunch of *fegelahs* and a man didn't have to worry when his wife said she was going to the beauty parlor.

"Why not on your money?" Johanna countered. And then, sugary, sweet: "After all, your money is my money. Or *will* be."

"Over my dead body!"

Mel's bland noncommittal expression stayed firmly in place through the venomous exchange that followed and even a little later, too, when Max and Johanna, their business left unresolved, the settlement papers left unsigned, left Mel's office hand in hand, trying to decide whether they preferred the St. Regis or the Waldorf.

But the instant Max got home he called his lawyer.

"That bitch wants a share of businesses," Max said. "I don't care what you do but lock 'em up, hide 'em, bury 'em!"

And locked, hidden, buried they were. The shopping malls disappeared into Bahamian corporations. The condos were re-registered in the names of untraceable nominees. The chain of real estate brokerages were insulated through three layers of Swiss, Andorran, and Lebanese corporations.

Johanna, Max told Lew, would have an easier time finding an ice cube in hell than a stray dime in the corporate affairs of Max Swann. In fact, Max confided, he was thinking of rescinding the five-hundred-thousand-dollar offer.

"It'll drive her crazy," Max said, chortling at the prospect.

"I'd be careful if I were you," Lew warned. "Johanna's greedy—and she's mean..."

The two points Wake Up, America had lost to AM/USA showed in the two martinis Hank Roman had for lunch and the two Tums he chewed for chasers. Hank was usually a one-Perrier man.

"Things that bad?" Al asked when the execu-lunches of grilled fish and watercress (at $16.50 a pop) arrived, and Hank ignored him, diving instead into the bread basket, spreading a sesame-seed breadstick with a thick slab of butter. Any executive who ate one calorie over three hundred at an expense-account lunch was parading his anxieties.

"Things aren't good," Hank admitted. "We keep trying to goose up the show. We've booked dog psychiatrists, a state senator's wife who teaches belly dancing in Albany, a horoscope/diet authority. Name 'em, we've had 'em. The freaks, the show-offs, the nuts. You know, your basic media mix. The moral majority and the immoral minority. Nothing works," Hank said in frustration, buttering a second breadstick. "Goddamn AM/USA! They're not doing much of anything we're not doing. I just can't understand it..." Hank began to eat the breadstick sideways, as if it were an ear of corn, gleaning the sesame seeds with his teeth.

"I know something—someone—AM/USA has that you don't," Al said, nibbling his grilled sole, knowing that at four o'clock he'd order up an English muffin to stave off the pangs of starvation that resulted from execu-eating.

"Who?" Hank asked, and before Al could answer, Hank said, "Well, I want him. Name a number."

"How do you know it's a 'him'?" Al asked. "It could be a man-eating parakeet."

"Come on, Al. Don't shit me." Hank attacked a third breadstick and signaled the waiter for more butter. "Who is it?"

Al talked about the Rangers, the prospects for the CBS cable station, and whether or not the affiliates would be able to block the proposed hour-long evening news. The two men finished coffee, and Hank signed the bill.

"So who is it?" Hank asked again as they parted in front of the restaurant.

"What difference does it make?" Al answered. "AM/USA

has the inside track anyway. So long, Hank," Al said and hailed the cab that happened to be passing and got in.

He spent the next hour and a half with a studio musician client who remembered Al's parents from the old days, and by the time Al got back to his office there were two phone messages from Hank Roman.

Urgent!

Al tucked the messages neatly into his desk blotter, called the coffee shop downstairs, ordered a toasted English, and, while he enjoyed it, returned Hank's call.

"Ellen Durban! That's who!" Hank practically yelled. "I looked at all the AM/USA tapes for the last six months. That's who! Okay, Al, you've got me. What do you want for her?"

Al and Hank backed and forthed on the phone for a while, and when Al got the bid up as high as Hank could go without getting upstairs' approval, he called Ed Salomay.

"Ed? I'm afraid you've got competition for Ellen Durban . . ."

Al leaned back in his chair and continued to talk to Ed. He couldn't believe how much he loved his work. It was almost illegal!

8

His professional life was, Al thought, compensation for his personal life. In 1973, Gail had come home from her consciousness-raising group and told Al that she had an announcement to make. The announcement, delivered in a flat tone of voice, was, in fact, an accusation. An accusation that Gail felt frustrated and unexpressed and unfulfilled, and that it was Al's fault.

"I gave up a promising career for you," Gail accused. "In the process I've become a second-class citizen, a support system for you and your glorious career. Marriage has reduced me to being a member of the service class," she said.

"But I wanted you to take your CPA exam," Al said, bewildered, resentful. Women's liberation seemed to have brought out an almost bottomless reservoir of rage in Gail.

"Your verbal message was one thing," Gail had said. "Your emotional message was another! I'm going to continue at Pace full-time. I'm going to get my CPA."

And before Al could say that he hardly objected, that he was, in fact, in favor of it and always had been, Gail informed him that she also wanted a divorce.

"I'll expect you to support the children," Gail said. "I,

myself, don't want a cent from you. I want to be my own person," she had bravely announced, and within the week she had moved out, into a two-bedroom apartment in Brooklyn Heights, and began attending Pace fulltime. It was a plan of action that had been developed with the advice, consent, and support of her women's group.

By the time Al got over the shock, the divorce had been granted. The children, now fifteen and sixteen, moved in with Gail, and Al found himself rattling around in the Long Island split-level they had bought two years after they married. Al sold the house for a staggering profit and rented an apartment in the city, in a comfortable but undistinguished building very far east on Sixty-second Street. Al, numb for almost three years after Gail's life-shattering announcement, was the envy of his married friends.

"Boy, those stewardesses and those gorgeous models! Hot stuff, Al!" they said, practically drooling.

When Al tried to tell them that the stewardesses usually had a boyfriend in each of the cities they regularly flew into and that he wasn't interested in a share-the-stew plan, his friends didn't want to hear it. And when he tried to tell them that the gorgeous models he met at Jim McMullen's or George Martin's tended to be sub-monosyllabic, they didn't want to hear that, either.

They wanted their fantasies; they didn't want to listen to Al's realities about the women he dated, the walking wounded.

There was the woman—a vice-president of a corporate public relations firm—with whom Al had had a brief affair. She owned a spectacular penthouse on Central Park West with magical views of Fifth Avenue, Central Park, and the Hudson River. She had had it custom-designed for her by one of the city's top architects. The result—subtly and elegantly furnished, with flattering recessed lighting, a glassed-in greenhouse-terrace, a stunning collection of Cambodian sculpture in lighted niches—had been featured in *Architectural Digest*. Yet the woman lived in a furnished apartment in a residential hotel on West Fifty-eighth Street. When Al asked her why she didn't live in her own beautiful apartment, she told him that the apartment "scared her," that it was "too much of a commitment," and she "wasn't ready for commitment..."

And another: A real estate broker who traded blue-chip townhouses and Park and Fifth Avenue co-ops and earned a yearly salary in the high six figures. Every night before she could go to sleep—even with a man in her bed—she called her mother and filled her in on every single detail of her day from the status of current negotiations to the details of what she had worn and eaten.

There were women who wanted a proposal of marriage after one date; women who wanted to keep Al on "hold" until their current affair either broke up or ended in marriage; women who would have wild sex with Al but who wouldn't sleep over; women who wouldn't confirm a date until very late the same afternoon, holding themselves open, Al knew, in case someone better turned up; women who were more interested in his bank balance than in him; women who accused him of being gay if he didn't make a pass on the first date; and women who accused him of being "just like all men—interested in only one thing" if he did.

The glossy, assured exteriors of the dynamic career women Al met did not fit in with the ragged and anxiety-dogged interiors. They seemed to be fighting battles they'd already won. They were women in conflict—not with the outside world but with themselves—and by the time Al had been divorced for five years, he was beginning to feel a little battle-scarred.

But he was aware of his own conflicts. He wanted a woman who could be a partner, who was independent, yet who was loving and who needed him the way he would want to need her. Did such a woman exist? And, if she did, would she want *him*?

It seemed to Al that most of the successful people he met were fairly unhappy, and he did not exclude himself. The problem was that he did not know what to do to change things. It seemed to be a fact of modern life: if your professional life was successful, your personal life went to hell.

And vice versa.

It seemed to be the curse of the age.

"Now that we've settled Ellen's salary, we can start the negotiations," Al told Irving Gold, the AM/USA lawyer who handled the talent contracts. Now that Al was down to the nitty-gritty with AM/USA, the execu-lunch stage was a thing of the past. Al and Irving were lunching on matzoh ball soup and lean pastrami at the Carnegie Deli. A bowl of sour pickles had been shoved aside for the papers they had spread out on the table. (No one ever pulled out a piece of paper bigger than a business card at a four-star execu-lunch.)

"I think AM/USA ought to take out ads to introduce Ellen's spots as a regular feature. The *Times*, the *News*, the *Washington Post*, and the L.A. *Times*. The Chicago *Trib*, too," Al said. "And *Variety* and the *Hollywood Reporter* go without saying."

"*Oy*," said Irving who ate his pastrami on rye from the crust on in. He liked the crust best.

"And I want a firm commitment from the promotion department. Ellen ought to be interviewed. She's a natural for the women's magazines, the supermarket magazines, the TV pages, and the food pages, of course."

"Of course," repeated Irving, mimicking Al's inflection. Irving was shortish, fatish, tigerish.

"Does that mean you agree?" Al asked.

"You know better than that," Irving said in a schoolteacherish tone. "It means '*oy*.'"

Irving and Al had negotiated dozens of contracts. They had the ritual down to an art form. They were now in the stage Al called the *oy* stage. It lasted for about two weeks. Then they'd graduate to the "budget-won't-go-for-it" stage, which would take another ten days or so. Al would then indicate, discreetly, that Wake Up, America was still hovering in the wings. *Their* budget might not be so tight.

They would then go into the straight horse-trading stage, which would result in Al getting a good half of what he asked in terms of promotion and advertising, and giving, in return, another six months' leeway in AM/USA's option-renewal period.

Al knew it; Irving knew it. But they had to go through the gavotte anyway. It was what Irving got paid for; it was what Al got paid for. It was the way things worked.

Irving finished his Dr. Browns, picked up the notes he had made of Al's demands, and said, "I'll get back to you tomorrow."

Al nodded.

"You know you're asking for the moon," Irving said. "No one's ever heard of Ellen Durban."

"But they will," Al smiled. "Thanks to AM/USA."

"What does she do anyway? Sing? Or play an instrument?" Irving was used to Al's musical clients.

"She's a cook and a caterer," Al said. "Don't you watch the shows you represent?"

"Who's got the time?" Irving said, putting the papers into a bulging briefcase. "Ellen Durban," he repeated. "Never heard of her."

"She's going to be the next Julia Child," Al promised.

"Terrific," said Irving gloomily. "It means my wife will go out and spend another five hundred dollars on fancy pots and pans she'll never use."

"Well"—Al smiled, leaving Irving—"who said it's a perfect world?"

"Five hundred dollars a spot! Two spots a week! That's a thousand dollars a week!" Ellen almost fainted.

"You don't think I'm going to let you work for scale, do you?" Al asked. And then he told her about scale: "Scale is what some dummy out of a nowhere journalism school with two years at a nothing station gets as a general assignment reporter."

"General assignment?" Al's show-biz jargon was Greek to Ellen.

"Yeah," Al said. "You know, the schmuck who pushes a microphone into the face of a woman whose husband and three children have just died in an automobile accident and asks, 'How do you feel?' That's general assignment."

"Oh," said Ellen, still trying to get used to the idea of a thousand dollars a week for thirteen weeks. *With*, Al had told her, options for four additional thirteen-week cycles. "A thousand dollars a week! That's a fortune!"

"You'd better get used to it," Al said, "because when they want to renew, your price goes nowhere but up. Way up . . ."

A week later:

"It's found money, Al," Ellen said, referring to her AM/ USA salary. "I don't want just to spend it and have it disappear. What would you think if I put it into a money market fund?" Ever since she and Lew had bought out Countess Tamara's business, Ellen had been reading the financial pages, something she had never done in her life. Something, she realized, that would have floored Phil—and rightly so.

"I think it's an excellent idea," Al said, wishing more of his clients made an effort to know a little bit about finance. So many people knew how to earn money but had never given a second's thought about what to do with it once they had it.

"You know, Al, I come from a poor family. I've never had any money in my life. Never," Ellen said. "Everything I earned at À La Carte went into supporting myself and the kids, and whatever was left over—and in the early years nothing was left over—went right back into the business. It feels nice to have some extra money," she confessed with an odd and appealing shyness, revealing a side of herself Al had never seen, a side that made her seem even more attractive than ever to him.

As she finished speaking, the telephone rang, and Al excused himself for a brief conversation.

"I've been stood up," he said when he hung up. "My date tonight had a better offer. So I have an extra ticket for the Rangers-Islanders game. Would you like to go?"

"I've never been to a hockey game," Ellen said. "I'd love to go, though. But I want to warn you that I don't know a thing about hockey."

"That's okay. Anything you need to know, I'll tell you. All you have to do is hope the fight is on our end of the rink."

"Al! I didn't know you were violent!"

Al winked at her and smiled. "How do you think I got you the thousand a week?"

When Al took her home that night and didn't kiss her goodnight, Ellen found, to her absolute amazement, that she had—without even knowing it—wanted him to. When, she asked herself, had she stopped thinking of him as good-old-pal/niceguy Al and begun to realize that Al was quite a sexy cat? What, she asked herself, was going on here?

What was she doing being attracted to a nice man? A man who, unlike Wilson, did not offer conflict and difficulty. A man who, unlike Lew, was available.

9

"ALL CHEM'S SHARE OF THE GERMAN MARKET HAS GONE UP fourteen percent in the last year," Sid Erlau told Brenda. German business, she knew, was highly desirable because the hard German mark was increasingly valuable against the inflation-eroded dollar. German-derived business weighed heavily in All Chem's annual balance sheet. "We want to open another German plant. In Munich. We'd like you to head up the lab side of things."

Sid paused and hunched his neck into his shoulders, like a bull about to charge. "How does the idea strike you?"

"Interesting," said Brenda, having learned from Heinrich Leben the value of not putting her cards on the table. "Can you fill me in on the specifics? Job description, salary, title, length of time overseas?"

Sid laid it out for her. The job would entail setting up the lab operations—she'd use the existing All Chem lab in Frankfurt as a model; the salary would be $27,500 plus bonuses; the title would be director of laboratory operations; the length of time overseas would be three months with three weeks back in the States, all travel paid by All Chem.

"I'd like some time to think it over," Brenda said, businesslike but positive. "It sounds very challenging."

"Good. Take your time. It's a big decision," Sid said. "Big for you. Big for us. I'm going out on a limb for you, Brenda."

He dismissed her, mixed emotions on her face. If she did well, he would look very good. They'd trot her out at every big All Chem meeting; there'd be positive press coverage; the PR department would make hay out of it; the brass would preen; and Sid Erlau would get the credit. If she didn't do well, he'd take the heat. Management felt that women were being pushed down their throats; and, although they had no choice but to go along with equal-employment acts and had hired three women—two chemists and an M.B.A. at Brenda's recommendation—they still didn't have to like it. And they didn't.

The bottom line was that Sid Erlau took a chance on Brenda because he thought she would do fine, just fine. She had so far turned out to be a real winner. There had never been the slightest sign that she was anything but an upfront broad.

Brenda left Sid's office knowing exactly what he was thinking. She was twenty-eight. If she took the offer, she'd not only be the youngest lab manager in all of All Chem, she'd also be the only female lab manager. It was exactly the kind of career starburst she and Toni had fantasized about since college.

Brenda could see herself getting on and off jets, heading up meetings at big rosewood conference tables, giving dictation to efficient secretaries—half of them female, half of them male. And she'd definitely be the first to reach thirty before thirty!

She told Sid she'd take the job. Not that he—or she—had ever had any real doubts. And she began to prepare her assistant—Diane Wyre, a chemist whose career she had mentored since she'd first met Diane at Radcliffe when she was touring campuses for MedLabs—to take over her own job.

And yet, yet . . .

Now that the moon and stars on a silver platter were being offered to her, she reacted with a divided self that surprised her. Half of her wanted to reach out and grab; the other half drew back as if from an unexploded and armed bomb.

"Now that I've almost got what I've always wanted, what do I do? There's still time. I can still back out. Say I've changed my mind," she told Toni. Toni had come to Boston for the weekend. Tuck was in Houston, where an oil client was engaged in a $250-million lawsuit over drilling rights in the Nevada Overthrust Belt. Toni, always quick, hesitated for a moment.

"Two years ago I would have said grab it. Even a year ago. But now...I don't know what to tell you. It depends. How does Jeff feel?"

"He says I should do whatever will make me happy," Brenda said, knowing that part of her resented Jeff for not being more demanding, more possessive, knowing at the same time that her resentment was irrational. After all, she and Jeff had married with the understanding that each would have maximum freedom. Now the freedom she had insisted on was beginning to feel like *too* much freedom. "The trouble is" she continued, "that I need him *and* my job to be happy. If I go to Munich, I can't be with him. It's not as if Jeff can move with me. It's not worth it for three months. Besides, he's licensed to practice here, not in Germany. What would he do? Be a lab assistant? I can't ask him to do that." Brenda shrugged slightly, a gesture of unhappiness, of bleakness. She wanted the job. She wanted Jeff.

"Tuck wants me to stop traveling," Toni said. She spoke with a wistfulness, a softness that was new to her. "He says I'm away so much he might as well be single again. He said we saw more of each other when we were living together. I reminded him that when we were living together, I was an office grunt, crunching numbers.

"Now I'm a head researcher with a specialty in high-tech companies. Most of which, unfortunately, are on the West Coast. I earn as much as Tuck, and I spend most of my money on long-distance phone calls to him." Toni laughed, but it wasn't a happy laugh or a bitter laugh. She had passed through the easy response of bitterness to the complexities of irony. "This weekend *I'm* home and *he's* in Houston. Whenever we're in the same city at the same time, we're happy. Unfortunately, we're not in the same city all that often." Toni paused. It seemed as if she were going to continue, and then, visibly, made up her mind not to say whatever she had been about to say.

"Is everything all right...with you two?" Brenda asked. She wondered what Toni had been about to say.

"No, not really," Toni admitted. "Tuck wants me to quit

my job and find something that doesn't involve so much traveling. But I worked very, very hard and put up with an awful lot of shit to get where I am. I'm not about to give it up." Toni made a reaching, a searching gesture with her hand.

"Brenda, I just don't know what to tell you. I can just tell you about us. Tuck and me. Our relationship prospers and fails in direct proportion to the amount of time we spend together. When we're together, it's fine; when we're apart, it's not so fine. And it's not like we fight. It's more subtle than that.

"It's like we're different people. It's because too much has happened since we last saw one another. I leave New York in one frame of mind and come back in another because of what happened in San Bernardino or Los Angeles. By then, Tuck has had a whole other set of problems. It takes us three days to catch each other up, and, by then, someone's usually going off somewhere . . ." Toni trailed off.

Brenda sighed, wishing things were simple, the way they used to be when husbands worked and wives stayed at home and everyone knew what was expected of him or her.

"What does your mother say?" Toni asked.

"I haven't told her about the offer. And I certainly haven't told her how mixed up I feel. All she'd say is, 'I told you so.' And, you know, Toni, she'd be right," Brenda admitted. "If my father were alive, I'd talk to him. He'd tell me what to do."

"Come on, Brenda! You sound eight. Not twenty-eight!"

"Don't remind me!" Brenda teased, and Toni ducked as Brenda threw a calico sofa pillow at her.

Still, after Toni left, Brenda was undecided about what to do and seesawed first one way and then the other, wishing, for the first time that she could remember, that someone would tell her what to do. She'd be grateful.

And she was left with an equally uneasy feeling about Toni. Toni had been about to tell her something—something important—and, at the last moment, hadn't. Brenda wondered what it was.

In the end, of course, Brenda decided to take the job.

"How can I turn it down?" she asked Jeff. "It's what I've been working for."

As Brenda got on the plane, she turned and waved to Jeff.

Her glowing smile and shining blue-green eyes concealed the divided halves of her soul.

The three months stretched into eight months. Brenda worked in Munich harder than she ever had, dealing with language difficulties, cultural differences, and the ten thousand details involved in setting up an ultra-sophisticated test lab.

She worked from an All Chem master lab-design plan, using the modifications that had been made in Frankfurt to adapt it to German law and procedure. She supervised the ordering and setting up of bunsen burners, centrifuges, sterile test areas; infrared photography equipment, electron microscopes, and the placement and storage of hardware and software for the in-lab computer systems linked to worldwide All Chem systems; the outfitting of shower rooms and changing areas; the locked-storage, limited-access, and public-access testing areas. She was in charge of five-million-dollars' worth of equipment, and all the time she kept remembering the months her mother had supervised the building of the big kitchen in New Rochelle. The procedures, the problems, the hassles, were the same—only on a vastly multiplied scale. She was, as she had been for Heinrich Leben, on time and on budget. She turned out to be, as Sid Erlau had hoped, a winner.

Sid Erlau was happy as the work progressed. So was Brenda—when she was at work. When she went home at night, to the All Chem apartment on Kirchestrasse, she was alone. And lonely.

And when she went home to Boston for her long-postponed three-week vacation at Christmas, Brenda knew by the way he hugged her but didn't kiss her, by the way his eyes never quite met hers—even before Jeff could get the words out—that he was having an affair.

"I never thought in a million years I'd do anything like it," he said. He looked miserable, hurt and angry, and guilty. "It doesn't make me happy. I feel terrible all the time." He was almost in tears.

"Oh, Jeff," Brenda said. "I don't like it. I hate it. But I understand it."

She did not tell him—and would not tell him—that occasionally she went to bed with someone in Munich. It had nothing—or not much—to do with sex. Going to bed with

someone was a Band-Aid for her torn-apart life, and it left
Brenda feeling worse after than before.

"What's going to happen?" she asked.

Jeff didn't know. He didn't have an answer. Did anyone?

During the week between Christmas and New Year's, Ellen
asked her if everything was all right between her and Jeff. For
a moment Brenda was tempted to lie. And then she decided
not to.

"Jeff's having an affair," she said. "It started when I was
in Germany."

"I'm sorry," Ellen said gently in a much more sympathetic
tone than Brenda thought she deserved. "Sorry for Jeff. Sorry
for you."

"I was sure you'd say 'I told you so,'" Brenda said. "You
warned me that having a career and a happy marriage wouldn't
be easy. But I thought I knew better."

"I thought I knew more than my parents, too," Ellen said,
knowing how conflicted Brenda was, seeing it on her tired,
pale face, in her sad, hurt eyes. "If you want to come back to
the States, you can go to work for À La Carte. We're very
busy now that we've bought Tamara out. And if the
KitchenWorks deal goes through, we'll really need more help,"
Ellen said. "Do you remember how we used to dream about
being in business together when you were a teenager and helped
me after school? Ellen and Daughter."

Brenda nodded. It seemed a century ago.

"But I'm a chemist. I'm an executive with a major multinational corporation."

"You're in the big time now," Ellen translated. "And you
don't want to lower yourself to the small time."

Brenda didn't answer. She didn't have to.

"I love you, Brenda," Jeff said on the night before she was to
return to Munich. "I love you and I want to be married to you,
but this isn't working out. You on one continent, me on another."

Jeff had realized that although his mother had brought him
up to respect women who worked outside the home, she herself
had always been at home, and he had always, unconsciously,
expected that his working wife would also, somehow, be there,
the laundry folded, dinner in the oven.

"Do you want a divorce?" Brenda asked, scared, not because she wanted a divorce but because she felt she had to give Jeff the choice.

"No," said Jeff, giving her the assurance she wanted, "but I don't want to live like this either."

"What should we do?" Brenda asked, a question to which there was no answer save tears, and, in tears, they made love and clung to each other, emotionally naked.

And they cried when they kissed good-bye.

As Brenda took her seat in first class, she waved away the steward's offer of champagne and wondered what she was doing with her life.

She was almost twenty-nine—married and alone. Successful and living in a company apartment in a foreign city furnished by a stranger. She was earning more money than her husband, and it bought her nothing except transatlantic phone calls and expensive clothes that she hid under a lab smock. She had, with her six-thousand-dollar bonus, even topped thirty thousand dollars that year, and when she had told Toni, Toni said, "I did it last year. I didn't even bother to tell you. It didn't seem very important anymore..."

The expensive lunch they'd joked about for so long seemed like a sad joke. It was all turning to ashes for Brenda, and when Toni offered to invest Brenda's six-thousand-dollar bonus in "a small company I've been following, a maker of silicon chips," Brenda agreed.

"Fine," she said. "Believe it or not, there's not one thing I want to buy."

And Brenda wondered about the future. She didn't want seats in first class and champagne at 35,000 feet anymore, or any more casual affairs with men she liked just barely enough to go to bed with. She'd had it with different jobs with different titles and higher salaries that felt the same day in and day out.

But how would she end up? Like the Sid Erlaus and Heinrich Lebens of this world? Looking over their shoulders, climbing over bodies and covering their asses all for the next promotion, the bigger office, the better title? For what? For whom? And why? Would she never get past being Brenda the winner? Brenda who got things done well, on time, and under budget? Brenda who got all A's?

It was uncharacteristic of Brenda to brood, to be introspective, but as the plane crossed the Atlantic she wondered what she was doing with her life and why success in a man's world according to men's rules and men's definitions wasn't making her happy. It crossed her mind that she felt barren.

As soon as the plane landed, even before she cleared customs, Brenda called Boston.

"If they ask me to go back to Munich, I'm putting in for a transfer," she told Jeff. "I want to be with you."

"Emesse and SwannCo, MaxCor and ShopCo, the shopping malls, have gone south," Mel Factir told Johanna at a meeting at his office. "To the Bahamas, to be specific. They no longer exist under their former names."

"So we'll sue under their current names," Johanna said, not seeing what the problem was.

"We don't know what their current names are," Mel explained. "Once the companies were transferred to the Bahamas, they were registered in the names of Bahamian banks, and Bahamian banking laws are as strict as Swiss banking laws. They won't tell us the new names of the companies."

"Can't we force them to?"

"We can't force bank executives to break the laws of their own country," Mel said.

"Well, what about the condos?" Johanna asked, wondering how much it must have cost Max to send his companies south. Plenty, she'd bet. Probably as much as she was seeking to get. It wasn't the money that bothered Max, she realized, it was that he didn't want *her* to get the money. "They couldn't have been shipped out to the Bahamas."

"No," said Mel. "But they are no longer registered in Mr. Swann's name. As far as we can determine, they've been put in the names of nominees."

"And what does that mean?" Johanna asked, although she had a pretty good idea.

"It means that they are no longer legally the property of Mr. Swann."

"And *that* means that Mr. Swann's about-to-be-ex-wife has no claim on them?"

Mel nodded. The bland, noncommittal expression on his face never changed. Never. He probably fucked with that face on, Johanna thought.

"And the real estate brokerages? I suppose they've disappeared too?" Johanna asked. "Have they gone north or south?"

"Well," said Mel, "as far as we can find out, they're currently in Andorra. In transit . . ."

"So I'm shit out of luck?"

"That isn't how it's described in a court of law," Mel said, "but that about sums it up."

"So, if I'm smart, I'll grab the five hundred thou?"

"If it's still on offer," Mel said. Johanna wondered if a punch in the teeth would change that bland expression.

"You mean that bastard is trying to weasel out of his offer?"

"It's his right," Mel said. "Mr. Swann is a difficult man."

"And *Mrs*. Swann," Johanna said, "is a difficult lady."

Of that, Mel had no doubt whatever. He thought if he ever married anyone like that, he'd fuck her until she turned purple and begged for mercy. But, of course, his expression remained bland and noncommittal.

"No assets are no assets," Mel said. Max Swann wasn't the only rich man involved in a divorce case who had pulled this trick; in fact, Mel had orchestrated the trick himself when he had represented the husbands. He had *told* Johanna to take the cash. "It looks like Mr. Swann has outsmarted us."

"No one outsmarts me," Johanna said.

"What do you plan to do?" Mel asked, thinking that she ought to grab the $500,000. A hefty portion of which would end up as his fee.

For once, Johanna had no answer. Or at least not right at the moment. She was sure something would come to her. Something always did. She simply would not let Max cheat her the way her mother had cheated her, the way her brothers had cheated her.

Sid Erlau had two words for Brenda: "Forget it."

Those words were followed by hundreds of other words. Words about goddamn women, unreliable women, undependable women. Words about how he had put himself on the line with top management suggesting her for the job and that he was not going to go back to them to say that she wanted out.

"You wanted the job. You jumped for the job. You worked for the job," he said, echoing Brenda's own words to Jeff. "Now you've got the job. You keep the job! You stick it out until *I* tell you different!" His voice blistered heat and fury over the transatlantic cable.

At some point in his tirade he asked her why she wanted a

transfer back to the States anyway, after all the time and effort she had put into getting the job in the first place. Brenda made the fatal mistake of telling him the truth: "I'm doing it to save my marriage."

"No man would *ever* say that! No man would *think* it! And you bitches wonder why the top slots are closed to you!" His scream turned into a wordless screech, and he slammed down the telephone, leaving Brenda's end vibrating before she had a chance to collect herself and accuse him of having a temper tantrum that men swore only hysterical, premenstrual women indulged in.

Maybe Sid was right was what Brenda told herself. Maybe no man would have put his marriage first, but she wasn't a man. Besides, men didn't even have the problem. Their wives followed them to overseas posts—the company even paid for their travel and relocation, helping them find apartments and set up housekeeping. But Brenda couldn't ask that of Jeff, couldn't expect it of him. He was licensed to practice in the United States, not in Germany. Would it be fair to ask him to put aside his career for hers? No. Yet women had followed their husbands unthinkingly forever. But women didn't have the careers men had. Women didn't, hadn't, but Brenda did. What was the answer?

She lay thinking in circles. Finding no answers. Only more questions, because when Brenda had told Sid Erlau she wanted a transfer to save her marriage, she had been telling only part of the truth. The rest of the truth was that she was now twenty-nine. Thirty had always seemed impossible, an outlandish fiction, something that happened to other people. Suddenly, thirty began to seem not only possible but real.

Brenda noticed that if she looked in the mirror in a certain southern light, she could see the beginnings of crow's feet at the corners of her eyes and brackets between her nose and mouth—lines that would one day be as pronounced as her mother's. And she noticed that, here and there, now and then, gray hairs grew in around her temples. Although she plucked them out, she could not pluck out the memory of their existence.

Brenda could no longer think of herself as a girl with the future lying in front of her in a limitless way. It was time to think of herself as a woman. She wanted to have a family. Her wish for children was becoming a hunger as compelling as hunger for food, for air, for breath.

She realized that the time for "later" had come to an end.
Later was now.

Brenda returned to Munich and stayed until the laboratory was
set up and in operation. On completion of the assignment, she
received a six-thousand-dollar bonus, which she asked Toni to
invest for her, thinking that the money would be a nest egg for
the child she so desperately wanted.

When she got back to the home office in Pittsburgh, Sid
Erlau seemed to have forgotten his screaming fit. All hot-shot
business, all chummily paternal, he told her that All Chem had
big plans for her, plans that included a projected new lab in
São Paulo. He complimented her on her former assistant, Diane
Wyre, who was doing beautifully in Brenda's old job as lab
section director; and told her that before the Brazilian plans
were nailed down, All Chem wanted to send her around to its
United States and Canadian branches as a lab trouble-shooter.
He presented the opportunity to her as if he were offering a
casket of diamonds, a longed-for and sought-after reward.

"No woman has ever had this assignment," Sid said, grinning mightily. "You'll have visibility at All Chem, Brenda.
Visibility!"

More diamonds.

Obediently, Brenda traveled to Cincinnati and Phoenix, to
Atlanta and Toronto, to Spokane and Ottawa. Every weekend,
no matter where she was, she flew home to Boston to be with
Jeff.

"You look fantastic!" Toni said over the asparagus quiche Brenda
made for lunch one rainy Sunday seven months later. "I've
never seen you look so pretty. What's the recipe? Some secret
formula you cooked up in your lab?"

"I'm pregnant," Brenda said, and it was the first time in all
the years Toni had known Brenda that she saw and heard a shy
pride in her friend's voice.

"Are you going to have it?"

"Toni, I would stand off Caesar's army to have it," Brenda
said.

"And what about your job?" Toni asked.

"Brazil is out of the question!" Brenda said. "And I'll have
to check on All Chem's maternity-leave policy. I haven't said

a word yet at the office." Then Brenda reacted to Toni's first question. "Toni, what makes you ask if I'm going to have it?"

Toni looked down, avoiding Brenda's eyes.

"I almost told you before you went to Munich, Brenda. I was pregnant..."

"And?" Suddenly the walnut oil on the salad—usually a luxurious treat to Brenda—seemed repugnantly heavy to her, overbearing in taste and texture.

"I had an abortion," Toni said. "I was in San Francisco to look over a maker of silicon chips. I spent all week at their plant outside the city, and after a Friday afternoon meeting I checked into a discreet clinic on Telegraph Hill."

"Does Tuck know?"

Toni shook her head.

"No," she said. "What he does know is that at the semi-annual Edder and Stern meeting, I'm going to be made partner."

"Do you regret... what you did?" Brenda asked.

"I don't know yet," Toni admitted. "I do know I'm thrilled about making partner," she said and smiled.

Brenda opened a bottle of champagne and they drank.

To Brenda's new baby and to Toni's fifty before forty.

10

AL HAD WARNED HER THAT TELEVISION WOULD CHANGE HER life, but, even so, Ellen was not prepared for the *extent* to which it changed her life. At first she thought it was because other people saw her differently; in the end, she realized it was because she had begun—finally—to see herself differently.

"Give me a quiche, Ellen!" hard-hats yelled when Ellen passed a construction site. She would respond with a wave and a big smile, thinking how much fun it would be to surprise them one day with a great big enormous quiche!

Strangers talked to her as if they'd known her forever. Women came up to her in supermarkets and asked for cooking tips; taxi drivers asked her how many bottles of wine they ought to buy for an anniversary party or if paper napkins were okay for a big party. A man behind her in line at the bank promised her he would send her his mother's recipe for Maine blueberry cobbler. He did, and it was absolutely delicious. A telephone operator, recognizing Ellen's voice when she dialed Information, wanted to know a graceful way to get rid of dinner guests who stayed too long. Once, as she waited for a red light to change near Lord & Taylor, a famous television star known for T & A told Ellen· that Ellen was her favorite television personality.

The director of a lecture bureau called. And kept calling. He wanted to sign Ellen and book her on a cross-country lecture tour. Ellen turned him down. And kept turning him down. She pointed out, reasonably, that she couldn't run À La Carte if she were running around the country.

Her rejection did not dissuade him; *au contraire*, there was a call from him every three weeks asking Ellen to reconsider, and two months after the first lecture bureau approached her, its biggest rival began to call.

A magazine for working women wanted Ellen to contribute a column on entertaining. Ellen was tempted, but she didn't see how she could fit in a column; she didn't have enough time to do a really good job. Between À La Carte and AM/USA, she was doing all she could handle.

A book publisher called wanting a book on entertaining. Ellen had lunch with the editor, a sporty, vibrant woman in her late thirties who was married and had three children. She commuted to Manhattan every day from Darien, and she and Ellen spent most of the lunch comparing notes on juggling a career and bringing up children. Not to mention, in the editor's case, a marriage!

"Two out of the three almost killed me," Ellen confessed. "I admire you. How did you do it? *Why* did you do it?"

"Easy," said the editor, a bemused expression crossing her face. "I only wanted everything!"

"And did you get it?" Ellen asked, thinking of Brenda.

"Yes," said the editor, "but most of the time I'm too tired to enjoy any of it."

Ellen didn't know what to say. Was there any woman anywhere who had resolved the conflicts between career and marriage, success and children, achievement and love?

The talk at lunch was ambiguous and inconclusive. The editor wanted the book to be full of hints, anecdotes, quick-and-easy menus—and, above all, she wanted it to be "snappy."

"But I'm not the snappy type," Ellen protested. "I'm nervous, insecure, and plodding."

"You don't look it," said the editor crisply. "You look snappy."

"I wish I felt that way," Ellen said automatically, unthinkingly, in a self-deprecating voice unchanged from her early twenties.

But . . . a moment later a more contemporary voice contradicted, admitting that, yes, sometimes she *did* feel snappy.

Charley, the AM/USA makeup man, had shown her how to do an almost professional makeup job using shadow and pencil to emphasize the shape of her striking blue-green eyes and where to place blusher so it looked natural-only-better-than-natural. She could now afford good clothes and shopped for silk and cotton and linen and wool, enjoying the simple shapes that suited her best and the pure, clean colors that best set off her auburn and peach coloring.

Sometimes when Ellen caught an unexpected glimpse of herself in a shop window or in a mirror she hadn't known would be there, she was pleasantly jolted at the glow in her face and the energetic swing of her step. She was, she realized, almost unrecognizable from the self-effacing, adoring wife she'd been when Phil had been alive. And she had long since understood that Phil had not "done" it to her—had not made her feel insecure, timid, and vaguely incompetent. She had made herself feel that way—she had, like every other woman she knew, gone along with what the women's magazines, the psychologists, and the movies were telling her she ought to be and want and do. She had become self-effacing because she had been told that men didn't like assertive women; she had not been able to balance a checkbook because an interest in money was "unfeminine"; and she had hidden the "terrific kid" in her because everything she saw and read told her that men weren't interested in women they couldn't take care of.

After Phil's death, Ellen's biggest problem—along with the practical necessity of earning a living for herself and her children—had been learning how to reclaim herself despite the pressures of a culture that insisted that independence and competence were "unfeminine." She had done a pretty good job, too, even if she said so herself, although she knew that her inner image did not match the confident exterior she projected. But now, no longer paralyzed by self-doubt and self-criticism, Ellen could smile comfortably at herself. Ellen realized with a start that, finally, at this supposedly late date, she had begun to like herself—and to accept the fact that she was what she appeared to be.

She liked herself too much to continue her long-term affair

with Lew. She felt that she deserved more: more than part of
a man's attention, more than shared and stolen love, more than
being the third side of a triangle that preserved Lew's marriage
And she knew that as long as Lew held claim to part of her
she'd never have a chance at more.

And she told him so.

"I've known for a long time that one day you would wan
to end it," he said. His eyes, normally lit with gold flecks
seemed to darken. "Sometimes I think I should have left Reenie
in the very beginning. We would have been very happy, you
know."

"Yes," said Ellen. "I know. And we *have* been happy—a
happy as we could be under the circumstances. But the fact is
you didn't leave Reenie."

"No," said Lew, "I didn't. And as the years go by, Reenie
and I seem to be getting along better and better."

"I know that, too," Ellen said with a wistful smile. "But
now you and Reenie will have to get along without me."

"You're not bitter," Lew said, not really surprised.

"No," said Ellen. "I'm not bitter. You needed me—for your
reasons. And I needed you—for my reasons. But now I want
more."

Lew nodded. He was sad; he was serious; he was accepting.
"I understand," he said, knowing he would never kiss her again.
"You deserve more . . ."

Business was better than ever. Ellen now had three full-time
chefs to take care of the cooking; she had a list of over a
hundred waiters, waitresses, and bartenders on call. Her old
New Rochelle kitchen—once a dream—was hopelessly over-
burdened. Should she enlarge it? Should she sell the house.
start from scratch, and build a kitchen in a more central Westchester location? Should she find a kitchen in New York to
take care of the increasing Manhattan business? And how could
she oversee all the details involved in building a new kitchen
now that she had the Westchester and Connecticut branches
she had bought from Tamara to superintend?

"I feel overwhelmed. What I need is another pair of eyes
and another pair of hands," she told Al at a Flyers-Rangers
game where the fights broke out all over the rink.

"What about Danny?" Al asked, aware that Ellen had once
offered a job with À La Carte to Brenda. He knew that she

had never really accepted Brenda's rejection and still, in fact, slightly resented it.

"Danny doesn't want to be a nepot," Ellen said. "And besides, he's enamored of Sophie De Witt. I can't compete."

"Then hire another pair of eyes and hands," Al suggested. "You hire cooks and waitresses. So hire hands and eyes."

And, later, over chili and beer at Anita's Chili Parlor—the kind of earthy, unchic food Ellen had come to prefer the more her professional life focused on nouvelle leeks-and-cream reductions, raspberry-vinegar glazes, and kiwi tarts—Al took an advance copy of the Sunday *New York Times* Arts and Leisure section out of his briefcase and handed it to Ellen.

"Page twenty-four," he said, with a smile a yard wide.

"Al!" Ellen exclaimed. Page twenty-four had a half-page ad for AM/USA featuring a large photograph of the host, the weathercaster, movie critic, and consumer reporter. In the upper corner, set off with a border, was a closeup of Ellen, smiling and confident, with a simple headline: STARTING THIS WEEK: ENTERTAINING WITH ELLEN. Al! This is fantastic! This is wonderful! Oh, Al! I could kiss you!"

"Then why don't you?" he asked.

"I don't call that much of a kiss," Al told Ellen as they left Anita's. "One day I'm going to kiss *you*. And, when I do, you're going to stay kissed..."

Johanna, dateless, was watching Sixty Minutes. The sight of Morley Safer interviewing Danny Durban about the success of Kitchen Works—the gourmet cooking-equipment company that had just been acquired by the company his mother had founded—made her ill, and she picked up the *Times* Arts and Leisure section to find out what else was on. And then she saw the AM/USA ad Al had just shown Ellen.

Johanna's envy triggered her anger, and her anger led her right out of the blind alley she had been stumbling around in ever since Mel had told her about the paper barricades Max had built around his fortune. Max had always dismissed Decor, treating it like a toy that was good enough to keep Lew occupied. The *real* business, the *real* money, the *real* action, in Max's opinion, was the real estate and the property. Decor, as Max said all the time, was strictly kid stuff. Mini-millions compared to Max's maxi-millions. And, unthinkingly, Johanna had agreed with Max, disdainfully considering Decor a mere drop in the bucket.

Now, she suddenly realized, Decor, which owned half of À La Carte, which owned all of KitchenWorks, wasn't such kid stuff anymore. She picked up the telephone and dialed Mel Factir.

"Mel, Decor is the key," she said. "Max owns half of Decor, and I'll bet you dinner at Lutèce that Max hasn't bothered to disappear it into an Andorran blind corporation. Check it out . . ."

Mel did. Johanna was right.

A month later, Ellen hired an assistant, an efficient, buoyantly humorous young woman named Norma who could cut through red tape like a laser, find a plumber when the species appeared to head the endangered and extinct list, plan a party with the most maddeningly indecisive client, and cook anything as long as the recipe was right in front of her.

An assistant! Every time Ellen thought about it, she almost had to pinch herself, but Brenda told her she should have done it a long time ago. Having an assistant was just good business practice.

"But not as nice as having a baby," Ellen said.

Brenda was in her eighth month, and Ellen couldn't wait to be a grandmother.

"*Nothing's* as nice as having a baby!"

Brenda smiled, happy at her mother's happiness. Privately, she thought that her mother was a little too mushy over the whole motherhood bit. Much as Brenda wanted her baby, the cootchy-coo routine wasn't her style.

But when, on the last day of 1979, the maternity nurse put Brenda's daughter into her arms, Brenda was overwhelmed at the reality of the tiny little girl: the perfect rosy fingers and toes, the gentle mouth already curved in a blissful smile, the delicate wisps of white-blonde hair that capped her fragile skull.

Brenda smiled at her hours-old daughter and then, overcome with emotion, burst into tears of inexpressible joy. Within twenty-four hours she had submitted her resignation to All Chem.

"She *what*?" Lew asked, not really believing what Ellen had told him as they took the elevator to the maternity ward at Boston General. Lew had taken the shuttle to Boston that morning after a long and extremely upsetting conversation with his father.

"She resigned," Ellen repeated. "All Chem has no maternity leave for executives—only for clerical employees. Brenda's boss told her that she could have two weeks, and apparently he wasn't even very nice about *that*. Knowing Brenda, I guess she told him what he could do with his two weeks."

"I can hardly believe it," Lew said. "At the rate Brenda was going, I was sure she'd end up president of All Chem."

"So did everyone," Ellen said and paused as Lew held the door to Brenda's room open. "But babies change the way women look at the world."

And Brenda confirmed it.

"Now that women have won the right to kill themselves with overwork, I'm opting out. I'm not going to kill myself. I'm going to stay home with my baby, with Caro. When she gets a little older, I'll go back to work."

"Caro?" Ellen asked. "After Caroline?"

Brenda nodded and handed the baby over to Ellen, who took her first grandchild into her arms. Everything, she thought, had turned out perfectly. She was happy, she was successful, she might even be falling in love. And everything had turned out perfectly for Brenda: she was happily married after the early struggles; she had a perfect, beautiful baby, and a whole, wonderful future to look forward to. Ellen felt her eyes fill.

Her tears of joy were also tears of thanks. One big fat wobbly tear fell on Caro's nose and slid down her little cheek. The tickling sensation made Caro smile into Ellen's eyes as Ellen cradled her in her arms and looked down at her.

"Look!" Brenda said. "She's smiling at you!"

And Ellen's tears turned to smiles and laughter, to a profound sense of pleasure and well-being. She felt she had never been more alive, had never had more to live for.

And Lew, watching Ellen's happiness, dreaded that he would be the one who would have to destroy it.

"My father and Johanna have never signed a divorce settlement," Lew said over a cup of coffee in the hospital cafeteria.

"I thought he offered her a lot of money," Ellen said, her mind on Brenda and Brenda's confident trust that, when she wanted to return to work, a job would be waiting for her. She thought of the difference between women of Brenda's generation and her own. She thought of how, when Phil had died, she had had no confidence whatever that she would be able to find work, that she would be able to support her family. These doubts had never crossed Brenda's mind, and Ellen envied her her automatic self-confidence, the confidence of the baby-boom generation.

"It wasn't enough," Lew said. "Johanna always wanted more."

"You always said she was greedy," Ellen said, not understanding why Lew had come all the way to Boston to tell her about Max and Johanna's eternal money squabbles.

"Now she wants Decor," Lew said.

For a moment, Ellen didn't understand.

"She's suing to get Decor as her divorce settlement," Lew said, staring at his coffee, not drinking it, not touching it.

Then, suddenly, Ellen understood.

"Decor owns half of À La Carte," she said. A stricken look appeared on her face as if someone had slapped her. "If Johanna wins, it means I'll lose half of what I've spent the last twenty years building—for myself, for my children. For Caro. And you'll lose everything. Everything . . ."

Lew said nothing. He merely nodded.

And Ellen put her hand to her mouth in shocked disbelief. Her stomach twisted, and the blood drained from her face.

11

In 1975, Sophie De Witt decided she was sick and tired of making other people rich. At the age of fifty-four, after thirty years of retail and mailorder experience, she decided to resign her job as gourmet-food buyer of Bloomingdale's and go into business for herself. One of the first people she confided in was her assistant, Danny Durban, the best assistant buyer she'd ever had, even though originally she'd hired him as a favor to her sister.

"I'm going to make you an offer anyone in his right mind would refuse," she told Danny in her airless closet of an office behind the delicacies department. Sophie, who had been considered unattractive as a girl, had become a striking woman. More than anything, she resembled an extremely handsome frog. She had wide-set brown eyes that missed nothing and a generous mouth that, if you looked carefully, seemed always ready to smile. She was tough; she was warm. Most people respected her more than they liked her, but the ones who liked her loved her. Danny was one of the ones who liked her.

"I'm leaving Bloomie's," Sophie continued. "I'm going to go into business for myself. I'm going to start a gourmet-food and cooking-equipment catalog. A mail-order Dean and De

Luca. I'd like you to come along as my assistant. I can't afford
to pay you as much as Bloomie's does, and you'll have to
work at least twice as hard. Furthermore, I can't even promise
you you'll have a job a year from now. Who knows? The whole
enterprise might turn out to be a disaster.

"On the other hand, since it *is* a lousy offer, I'll sweeten it
by giving you stock options in the new company. That way,
if it *does* succeed, you'll be an owner. Now, Danny, what do
you think?"

"I think," Danny said, his hazel eyes—his father's eyes—
intelligent, wary, thoughtful, "that I'll have to think about it."

Danny had learned—the hard way—that liking someone
and going into business with her were two very different mat-
ters.

Sophie was Danny's second boss—second *woman* boss—and,
when he told people she had asked him to leave Bloomie's to
go into business with her, they told him he was crazy. Hadn't
his experience with Sherri Phrainer taught him to watch out
for female entrepreneurs?

Brenda warned him against Sherri; Ellen was dubious; Toni
was negative ("Stay away!" she advised. "Stay far away!").
Danny decided they were jealous of Sherri and were just being
bitchy.

When Danny graduated from the University of Pennsylvania
with a degree in finance and economics in 1973 and two summers' experience working for Wilson, two working for a bak-
ery, and a lifetime helping his mother with À La Carte, he
naturally looked for jobs related to food and food service. After
rejecting a trainee position with a fast-food chain ("Portion
control doesn't turn me on," he said) and a junior executive's
slot with a company that catered airline meals, Danny decided
to take a hell of a risk—in the hopes of making a hell of a
killing.

Pita Perfect was a quality fast-food concept, and Danny
thought it had big bucks written all over it. The Pita Perfect
shops would offer a menu of twenty-six fillings stuffed into
white or whole wheat pita. The fillings ranged from coffee-
shop-basic tuna salad and egg salad to exotic coriander-sea-
soned kebobs and cumin-spiked eggplant purée.

The food was fast, high-quality, different, and inexpensive.

The idea, Danny thought, was excellent, and the idea was Sherri Phrainer's.

Sherri insisted she had thought it up herself while cruising the Greek islands during her marriage to a California computer tycoon. Others insisted she stole it from a small storefront operation on Atlantic Avenue in Brooklyn. Anyway, by the time Danny appeared in Sherri's life she had her idea—and not much else. She needed money (most of which her ex-husband would supply), she needed locations, she needed chefs, she needed a good start on a fast track.

"I don't know a *thing* about business," she confessed to Danny during the interview, which she conducted in the white-and-cream mirrored living room of her Beresford penthouse. Sherri had masses of silky blonde hair, legs that wouldn't quit, and smoky green eyes men tended to fall into. She looked like a model in a jeans commercial, not someone who was trying to become a fast-foods tycoon. Danny couldn't take his eyes off her. "I'm an idea person. I need someone to do the business parts for me. Wilson says you know all about that end of things..."

Her soft, apricot lips parted, waiting for Danny's answer.

"'All' is an exaggeration," Danny said. "But I did study business and finance in college. And I've spent my whole life around the food business. My mother is a caterer, and I've handled her books since I was twelve. I was the only twelve-year-old kid I ever heard of who asked for—and got—an adding machine for his birthday.

"Summers I worked in the comptroller's office of Better Bakers in Queens. I helped handle the contracts, the purchasing, the billings, the invoices, the receivables. In fact, they offered me a permanent job when I got out of college."

"That's impressive. Really. *Impressive!*" Sherri said, thinking how good-looking Danny was. He was a mixture of clean-cut preppy and riverboat gambler—a devastating combination. Except that he was so young—at twenty-one he was five years younger than Sherri, who was turned on only by older men. *Quel dommage!* "That's just what I need... someone with a head for figures. Someone like you."

"But I want to be honest," Danny continued, not wanting to overstate his experience. "I haven't had much experience outside my mother's business and the summer job."

"Wilson says you're sharp. Really. *Sharp!*" Sherri said.

"What I need is someone to pull the whole thing together for me. To take care of the details . . . to coordinate the lawyers, the accountants, the real estate deals, the buying. You know, I used to watch my husband run his business. Ex-husband. He told me that the creative part is everything and that the rest could be handled by halfway-decent administrators. Now, I'm great with ideas . . . what I need is a partner to help with the business side of things. Do you think you'd be interested?"

"Partner?" Danny couldn't believe his ears. Partner? It was beyond his wildest dreams—and his wildest dreams were very ambitious indeed.

"Well, not a *full* partner," Sherri said, "but a limited partner."

"I'd certainly be interested," said Danny, trying to hide his excitement, visions of empire-building dancing in his head. He was excited by the idea of helping a business grow from the ground up the way he had seen A La Carte grow; he was excited by the prospect of being a partner; he was excited by the Pita Perfect concept—it was, he thought, a real winner. And he was excited by Sherri Phrainer—she was, he thought, a real winner.

He was impressed by her apartment, and he was dazzled by her. She was gorgeously beautiful, jet-setty, and obviously smart as hell—it added up to a dream-mirage of money and pleasure. Who could resist her? Not Danny. And not, as he would find out, any other man between nine and ninety.

Danny threw himself into Pita Perfect with a passion.

He hired a restaurant designer and worked with him on developing a "look." The Pita Perfects would be Greek-island-inspired white stucco with blue trim, primitively hewn tables and rush-seated chairs like the ones in Greek tavérnas. The "look" was clean and simple. It was easy to maintain, inexpensive to construct, and had a memorable, strongly themed style.

"It looks like the waterfront tavérnas in Mýkonos," Sherri raved. "People will think they're in the Greek islands. It's perfect. Really. *Perfect!*"

Danny glowed, and she hugged him and kissed him and invited him to lunch at Mortimer's, where she introduced him to the gorgeous model who was on that month's cover of *Vogue* and with whom Danny fell briefly and madly in love.

Danny spent so much time with real estate agents that he

joked he ought to marry one. He was looking for the right upscale location at a sane rent.

He rejected the midtown forties as too commercial, the east sixties as too elitist, Columbus Avenue as ideal but too far from the heavy noonhour traffic Pita Perfect would depend on. The Village was out for the same reason, and so was SoHo.

Danny considered space in the Wall Street area—for about ten redhot seconds—until he realized that while lunch business would be sensational, evening business would drop off to zilch. What he wanted was the area around Bloomingdale's. So did everyone else, but, miracle of miracles, Danny found an ideal location on Third and Fifty-ninth. Contracts were drawn and about to be signed when the owner of the Chinese restaurant two doors away found out and raised hell. No way did he want a competitor selling inexpensive food right in his lap. He threatened to pile garbage in front of the entrance; he threatened to poison Pita Perfect's food deliveries; he threatened ominous Tong Society deeds and obscure oriental curses. Every time Danny saw him, he carried a murderous-looking meat cleaver in his hand.

Both Danny and his would-be landlord had the identical reaction: Who needs this hassle? And the deal fell through.

Danny persisted and finally, finally, found an ideal spot. A Sixtieth Street boutique that sold high-style plastic resin jewelry went out of business before its lease was up. The owner was happy to sublet to Pita Perfect at its (comparatively) inexpensive pre-double-digit-inflation rent.

"You're a genius. Really. A *genius!*" Sherri told Danny the day she, as president of Pita Perfect, signed the lease. She appeared in her lawyer's office dressed as she always dressed for business meetings—in the ultimate dress-for-success outfit.

She wore skin-tight jeans, high-heeled sandals, and a thin silk blouse unbuttoned to the fifth button. She wore no bra, and every time she moved, a glimpse of breast appeared and then quickly disappeared. Sherri's lawyer, the renter's lawyer, the landlord, the landlord's lawyer, the broker, the jewelry maker (who was gay and theoretically shouldn't have cared less), and Danny were all totally mesmerized.

After they left the lawyer's office, Sherri invited Danny to a party she was giving that weekend in her Bridgehampton beach house, where she introduced him to a lovely and successful fashion designer with whom he spent a blissful weekend.

"You're fantastic. Really. *Fantastic!*" Sherri told Danny on the drive back to New York. She was thrilled—Really. *Thrilled!*—that a location had been found and that Pita Perfect was that much closer to being a reality.

"You're much more than just an administrator, Danny. You're creative, and you're a demon worker. I've been thinking, and I've decided that just a salary isn't enough for you. We wouldn't have that location without you, Danny. I think you ought to own some stock in the company. Billy told me I ought to incorporate Pita Perfect and that the stock ought to be owned by the key people. You, Danny, are absolutely key. And I'm going to tell Billy to issue some of the stock in your name. It's the least you deserve. Really. The *least!*"

Billy was Billy Howe, Sherri's lawyer and Monday-to-Friday lover. Weekends, Billy spent with his wife. Weekends, Sherri spent with her ex-husband. Theirs was a very "now" romance.

"That's terrific of you, Sherri. I have very good vibes about Pita Perfect, and there's nothing I'd like more than owning some stock in it," Danny said, and he leaned back in the passenger seat and inhaled the lovely scent of the leather upholstery of Sherri's BMW mingled with her Opium. He closed his eyes and thought he'd died and gone to heaven.

"You're key, Danny," he heard Sherri say from his dreamy distance. "Really. *Key!*"

Now that Danny was a stockholder, he ate, slept, dreamed, and connived Pita Perfect. His twelve-hour days turned into eighteen-hour days.

He interviewed cooks: artistic Italians, non-English-speaking Koreans, Chinese philosophers, sullen Armenians, robust Poles, aggressive Israelis, handsome Yugoslavs, cheerful Greeks, hard-working Puerto Ricans, and cleaver-wielding Peruvians. Hiring a cook was a crucial decision. Restaurant owners Danny knew had told him that cooks usually lasted seven years; after that, the unrelenting heat of commercial kitchens drove most of them to the bottle or to another line of work. And after the exotic parade, Danny finally hired a Culinary Institute of America graduate, a handsome Iowan who used to work part-time for his mother.

Danny conferred with Billy Howe over copyright procedures for Pita Perfect to ensure that no one could steal Sherri's idea. He interviewed a half-dozen insurance brokers to get the best coverage at the best price. He patiently sorted through Department of Health red tape and sought out the best and best-priced food and beverage suppliers. He negotiated with restaurant workers' unions, met with fire department inspectors, and let the bids for contractors to build the first Pita Perfect.

"I don't know what I'd do without you," Sherri said over cheeseburgers at the Broome Street Bar. "You're just incredible. I told Billy last night that you're literally invaluable and that you ought to be an executive of the company. Vice-President."

Vice-President! Danny remembered Brenda with her thirty before thirty and decided she had been thinking small. *He'd* be a millionaire by thirty! Danny's eyes gleamed at Sherri's compliments, saw visions of money and executive status. And why not? Born in 1953, Danny was a full-fledged member of the Unlimited Expectations Generation—a generation that had seen the standard of living go only one way: up.

"Sherri," he said in thanks, "you're one in a million."

"Not me. You're the one in a million," Sherri said, running her fingers through her cascade of blonde hair and shaking it out sexily. "Really. *One in a million!*"

Working for Sherri was as good as falling in love. Danny glowed. Brenda noticed. Ellen noticed.

"Are you in love with this Sherri Phrainer?" Brenda asked.

"Yes," Danny said. "But not the way you think. Unfortunately."

"Who exactly is this Sherri Phrainer?" Ellen wanted to know. "What do you know about her?"

"She's wonderful!" Danny said.

Ellen arched a dubious eyebrow.

"Oh, Mom," Danny said. "For a liberated lady, you sure come on old-fashioned!"

After fourteen months of slave labor, Pita Perfect turned out to be an instant success. Four days after it opened, lines of people stood on Sixtieth Street to try the new rage. Office, bank, and retail workers lunched there. Lady shoppers snacked there; filmgoers had a bite before or after the movies; and the disco freaks refueled in the early hours.

The media loved it—or, rather, they loved Sherri, who was young, beautiful, successful, and female! It was the age of women, and Sherri was one of the women of the age. She was interviewed, photographed, and written about; she was asked for her success recipes (as if there were a recipe for success just as there was a recipe for veal Orloff); she was admired for her business head and super bod, and held up as a model for other women to emulate.

When the fourth Pita Perfect within sixteen months opened, Danny asked for his shares of stock. Sherri put him off with an invitation to a party at Studio 54. The second and third times he asked, she said she'd speak to Billy—she wasn't too sure where the shares were kept. The seventh time he asked, she said she'd get to it the *instant* she got back from Marbella, and the tenth time she said that she didn't really understand "all that business stuff" and suggested he speak directly to Billy.

Who told Danny that, although he did own shares in Pita Perfect, that Pita Perfect was now legally defunct. Its ownership had been transferred to a holding company registered in Delaware and owned by Sherri, Billy, and Sherri's ex-husband.

"Well, then, doesn't the holding company have to buy my shares from me?" Danny asked.

"Since the shares were never actually issued," Billy began, and Danny understood even before the slippery sentence was out of Billy's mouth that he'd been *shtupped*. By Billy. By Sherri's ex-husband. And most of all by Sherri, who understood exactly how to take advantage of anything and anyone who came her way. Sherri was, Danny thought, in a scary way, impressive. He'd been had—and he'd loved every minute of it up until the very end.

12

In Sophie's time—as in Ellen's—attitudes toward women and work had shifted 180 degrees—the same 180-degree shift that had occurred in attitudes toward women and sex. Specifically, from Nice Girls Don't to Nice Girls Do—and love every minute of it. Sophie—and Ellen—had been brought up on the Romance of Sex; their daughters' generation was being brought up on the Romance of Work.

In Sophie's opinion one was just as much a crock as the other. She had worked for the reason most people work—to support herself. As a girl, her looks had not attracted a man who might have offered to rescue her from work. As a woman, she had become handsome, and the men who might have interested her thirty years before had become dicey specimens at best: heart attack candidates, middle-aged fools chasing girls young enough to be their daughters, arteriosclerotic divorcés and widowers who wanted someone to take care of them—and their doped-out kids.

Thanks but no thanks. Which is why Sophie, after thirty years of working her way up laboriously from salesgirl to assistant buyer to buyer, decided it was time to make a bundle for herself. She had had enough of work; she wanted to see what fun was like.

So when she went into business for herself, she had no intention for it to fail. She sensed the time was right for an imported-food and elaborate kitchen-equipment catalog. By the sixties anyone who read the food column of *Playboy* considered himself a gourmet, and in the seventies three items blew everything else on the sales counters away: the CB radio, the calculator, and the Cuisinart. Sophie put her money on the Cuisinart.

She spent four years planning KitchenWorks, from the line of merchandise it would carry to the pricing strategy, the promotion and advertising, the capitalization, the mailing lists it would buy, down to the type of paper the catalog would be printed on. For those four years she had worked with Danny and found that what her sister had told her had been absolutely true: he worked like a dog, was pleasant and imaginative, and had a nose for a buck. Also, that he had been burned and was wary.

"I hired you as a favor to my sister," Sophie told Danny after he'd worked for her a year at Bloomingdale's.

"Who's your sister?"

"Lillian De Witt."

"Never heard of her," Danny shrugged, mystified. "Should I have?"

"You'll recognize her married name," Sophie said. "Lillian Phrainer . . . she's Sherri Phrainer's mother-in-law. Ex-mother-in-law. She never exactly liked Sherri, and she was appalled at the way Sherri treated you. When I told her that my assistant was leaving to go to Nieman's, she suggested I hire you. I didn't want to—when I met you. You seemed such a sad sack. Lillian practically forced me to give you the job. She said that passing you up would be the stupidest thing I'd ever done. So I hired you"—Sophie grinned—"to shut up my sister."

"I don't blame you for not wanting to hire me," Danny said, remembering the six months he'd spent in a depressed funk after realizing that he'd been aced out of his share of Pita Perfect. He hadn't known what he wanted to do next and had spent his time working for his mother, only to find out that sons, or at least *this* son, couldn't—and shouldn't—work for their mothers. He and Ellen had been in constant conflict the way Ellen and Brenda had been when Brenda was younger.

With the purchase of Tamara's shops, Danny had begun to

see À La Carte as a way to make a family fortune. Ellen saw it the way she had always seen it: as a personal business in which she had a huge personal stake. She cared only that it be good—be the best.

"À La Carte could make us rich," Danny told his mother. To Ellen he sounded like Phil with his extravagant dreams— dreams that, despite Ellen's success, still seemed impossible and unrealistic.

"I'm rich enough," Ellen told him. "I care that A La Carte be the best—serve the best food, offer the best help, and do it at the best prices."

"You can do both," Danny insisted. "By being the best you can get rich."

"Danny," Ellen said, ending the conversation, "I'm happy the way I am."

When Sophie had offered Danny the job as her assistant, both Danny and Ellen had been relieved. And when Sophie invited Danny to leave Bloomingdale's and help her start up KitchenWorks—that was the name she had chosen for her about-to-be-launched company—Ellen had encouraged Danny.

"Sophie's no Sherri Phrainer," Ellen said, making her opinion of Sherri clear in the way she pronounced the name. "By all means, take the chance. *If* you want to . . ."

"I trust Mom," Brenda said. She thought that sex tended to blur Danny's instincts—a weakness Sherri Phrainer had taken full advantage of. Not that she blamed Danny. After all, why should he be different from the rest of the human race? "If she likes Sophie, then so do I."

Toni had some practical advice: "Don't trust promises. You can't take promises to the bank," she said, not having been made an Edder and Stern partner for nothing. "Get everything in writing. And get it *first . . . before* you leave Bloomingdale's."

And Toni gave Danny a few, very specific suggestions about what to ask for. "Remember," she said, "the best time to negotiate is when they want you—*before* they've got you. That's when you hold most of the cards."

"I've been thinking about your lousy offer," Danny told Sophie a few weeks after she'd made it. "And I might be interested. But there are conditions . . ."

"Such as?"

"Such as you offered me stock in KitchenWorks. I want the shares—in my hands—*before* I leave Bloomie's. Second, I want full access to the books at all times. And I'd like that in writing—*before* I leave. Third, since I'm your assistant here, I want to be your assistant there. I'd like the title assistant to the president. I'd like it in writing—"

"*Before* you leave Blõomie's," Sophie interrupted.

"Before I leave Bloomie's," Danny confirmed.

"Smart boy," Sophie said, approvingly. She liked people who knew how to take care of themselves. There was so much less possibility of hard feelings later on. "Smart boy."

Danny had once told his mother that he would walk through fire for Sophie De Witt, and in the first year of KitchenWorks' existence, he did. Literally:

The Wisconsin factory that made the all-purpose twelve-ounce stemmed glasses featured in the first holiday catalog burned down in the summer of 1975. The day of the fire, a sweltering mid-August sizzler, Danny flew out to Sheboygan with Sophie and, while the ashes were still warm, he went through the burned-out shell of the factory with her, salvaging as many cartons of the glasses as they could, personally loading them on the trucks that would take them to the KitchenWorks shipping facility in Long Island City. The glasses had drawn well and promised to be a big holiday item. There was no way Sophie was going to disappoint the customers who had ordered them.

The fire was followed by a flood. The small cooperative northwest of Dublin that made what Sophie considered the best rough-cut bitter orange marmalade flooded when the pipes that supplied the washing vats burst, and an entire season's shipment of marmalade made expressly for KitchenWorks was ruined.

"I suppose," Sophie said, bracing for the biblical worst, "the next thing is famine..."

"Impossible!" Danny said and gestured toward the stacks of cheeses, cartons of jams and jellies, boxes of candies, crates of oils and vinegars and olives and pickles, sacks of grains, and towers of teas and coffees that crowded the shipping room.

Sophie smiled. Sort of. Business was not something she tended to joke about.

* * *

In its first year, KitchenWorks operated from a rented office on East Twenty-sixth Street and leased warehousing in Long Island City and grossed $350,000.

In its second year, KitchenWorks outgrew its office and leased warehousing, and that year, 1976, just before real estate values in Manhattan went through the roof, Sophie bought a derelict building on Mercer Street that had once housed a sewing-machine factory. The cavernous ground floor was turned into a warehouse and the top-floor was converted into a spacious skylit loft that was used for offices. In that same year the catalog grew from a 70-item book to a 120-item book. Business that year doubled business the first year.

In its third year, the KitchenWorks catalog featured almost two hundred items, many of them exclusive, grossed a million dollars, and Sophie turned down the first offer to buy out KitchenWorks. The offer came from a giant maker of frozen foods, and Sophie said, "I'm not going to let them get their icy fingers on my hot little business."

She was equally disdainful of the (financial) courtship of a Tennessee-based fried chicken fast-food chain and the overtures of a Milwaukee manufacturer of processed cheeses who wanted to diversify.

"But I thought you *wanted* to sell," Danny said.

Sophie had told him right from the beginning that her goal was to make money and that her accountant had advised her that the way to do *that* was to build a business and sell out.

"I do," Sophie said. "To the right buyer."

Her words triggered a memory of Danny's: the story his mother had told about how, in Eilberg's eyes, Reinhardt Estes had been the right buyer and how, in Estes's eyes, Lew Swann had been the right buyer.

It gave him an idea.

"Sophie wants to sell KitchenWorks—on her terms," Danny told his mother. "But she's fussy about who to. As fussy as you always said Reinhardt Estes was. She wants to hang on to some of the stock, and she says she intends to live high on the hog—very high—off dividends and capital gains. In her eyes, the right buyer is going to be the buyer who makes the biggest success out of KitchenWorks."

"And that person would be you?" Ellen asked, interrupting.

"How did you guess?" Danny asked with that devilish twinkle and piratical smile.

"But it would cost a million dollars!" Ellen exclaimed.

"You're thinking small," Danny said. "A million—at least!"

Buying out Countess Tamara's chain of catering businesses and purchasing the brownstone on East Fiftieth Street had accustomed Ellen to thinking of money in fairly large sums; her success on AM/USA had accustomed her to making money in large amounts. But, still, a million was different from thousands.

"A million—at least!—is out of my league," she told Danny, wanting to conclude the conversation. "Way out of my league."

"Says who? I remember the first time you earned a hundred dollars," Danny said, refusing to pick up on Ellen's clue. "You woke us up after midnight to show us the check. Don't you remember?"

Ellen nodded. "I remember," she said. She hadn't thought of the incident for years and years. Now, a hundred-dollar order was rare. A nuisance, in fact. She looked closely at Danny. She had graduated from hundreds to thousands. Why close her mind now? "Let me think about it. I'll talk to Al. And to Lew . . ."

The negotiations for À La Carte, a division of Decor, to buy out KitchenWorks began in the spring of 1978. And Ellen found out that a million-dollar deal did not mean running down to the bank and drawing out a million dollars. It meant a transfer of stock for part of the purchase price, because Sophie insisted on retaining stock and paying out the balance in monthly sums over a period of time, most of the payout to come out of KitchenWorks' earnings.

Although a million dollars was still a great deal of money, by the time negotiations were completed—at terms satisfactory to Sophie and to À La Carte—it was no longer an impossible, terrifying amount of money. In fact, Ellen reminded herself, the first years of À La Carte when she literally could not pay the bills had been much, much scarier, much, much more intimidating.

Perhaps the difference was experience; perhaps the difference was confidence. Perhaps the difference was Ellen herself—the woman she had been, the woman she had become.

The papers were signed almost a year after the negotiations had begun.

"You're a millionaire now, Mom," Danny said.

"You're an optimist—just like your father," Ellen replied, thinking that the difference between Danny and herself was the difference between seeing a glass that was half-filled with water as half-empty or seeing it as half-full. "The way I look at it is that I *owe* a million."

Danny laughed and shook his head. "One day you're going to wake up and think like a millionaire," he said. "I just want to make sure I'm around when it happens."

"Me, too!" said Ellen and laughed at the impossible thought.

"Anyway," Danny said, now serious, "I want to thank you. You won't be sorry. I promise."

"I know, Danny," Ellen said, overwhelmed with love and admiration. Danny, who had grown up without a father, had always been a rock. "I know . . ."

And she wasn't.

Danny was full of ideas. He commissioned the top fashion photographer in New York to do the catalog and the reigning prince of pop art to design the cover. The KitchenWorks catalog became a collector's item, and business the first year that Danny ran things grossed $1.7 million.

The next year he introduced an innovation: two never-before-published recipes contributed by Julia Child. That second year business grossed $2.2 million, and Danny was two years ahead of schedule in the buy-out agreement.

KitchenWorks—and its twenty-seven-year-old chief executive—was the subject of a "Sixty Minutes" feature, a photographic essay in *Fortune*, and a front-page *Wall Street Journal* story. Everyone who breathed had heard of KitchenWorks and KitchenWorks' success, and everyone celebrated the success in a different way.

Ellen and Lew gave Danny the title he wanted—and had earned: president of the KitchenWorks subsidiary.

"My son, the president," Ellen had laughed, tears of pride and joy in her eyes, at the big champagne dinner she had given to make the announcement.

Sophie bought herself a sable coat.

Sherri sent Danny flowers, a magnum of Dom Perignon, and told the press that she had taught him everything he knew.

And Johanna told Mel Factir that it was time to stop fooling around. In late March—ironically in the same week Phil had died—Ellen answered her door.

"Mrs. Durban?" asked the stranger. She was a well-dressed woman of middle-age who, Ellen thought, seemed nervous.

"Yes?" Ellen replied, thinking that new clients didn't usually just show up at the front door.

"Summons," the woman said and handed Ellen the paper. She looked at it as if it were a bomb.

13

ELLEN CONSULTED THREE DIFFERENT LAWYERS IN HER SEARCH for someone to take À La Carte's case against Johanna, and they all dished out the same advice: settle.

Settling would be easier and cheaper than fighting. Fighting would be expensive, time-consuming, and there was no absolute guarantee that, in the end, Ellen would win. No matter how liberated the media proclaimed women to be, the fact was that most judges tended to be conservative, tended to be on the side of wives. Particularly wives whose husbands had gone to great lengths to conceal assets in divorce cases.

Settle.

Lew's lawyers told him the same thing. Settle. It'll cost you more to fight than just to pay her off and shut her up.

And Max's lawyers followed suit. Settle, they said. Pay her off and shut her up.

"I'll do my best," Max said. Johanna's attack on Decor had roused Max's fury. He didn't care what embarrassment had cost him personally. After all, he was a big boy. But he went blind with rage when Johanna moved to seize Decor as a divorce settlement. Decor was family. Decor had been founded by his father, passed down to his son. And, although Max might tease

Lew, although he might joke about Decor as kid stuff, let anyone else raise a finger against it and Max went berserk. "I'll give her the goddamn million she wants."

He took her to Acapulco for a week—a trip he wrote off as a business expense. On the plane coming back, Max told Johanna that he'd decided to give her her million.

"Get your lawyers to back off Decor and you'll get your million," he said.

"A million isn't enough," Johanna said, sticking her tongue into his ear. "I want two million."

"You're crazy!" Max pulled away from her.

"No," she said. "Not crazy. Just good at arithmetic. Decor now has seven divisions. Including À La Carte, which owns KitchenWorks. My accountants value Decor at over eight million dollars. I'm only asking for a quarter," she said generously.

"You'll never get it!" Max said. "You'd better take the million while the offer is still good."

"A judge will think I'm being reasonable," Johanna said. "If we go to court—"

"Take me to court!" Max exploded. "All I have to do is let a judge know about the screwing around you did while we were married—"

"Don't threaten me, Max," Johanna warned. "Because you're not the only one with some dirty linen to wash. If you don't come up with the two million, I'm not only going to keep after Decor until I get it, I'm going to break up Lew and Reenie's marriage."

"We've been through that!" Max exploded. Lew and Reenie's marriage was the only Swann marriage intact, and the longer it lasted, the more fiercely protective Max became of it. "Anyway, what could you do at this late date?"

"Remember the letters?" Johanna asked in a perfectly reasonable tone. "From Reenie to Phil? Love letters, Max. Explicit love letters."

"You burned them."

"But first I Xeroxed them," Johanna said, sweet as pie.

Max turned pink, red, and purple as Johanna continued. "All I have to do is show them to Lew. Then I'll tell Reenie about Lew and Ellen. You'll not only have me suing to get Decor, but Reenie is going to want her share, too. Then, my dear Max, you and Lew won't have shit left."

* * *

"She's raised the ante," Max told Ellen. "She wants two million dollars."

"Lew told me," Ellen said, awed at Johanna's nerve. Awed and disgusted. "What are you going to do?"

"Give it to her." Max, for the first time since Ellen had met him, looked his age. He seemed gray and lined, and his usually robust frame seemed shrunken.

"Give it to her!" Ellen was appalled. Ever since Johanna had begun her lawsuit Ellen had felt she was in a time warp. She didn't think women lived off men anymore; she didn't think women married men for money anymore She was beginning to realize how naive she was, what a protected life she had been leading, because now every woman she knew worked.

"If I don't, she'll get nasty," Max said. "Really nasty."

"What's nasty?" Ellen asked. "How much nastier can she get? She's trying to take the company Lew's spent his whole life building . . . not to mention half of À La Carte. And she's never spent one hour of time or one penny of money to contribute to their success."

"I didn't tell Lew the whole story," Max said obscurely. "That's why I wanted to talk to you."

"It's not like you to be mysterious, Max," Ellen said. "You're the world's most outspoken person. What's the whole story?" she asked. And then, "Does it involve me and Lew?"

Max nodded. "Johanna threatened to tell Reenie."

"But it's been over for some time," Ellen said, thinking that the affair that had meant so much to both of them—personally and professionally—had run its course. And in its course had saved Lew's marriage.

"That's not how Johanna would present it," Max said. "She'd let Reenie think it's still going on."

"We could tell Reenie the truth," Ellen said, sick at the thought of a confrontation. "She'd believe us. We could make her believe us because we'd be telling the truth."

"Even if you could, it wouldn't do much good," Max said, "because she's also threatened to show Lew the letters Reenie wrote to Phil."

"Reenie wrote letters to *Phil*?" Ellen asked, stunned, not believing she had heard correctly.

She saw the color drain from Max's face. She *had* heard correctly.

"I thought you knew . . ." Max looked at everything in the room except her.

Ellen shook her head, unable to find her voice. She closed her eyes and gasped for air. She felt as if she'd been punched in the stomach.

"Are you sure?" Ellen finally asked, *knowing* that Max never lied but still compelled to ask the question. "Have you seen them?"

Max nodded. "The originals. Johanna burned them. But first she made Xeroxes." He'd give anything to take back the words he'd said, the secret he'd inadvertently revealed.

"Has Lew"—Ellen paused to swallow hard—"seen them?"

"No," said Max in almost a whisper, appalled by the extent and degree of Johanna's destructiveness, wondering what there was in him—what fatal weakness—that had attracted him to her. "Apparently not."

"I didn't think so," Ellen said. "He was always so guilty . . . about us. So afraid of hurting Reenie . . ."

"Lew's a straight arrow," Max said. "Too straight a lot of the time."

Ellen nodded. And then she said what had been going through her mind: "So you mean if you don't give her the two million dollars—for two years of marriage!—that Johanna will go ahead until she gets Decor *or* breaks up Lew and Reenie so that Reenie will also go after Decor?"

"Exactly," said Max. "Exactly right. I'm going to give her what she wants. I don't have any choice."

Ellen almost let the conversation drop at that point.

After all, what was she fighting for? It was Max's money. Max's marriage. Max's greedy ex-wife.

And then she thought *no!*

"No!" she suddenly said, startling Max. "Absolutely not! I don't care what's between you and Johanna. That's your business. But blackmail is something else! And that's what she's got in mind. Max, tell her to go to hell!"

For days Ellen walked around with what felt like a large lump at the top of her stomach. Phil. Her suspicions had been valid, after all.

And what would she have done if she had known at the time? Would she have demanded a divorce? Would she? With two small children? With two small children and no way to support them? With two small children and no father to help bring them up? Would she? Would she have chosen what fate had given her no choice about?

She knew that she would not have. She would not have been brave enough, confident enough, strong enough. She would have found a way to live with it. To live with the angry, bitter knowledge that would never have gone away. That would have eaten into every moment of every day. That would have been there when she and Phil trimmed the Christmas tree. When they shared the Sunday *Times*. When they fought or made love or did the dishes.

And she wondered what kind of woman she would have been. A bitter, angry woman—that she knew.

Still, she kept trying to swallow the painful lump that rose up in her.

But it wouldn't go away. Gradually, the rawness of the pain began to subside, and, little by little, Ellen was able to think and to remember as well as to feel.

She remembered how Phil used to tease her about how attracted Lew was to her; how Phil actually seemed to encourage her to consider Lew as a romantic possibility for herself. At the time, she had been uncomfortable—and uncomfortably flattered. She had accepted Phil's words at face value, had accepted that Phil saw something in Lew's response to her that she didn't. Now she began to think that something was behind Phil's "teasing"... and that the something was guilt. He'd have felt better if *she* had been unfaithful... too.

And, as she assembled the mysterious fragments of Lew's marriage, they all fell into place like a jigsaw puzzle. Ellen suddenly understood the behavior that Lew had never understood, Reenie's running hot and cold—passionate now, frigid then. And Ellen could even construct a timetable based on what Lew had told her. Passionate in the year before Phil's death; cold for some time after his funeral. And Ellen constructed a theory—only a theory, but it made sense to her—that Reenie's mysterious hot and cold spells probably had to do with the presence—or absence—of another man in her life.

Ellen recalled Lew's devastating guilt about their affair because of Reenie and thought it was probably wasted emotion. She could, of course, tell Lew about Reenie. But she wouldn't. Why? Lew and Reenie seemed to have made something good of their marriage. What was the point of undermining it with news of an old affair?

Telling Lew wouldn't make Ellen feel better. Only time would.

And then she asked herself as dispassionately as she could: Why did Phil do it?

At first she assumed it was her fault. Was there something wrong with her? Something inadequate? Was she not enough for him?

But then, after a while, Ellen began to ask herself still other questions. Had too much of a burden been placed on marriage back when she and Phil were young? The woman renouncing self to be wife and mother; the man renouncing vulnerability and fallibility to be sole support, sole strength, sole provider? Did people's idea of marriage back then place too many demands on husband and wife, rigidly forcing them into "approved" roles? And was an affair simply an attempt to escape from the impossible demands?

Johanna's lawyers filed papers that would make Decor and all its subsidiaries, including a 50 percent interest in À La Carte, part of the financial settlement in the divorce case of *Swann v. Swann*.

Lew's and Ellen's lawyers filed papers requesting that the judge dismiss Johanna's suit.

The legal papers were supported by accounting documents. The files took up almost half of a file drawer, and Ellen's initial legal and accounting bills came to almost ten thousand dollars.

When she wrote out the checks, she did something she hadn't done in a long time: she cried.

All that money, she thought, just to hang on to what she had, slowly and painfully, dollar by dollar, hour by hour, built to support herself and her children and to leave as a legacy for her children and grandchildren. All that money just to stay where she'd been in the first place. All that money to fight a battle she could never hope to win—all she could hope to do was cut her losses.

"Maybe my high and mighty moral stand against blackmail is just too expensive," she told Al in a moment of despair.

"No," Al said. "You're doing the right thing."

And Al gave her the courage and the energy to go on.

She didn't know what she'd have done without him.

The judge's decision denied Ellen's and Lew's petition to dismiss the case. He would hear Johanna's case. He wanted further particulars.

Further particulars meant more lawyers' and accountants' bills, and Ellen wondered once again whether she was being an idealistic fool.

The decade that had begun with Vietnam ended with Iran. Interest rates were in the double digits and so was the inflation rate; the bond market was in ruins and high mortgage rates had devastated the housing industry; the Dow Jones Industrial Average, which had been kissing a thousand, sank below 900, then below 850. The quart of milk that had cost 33¢ in 1970 now cost 63¢; a new car, a compact, gas-saving foreign import, cost almost ten thousand dollars—more than most people could afford; and, according to the Department of Housing and Urban Development, in 1980 nearly two-thirds of all American families could not have afforded to buy the houses in which they were living.

People still wanted to entertain, but everyone, even the richest people, was now money-conscious. Ellen had adapted to the times. She now suggested cassoulets, Indian and Middle Eastern food, pasta and rice and lentil dishes that were both delicious and economical. *Coq au vin* and *boeuf bourguignon*— dishes that Ellen had made hundreds of times when she first started À La Carte and that had been, at that time, the height of sophistication—had become embarrassingly clichéd and "out" in the seventies, when nouvelle cuisine was coming "in." Now their earthy straightforwardness seemed appealing; and, when one of the food magazines Ellen subscribed to had a lead article about the new chic of French provincial cooking, Ellen felt satisfyingly ahead of the trend. She had begun, once again, suggesting those old favorites for dinner parties. Fashion and taste had come full circle... and, in a very difficult year for business, À La Carte not only held its own but, because of Danny's innovative merchandising and continuing success with KitchenWorks, actually increased in profits—which increased Johanna's greed and determination.

Encouraged by the judge's first favorable-to-her decision, Johanna had Mel Factir file an amended demand raising the amount she wanted in settlement.

The consequence was that Ellen and Lew would have to answer her new demands with a new defense. Ellen was faced with another ten thousand dollars' worth of legal and accounting fees. At least.

"Maybe we ought to settle," Lew said. "Maybe the lawyers are right . . ."

"No," Ellen said. Because now she felt she was not only fighting Johanna's crude blackmail attempt, but that she was fighting on behalf of every woman—and every man—who had struggled for success against those who wanted to take without giving, to profit without contributing.

And an expression Lew had never seen crossed Ellen's face. Anger. Real anger. Followed by determination.

"I'm not letting her take what you worked for and what I worked for. If you won't fight, Lew, I will. And I'm going to win. I don't know how. But I'm going to win."

14

"I DON'T KNOW KNOW TO TELL YOU THIS," TONI SAID TO
Brenda in an unusually hesitant voice. "I never thought it would
happen..."

At thirty-one, Toni was a full partner in Edder and Stern
and well beyond the thirty by thirty. She was also beyond the
rigid matched suit and uniform silk blouse. She wore a soft
suede dress in sage green, belted with a crush of woven leather
held by a hand-crafted sterling silver buckle. Her buttery low
boots cost more than Brenda had spent on groceries for a whole
month. She was very slim, slimmer than Brenda had ever seen
her; and with a short, almost boyish, yet softly waved haircut,
Toni seemed neither womanly nor girlish. There was an attractive androgynous quality about her, as if she had been newly
minted. Only the expression in her eyes showed that she was
far from untouched.

"Tuck and I are getting divorced," Toni said, sipping the
black currant tea Brenda had made. Brenda had given up caf-
feine now that she was pregnant a second time. Caro was
napping in the dining ell Brenda had turned into a nursery. "An
amiable divorce."

Brenda wasn't surprised, but she still didn't know what to

say. Are you happy? Are you sure? Is there someone else? Finally, she said what she felt: "I'm sorry."

"So am I," Toni said. "But we couldn't go on. I'm on the road more than two weeks a month. We thought that once I made partner I'd spend more time in the home office, but it hasn't turned out that way at all. Now that I'm a partner, companies think more of me and want to see more of me. Do you know that except for a bed and a table our apartment is still unfurnished?" Toni asked.

Brenda nodded; she understood. When you were absorbed in your work, when you were, as she had been, on the track—maybe—of the obesity-causing factor or, in Toni's case, on the scent of an undervalued company ripe for takeover, who wanted to think about curtain fabric or whether the living room furniture ought to be French provincial or Conran contemporary? It seemed so trivial, so unimportant.

"It's sad," Toni went on picking at a well-groomed, nicely buffed fingernail, "but we ran out of love. I can't even remember what it felt like. Neither can Tuck. We've talked about it a lot. We can feel a lot of things—ambition, competition, happiness, excitement, pleasure, jealousy, disappointment. But not love. You know, Brenda, of all the couples in our class, you and Jeff are the only ones who are still together."

"Sometimes I didn't think we'd make it," Brenda admitted. Toni knew about Brenda's affair with Sandy, about Jeff's affair that had brought Brenda back from Germany. "And it wasn't just Jeff's thing with that girl from the clinic. We had become strangers who shared an apartment. I was involved in my career; Jeff was involved in the clinic. We didn't have anything left over for each other."

Toni nodded. "You know what Tuck told me? That he's not even interested in having an affair. That he just doesn't have the time or the energy." Toni sipped her tea. "We're liberated, but it's some hell of a liberation. Sometimes I meet someone through work. And we're attracted. I've gotten so liberated that when it happens, the guy and I talk about it. We ask ourselves if going to bed is going to get in the way of our business relationship. We almost always decide that it will. We have a second drink, agree not to go to bed, shake hands, and say goodnight. That's it," Toni said. "That's the end result of the big-deal sexual revolution. Talk and a handshake!"

"The amazing thing is that you don't sound bitter." Brenda poured a second cup of the fragrant tea for Toni.

"I'm not," said Toni. "I made my choice. I wanted to have a terrific career, and I do. And I'm happy with my choice. But, you know, Brenda, I admire you for doing what you did. I wouldn't be able to give up the money, the power, the perks, the excitement, the deals. It's addictive, like a drug," she concluded. "And, like a drug, there are side effects. Not all of them pleasant. Like no marriage and an empty apartment. Still, I don't know if I'd be able to do what you did."

"I miss working. And not just for the excitement and satisfaction. For the money. Everything's so expensive now. We're not used to struggling along on one salary," Brenda said. "Before I got pregnant again, I tried to get a job with All Chem's New England branch. I call Diane Wyre . . . you remember her. I was her mentor. I hired her, got her my old job when I went to Germany. I had to call three times before she'd return my call. I asked if there was anything in the New England labs, and she said no, and that was that. She didn't offer to ask around, didn't say she'd speak to her friends at other companies . . . nothing." Brenda was confused, hurt.

"You remember sisterhood from the old days," Toni said. "When all the women pulled together. When we were a united minority. It's not like that anymore. The economy's rotten. There are very few top jobs and barely any for women, no matter what propaganda you read. The few women who do have top slots aren't looking for competition, believe me."

Brenda sighed. Toni was, unfortunately, right.

"Anyway, now that I'm pregnant again, a job is out of the question. And I've got other problems . . . like finding a place to live. I always assumed once we had children that we'd move out of the apartment and into a house. I've been looking, and although there are a lot of houses for sale, we can't even afford the down payment, never mind the mortgage. The Reagan cuts are affecting the clinic, and Jeff's worried about being out of a job," Brenda said. She had never realized until she had stopped working how spoiled she and Jeff had been with two salaries to spend. They had thought it would go on forever, had never saved a dime. And Brenda, for the first time in her life, nervous, insecure, anxious about the future, finally began to understand what it must have been like for her mother when her father died. How frightening, how overwhelming, how unprepared her mother must have been. "We're going to be awfully crowded when the second baby comes along."

"Why don't you sell your stock and use the money to buy a house?" Toni asked. "The bonus money you gave me to invest for you."

"How much is it worth now?" Brenda asked. She never thought about that money; she wanted it to be a nest egg for Caro and any brothers or sisters she might have.

"Seventy thousand dollars," Toni said.

"Seventy thousand dollars!" Brenda thought she'd faint.

She barely heard Toni's explanation. The orginal investment in the silicon chip company had quintupled.

"I sold out and bought Conoco. When Dupont took over Conoco, I took the profits and bought Marathon Oil. At the close of the market yesterday, you were worth seventy thousand dollars."

"Oh, my God! Toni! You're a genius!" Brenda, pregnant as she was, jumped up and down and hugged her friend. "Wait until I tell Jeff when he comes home tonight! Maybe we'll have to choose between a nest egg for the kids and a house to bring them up in. But at least it's a choice! Oh, Toni, how can I thank you?"

Toni smiled. "Maybe one day I'll ask you to introduce me to someone I can love."

But when Jeff got home, there was an expression on his face Brenda had never seen before.

"The clinic's closing...the Reagan cuts," he said. "I don't have a job anymore, Brenda. I've been fired..."

The further Ellen got into the lawsuit, the angrier and more frustrated she felt. Defending Johanna's amended demands was forcing her to start all over again with the lawyers and the accountants.

"It's costing me thousands and thousands of dollars at a time when it's harder and harder just to break even," Ellen told Al. "Sometimes I think I ought to do what Sophie did and sell À La Carte, take the money, invest it, and live off the incomce. The trouble is, I don't know what I'd do with myself. I'm used to working. I *love* my work. How many cruises could I take? How many massages could I have? How many days a week could I spend in Saks?" Ellen seemed pale and drawn.

"You look tired," Al said.

"Tired?" Ellen asked. "Exhausted is more like it."

"Too tired for *Evita*?" he asked. "One of my clients is stage manager. I have house seats. Are you free?"

As Ellen sat in the theater watching Eva Perón take over Juan, his country, and then a good slice of the world in song and dance, an idea came to her that was so bold and daring she was electrified with excitement.

"You look fabulous," Al said as they left the theater. Ellen was glowing, her eyes sparkled, even her posture seemed light and buoyant. "Almost as if you've had a rest cure!"

And Ellen looked at him, her blue-green cat-shaped eyes shining, and said, "Eva Perón! Katharine Graham! Estee Lauder! Golda Meir! Mary Wells Lawrence! And me! Ellen Durban!"

And before Al could ask her what on earth she was talking about, she threw her arms around him and, in the middle of the theater crowd, kissed him right on the lips.

"Bet you wouldn't do that when we're alone," he teased when she had finished.

"Bet you I would!" she answered, and the small crowd around them, many of whom recognized Ellen from AM/USA, applauded.

"Lew, have you ever thought of selling Decor?" Ellen asked. She had called him the minute she had gotten home and had asked to see him as soon as possible. They had breakfast the next morning at Lew's Manhattan *pied à terre*. Lew sat in his usual chair and Ellen in Max's. The small Sony was tuned to AM/USA, the sound turned off. As Ellen spoke, Lew was distracted as her image flickered on the screen.

Lew shook his head. "Of course not. Why should I?"

"To protect it."

"Protect it?" he asked mystified. "From what?"

"From Johanna," Ellen said.

"Who'd buy it? A company involved in a lawsuit?"

"Me."

"You?" Lew blinked.

"Me," Ellen repeated and reached over and switched off the Sony. She wanted Lew's undivided attention.

"Suppose the little fish swallows the big fish? What I mean is, what if À La Carte buys Decor? À La Carte, after all, is my company. Incorporated in my name. If I own Decor, there won't be anything for Johanna to sue. After all—thank God!— she didn't marry me!" Ellen paused, waiting for Lew's answer. Her eyes gleamed with intimations of wicked revenge.

Lew, who had admired her, who had loved her, was now astonished by her. Would she never cease to intrigue him? Would she never cease to attract him?

"Ingenious!" he said, his slow smile reflecting back to her the identical note of anticipated delicious vengeance. "Beautiful! Brilliant!"

"Ingenious! Beautiful! Brilliant!" Max agreed. "But expensive as hell. Where's she going to get the money?"

"What she can't raise directly she's going to borrow."

"Good for her!" said Max. "Where do I get in line?"

The line was longer than Max—or Ellen—had even begun to imagine. It began with Danny.

"*Now* you're thinking like a millionaire!" he said with a piratical grin when Ellen told him her plan. "You can have my savings *and* every dime I can borrow against my KitchenWorks stock. *And*, if you still need more, I'll hold up a bank!"

Toni, now a partner-director of Edder and Stern's Venture Capital Fund, was enthusiastic. With the approval of the Edder and Stern board, she invested a large pool of her clients' money in the purchase of Decor by À La Carte.

"Food services and home-improvement resources look good in a recessionary and/or stagnating economy," she told her clients. And they went along with her because Toni had credibility.

"Credibility and a red-hot track record," Danny said and invited her to the opening of the first KitchenWorks retail shop on the renovated ground floor of a cast-iron building in TriBeCa.

"I'd love to," Toni said, and she looked at Danny with new eyes. He was tall, over six feet two; he wore, casually, an impeccable hand-tailored suit. He was undeniably handsome, and his obvious confidence and capability were perfectly complimented—if you knew him very, very well—by the maturity of a man who grew up thrust into an adult's role at a very young age, by the sensitivity of a man who had grown up with women and who really liked them.

Toni asked herself, in wonder, what had happened to the four-year difference in their ages that had once seemed so enormous.

* * *

Caroline was hurt at not being included.

"Danny told me about your plan to buy Decor," she told Ellen one afternoon over tea and homemade English muffins in Ellen's comfortable kitchen. "I feel left out because you didn't come to me, Ellen. I want to help," she said, handing Ellen an envelope.

"Thank you!" Ellen said, surprised at how much it contained, and then, noticing the penciled notation on the envelope, asked, "What's XON?"

"Exxon," Caroline said. "It's time to sell the oils. OPEC isn't the money-machine it used to be."

As Caroline spoke, a sudden memory came to Ellen, a memory that had been buried for years.

"PPG," she said. "Caroline, is there a stock called PPG?"

"Pittsburgh Plate and Glass," Caroline said instantly. And then, with a fond smile: "I made a bundle on it."

"Caroline, did you used to . . . lend . . . Phil money?"

Caroline nodded. "I loved him," she said softly. "He was my only child. I gave him everything. Too much, perhaps. It made him think he could afford his dreams. Do you think I was wrong?"

"No," Ellen said. "I don't think you were wrong. And if Phil had lived, he probably would have made his dreams come true himself." Then another question came to Ellen: "But how did you afford it? Phil was always so lavish with money . . . your money, I now realize. You must have . . . lent . . . him a great deal."

"I suppose I did," said Caroline with a smile both wistful and proud. "I'm an ace bridge player. Always was. Plus I inherited a tiny trust fund. One day I decided it was stupid to spend all my winnings on clothes and makeup, and I began to follow the stock market."

"Tommy must be proud of you," Ellen said, recalling the time Danny had quoted Caroline's investment opinions as if quoting an oracle.

"Tommy doesn't know. He thinks any woman who's interested in money is unfeminine," Caroline said. "So it's my little secret. After all, what good would it do me to ruin Tommy's illusions about me? I know that it's fashionable now to 'let it all hang out,' but it's a fashion I don't happen to agree with."

"Disagreeing with fashionable thoughts," Ellen said, speaking from costly experience, "is one of the hardest things in the world to do."

And she suddenly understood why, all these years, thinking about money and talking about money had been by far the most difficult part of running À La Carte. She, too, had thought money was unfeminine because that was what Phil had thought, and it was what "everyone" thought. As if money had a sex!

"Caroline, I wonder if I'll ever stop learning," Ellen said as her mother-in-law, in her mid-seventies, beautifully made-up and groomed and flatteringly and youthfully dressed, prepared to leave.

"Not if you're lucky," Caroline said and left in a cloud of Chloë, not wanting to be late for her masseur.

Max, as usual, took the blunt approach: "How much do you need, kid?" he asked. "I've got a numbered account Johanna never ferreted out."

And he wondered, as he did from time to time, why he had never had the brains to marry a woman like Ellen. Not that he was planning to give up. Who knows? he asked himself. Maybe next time. Because there would definitely be, for Max, a next time. And, if that didn't work, a time after that.

"I was there at the beginning," Al reminded her with affection. "I've always *felt* like a partner. Now's my chance to *be* one!"

And he cleaned out his money market fund for her.

"Partners?" he asked when he handed her the check.

"Partners," Ellen said, giving the word a double meaning that made Al, who had always envied the partnership his parents had—a partnership in marriage and career—very happy indeed.

The line even included Edwin Garren of County Mercantile.

"We'd be happy to extend you a line of credit," he offered at the monthly officers' lunch, which Ellen had been catering for years. "We'll make a special arrangement," he went on, his mouse face intense and anxious-to-please. "A point under prime."

"Thank you," Ellen said politely. And then she got to say the most luscious, juiciest words she had spoken in a long, long time: "But you're about twenty years too late . . ."

* * *

And the line ended with Brenda.

"I have seventy thousand dollars," she said. "Let me give it to you so you can buy Decor."

"But I thought you were going to use your money to make a down payment on a house," Ellen said, surprised and touched.

"A house isn't as important to me as you are," Brenda said. And then, tentatively, afraid of being rejected, aware of how often she had done the rejecting: "If you'll let me, I'd like to open a branch of À La Carte here in Boston. People know who you are from AM/USA, and they've been asking me to—"

"But you swore you'd never get involved in À La Carte," Ellen reminded Brenda. "And didn't I hear you say you'd never work until your children were much older?"

"That's what I said," Brenda admitted. "I didn't realize what a luxury I was taking for granted. Jeff is still trying to find another job. I *have* to work. And the way things are going, the odds are most certainly that Caro will have to work and so will her sister. Just like I do. Just like you did. And growing up with a working mother sets the best example in the world. I just never appreciated what happened to you until it happened to me. I love you," she said.

And the lump in Ellen's throat did not stop her from telling Brenda how much she loved her.

"She can't!" Johanna told Max furiously. She addressed him as if Ellen were not even in the room—the big corner office Johanna had once decorated for Lew.

"She can. And did," said Max. "Buying a company isn't against the law."

"But she can't do this to me! She just can't!" Johanna repeated, totally focused on Max.

"Tough," Max shrugged. "Besides, she already did."

The papers had been signed a week ago. Decor was now a fully owned subsidiary of À La Carte. The combined companies had a current value of ten million dollars. Ellen Durban was president; Lewis Swann, vice-president; Danny Durban, treasurer.

"But what am I going to do?" Johanna literally wrung her hands in anguish and frustration. There was no Decor left to sue: Max had sold out every single share and wiped out his own cash accounts to help Ellen buy him out.

"You can try to earn a living," Max said. "You've still got the hairdresser's in General Motors Plaza. Build it up. Make it work. Be like Ellen."

Max had waved the red flag in front of Johanna, but before she could speak, Ellen did.

"And I'm not finished with you, Johanna," she said, entering the conversation for the first time. "I want those letters. And I want them before Lew gets back to the office."

"You'll never get them," Johanna said. "They're all I have."

"Bull!" said Ellen, borrowing vocabulary from Max. "You'd better give them to me, Johanna. Because if you don't, I'm going to prosecute you for theft. Those letters are my husband's property. Property of his estate, now. And I'm the executor of that estate. If you don't give them back—*all* the copies—you'll find yourself in court again. And *this* time as the defendant!"

"Max, she can't!" Johanna implored, still not deigning to address Ellen.

"I most certainly can," Ellen broke in, infuriated at the way Johanna ignored her. "And I will if you don't hand them over. I want them by two o'clock, or my lawyer is going to recover them on behalf of Phil's estate."

Ellen pushed the formidable-looking legal papers her lawyer had prepared over the desk toward Johanna.

"Do I have any choice?" Johanna asked, subdued, finally looking at Ellen and addressing her directly.

"No," said Ellen. "None."

Even in the early 1980s, a female president of a $10-million company, who had gotten there herself without being someone's daughter or someone's wife or having a strong someone (male) in the background pulling the strings, was a rarity. When the announcement of the purchase of Decor by À La Carte was made public, Ellen became a heroine: to the business press, to women's page editors, to the deans of business schools. She was *People*d and *Fortune*d; *Vogue*d and *Ladies Home Journal*d; *Donahue*d and *Signature*d.

Almost everyone wanted to know what her "secret" was. As if the "secret," once known, was copyrightable, merchandisable, adaptable, borrowable, or stealable, available for instant success by anyone who cared to apply it.

"There is no secret," Ellen kept saying over and over. "Or, if there *is* one, *I* certainly don't know what it is."

"What was the hardest part?" she was asked over and over. "Was it getting started? Was it getting clients? Was it the cooking? Was it the ups and downs in the economy? Was it the threats of competitors? Was it keeping up with changes in food fashions? The time pressure? The fatigue? Balancing children and a career? Finding the time for a personal life?"

"All of them were hard at one time or another. But the hardest thing of all was discovering and defining an identity independent of what 'everyone' said women were, ought to be, or should be," Ellen answered. And then she added, wryly, "The hardest part of becoming a self-made woman was becoming a *self*..."

"And can anyone do it?" they wanted to know.

"If I could," Ellen said with a serious smile, "anyone can..."

And then she discovered that there was one more step to take.

She was impressed with Brenda.

Proud of Danny.

Indulgent with Caro and her sister.

Comfortable with Lew.

Admiring of Caroline.

Playful with Max.

Contemptuous of Johanna.

Awed by Toni.

Self-confident with her clients.

Pleasantly businesslike with her staff.

Charming on AM/USA.

Creative at menu- and party-planning.

Tough when she had to be tough.

Humorous when things were funny.

No-nonsense when they weren't.

And, with Al, she was even more.

She comforted him when he needed comforting and expected—and received—the same from him.

She wanted him to applaud her triumphs on the days she was better than she thought she could be, and to buck her up on days she thought she was worse than she could have imagined.

She wanted cuddling and tenderness, a good fight now and then, a responsive ear, a steady shoulder, and a loyal heart.

What she wanted she gave—and so did Al.

"It wasn't a self I had to find, after all," she told him. "It was selves—and they were there all along."

And she discovered something about happiness. It wasn't success or money or celebrity that made her happy. It was the same familiar things that had *always* made her happy: her family, her friends, someone to love who loved her.

And she was never happier than when she was in the kitchen, all the burners lit, cooking something delicious for someone she loved.

"It's been a long time since I've cooked for two," she told Al early in the spring of 1983. "And Reinhardt's just sent over some beautiful quail—he's added perfect quail to his perfect chickens. I'm just in the mood to cook them—with juniper berries and wild rice. Do you like quail?"

"At least as much as I like juniper berries and wild rice," Al said.

"Then would you come to dinner?" Ellen asked. "The last dinner at 76 Dogwood Lane?"

She was about to move out, the new owners were moving in. She had sold the house to help raise the money to buy Decor. The house she had once been unable to sell for thirty thousand dollars now brought almost one hundred and fifty.

"Just the two of us?" Al asked.

"Just the two of us."

"Because there's something I want to ask you..."

Ellen smiled.

She was almost sure what the something was. And she was absolutely sure of what her answer would be.

ABOUT THE AUTHOR

Ruth Harris grew up on Long Island and graduated from Sarah Lawrence. She has worked in publishing and has written several novels. She currently lives in New York City with her husband, Michael.

THE MARRIAGE BED
by Constance Beresford Howe

As a teenager, Anne had planned to marry a rich Older Man. This scheme had come to nothing when Max, the first suitable candidate to come along, had perversely married her mother instead.

The next plan was to have a brilliant career. This scheme in turn rather fell apart because, unaccountably, her biology degree didn't teach her to master the practice of birth control.

So, still in her early twenties, she has become the mother of two delightful accidents, aged three and one. A third mistake is on the way.

All this has got to be too much for her husband who fled to a commune, taking his secretary with him.

Then it is that more plans are made: by her mother, her mother-in-law, a neighbour, her step-father, even the family doctor. And more plans mean, of course, more confusion ...

'Funny, moving, thought provoking'   *Woman's Own*

'Warm, thoughtful and critically acclaimed'
                                        Books and Bookmen

NEW ENGLISH LIBRARY

Book Tokens

**Give them
the pleasure of choosing**

Book Tokens can be bought
and exchanged at most
bookshops in Great Britain
and Ireland.

NEL BESTSELLERS

Even Chance	*Elizabeth Bennett*	£1.50
The Marriage Bed	*Constance Beresford Howe*	£1.75
Lights, Laughter and a Lady	*Barbara Cartland*	£1.25
Forefathers	*Nancy Cato*	£2.50
Maura's Dream	*Joel Gross*	£2.25
Memory and Desire	*Justine Harlowe*	£2.50
Only Perfect	*Rochelle Larkin*	£1.75
Sisters	*Linda Lauren*	£1.50
Almonds and Raisins	*Maisie Mosco*	£1.95
The Enticers	*Natasha Peters*	£1.95
Believing in Giants	*Charlotte Vale Allen*	£1.75

All these books are available at your local bookshop or newsagent, or can be ordered direct from the publisher. Just tick the titles you want and fill in the form below.

NEL P.O. BOX 11, FALMOUTH TR10 9EN, CORNWALL

Postage Charge:

U.K. Customers 55p for the first book plus 22p for the second book and 14p for each additional book ordered to a maximum charge of £1.75.

B.F.P.O. & EIRE Customers 55p for the first book plus 22p for the second book and 14p for the next 7 books; thereafter 8p per book.

Overseas Customers £1.00 for the first book and 25p per copy for each additional book.

Please send cheque or postal order (no currency).

Name ....

Address ....

....

Title ....